ORIGINS

The Greatest Scientific Discovery

Phillip Day

Origins

ISBN 1-904015-24-7

Manufactured in Great Britain
Credence Publications
PO Box 3
TONBRIDGE
Kent TN12 9ZY UK
www.credence.org

WARNING: The information contained in this book is for information purposes only and should not be construed as medical advice for an individual's given condition. A medical practitioner's qualified opinion should always be sought in the matter of serious illness.

1st ed.

TABLE OF CONTENTS

AUTHOR'S NOTE

The book you are about to read is a compendium of research material compiled on a complex but enthralling series of subjects. During the course of my travels and teachings over the past 26 years, I resolved to do some leg-work and gather some principle sources, drawing together the raw data, differing opinions, research and commentaries and present them to you in some sort of cohesive form. Now you can sit back in your armchair with more than a few facts at your fingertips, the hard slog is done. And if you want to investigate a particular point further, adequate sources and recommendations are given in the text and footnotes.

Often, seemingly meaningless information takes on a new significance when placed in context with other pieces of the overall jigsaw. This is the excitement of working the information puzzle. For instance, putting together different events in history known to have occurred at the same time gives a greater clue as to why historical characters acted the way they did and why the world is as we find it today. Many personalities have spoken out and commented on one or more of the subjects covered in the following pages. It has been my aim to quote them as accurately as I can and scour book and article releases to reflect the most up-to-date positions on these issues for your consideration.

I have included sources that do not necessarily reflect my own views but enhance the subject matter, and quoted much source material verbatim with adequate references where possible (see *Bibliography*). Where newspapers are cited, those selected are typically publications representing the wider readerships. Biblical commentaries are from a wide spectrum of denominational camps and quotes are from the Authorised King James Version unless indicated. Forgive me for underlying sections of quotes to draw the reader's attention to something specific. Scientific and medical data are indexed where appropriate and intended for educational purposes only. Specialists in certain of the subjects covered are quoted and their opinions discussed.

The reader must, of course, appreciate that no source is 100% accurate or unbiased, not even this one. However neither should a particular source be discounted because the position held is contentious. As always, it is up to you, the reader, to consider your verdict.

Phillip Day

INTRODUCTION

"I know that most men, including those at ease with problems of the greatest complexity, can seldom accept even the simplest and most obvious truth if it would oblige them to admit the falsity of conclusions which they have delighted in explaining to colleagues, proudly taught to others, and which they have woven, thread by thread, into the fabric of their lives."
- Leo Tolstoy

Who are we?
Where did we come from?
What are we doing here?
And where are we going when this life is over?

Four more fundamental questions cannot be imagined, questions each of us will ask ourselves at some stage in our lives. At the birth of our child. At the funeral of a loved one. When we become seriously ill or scared, wondering what will become of us. What has it all been about?

There's a war going on and control over the public mind is the prize. The purpose of this book is not to pick a fight, it's an attempt to get some of the hard questions answered through science, observation and intelligence. Like you, I am an end-user of all this civilisation and justifiably concerned about the truth of the science, politics, economics, commerce and medicine daily squirted at us through the newspapers, magazines and TV. If I'm sick, I want to know doctors can fix me. If we're to march off to war, I'd like to be settled that the reasons given are just and there is no other way.

Most of what we learn comes through the mass communications media, which sculpts the public psyche with information. It's not that the media lies, it's just selective about the information it gives us. Richard M Cohen, senior producer of CBS political news, remarked:

"We are going to impose our agenda on the coverage by dealing with issues and subjects that we choose to deal with."

Richard Salant, former president of CBS News, believes:

"Our job is not to give people what they want, but what we decide they ought to have."

Intellectual gerrymandering. You brainy scientist, me thick member of the public. Yet unprejudiced review reveals that we thick members of the public are the ones scientists, politicians, captains of industry, doctors, professors and chemists ultimately depend upon to maintain their station and bank balance. Many of these professionals are well-meaning and honest, while an ever-growing percentage are, as we'll discover, utter carbuncles on the backside of 21st century humanity. Don't misunderstand me. I have tremendous respect for those who have dedicated their lives to a particular cause in all honesty, but as I'm oft fond of saying, you can be sincere, and you can be sincerely wrong.

This book will expose just how far we've been bamboozled by 'the experts', who have robbed us of our faith, sold us a shoddy bill of goods and even killed us. Such 'experts' have by their greed and unassailable sense of right eschewed the passion for going where the evidence led them and finished up snake-oil charlatans posing as men of learning, dreaming up their own fairy-tales and flogging them to the public as fact.

I am not anti-capitalist, anti-science, anti-politics, anti-religion, anti-medicine or one of those slipper-wearing, tree-hugging potato-heads trying to bust us back to the Wind Age. I'm an ordinary citizen and I'm fed up. In fact, I've been fed up for quite a while now, so I'm taking you on this little excursion so you can consider to what extent we've been sold down the river by intellectual prostitutes, who mock the public's intelligence, pontificate absurdities and expect us to believe them. I've always wanted to do a book like this.

No area of science and religion, no zone of society has been immune from their brutality. Overarching the lot is the quackery of evolution, which I studied for years in one of Britain's great learning institutions, Charterhouse, before realising I'd been had. Evolution is the idea that we're nothing but a piece of pond slime that washed up on a beach four billion years ago, then began evolving through a series of blind, random mistakes into the splendid creatures we are today. All this in spite of the Second Law of Thermodynamics which, author Wendy Wallace takes haste to remind us, holds that we're actually devolving back into pond scum and our minds are so far along in the process we can't figure it out.[1]

Most of us know something of the creation/evolution debate. It's joked about on *Friends* and *The Daily Show,* though taken more seriously in the hallowed halls of academia. In the liberal establishment, the debate is misunderstood to be between quiet, rational men of science on the one hand, and wild-eyed 'Sarah Palin clones' frothing scripture on the other. Notwithstanding the absurd degree to which evolution is promoted in schools, universities and the media as 'established science', a whopping 92% of Americans believe in God or a universal spirit.[2] The world certainly looks ordered, *but is it?* A shark surely looks like a designed killing machine, *but is it?* And if Darwin's right and there is no design - no God, Jesus, Mohammed or Allah - are we free to toss out the Ten Commandments, kill whomever we want, rape, cheat and steal, for tomorrow we die? Author Sean McDowell believes there is no greater question than the ultimate secret to why we are here. What meaning, if any, can we attach to this miraculous journey we make to the day of our deaths? What's life all about? And after death, then what?

---

[1] **Wallace, Wendy** *The Four Horsemen of the Apocalypse,* POB 3109, Prescott AZ 86302, USA

[2] *Washington Post,* 24th June 2008, p.A02

13

"Evolution raises fundamental questions about what it means to be human. Are we accidental by-products of blind forces in nature? Or are we the pinnacle of creation intended by a personal and loving God? Can all the beauty, complexity and diversity of life be explained by random variation and natural selection? Or is the natural world best explained as the workings of a designer?"[3]

The evolution/creation debate is not a new one and even pre-existed Darwin, but it has fully raged since the 1859 publication of Charlie's *On the Origin of Species*. Successive generations on both sides of the battlefront have duked it out, the debate essentially for or against design, the existence or denial of purpose in the universe. The ramifications of evolution as a belief system are extremely far-reaching. If we are nothing but by-products of accidental biogenesis, then life is essentially meaningless. Why bother getting out of bed in the morning? Why not toss the alarm clock into the laundry basket for a few more hours of sleep? Live on the dole? Who cares?

In his own day, Charles Darwin's big idea grew wings to the horror of the Victorian clergy and became the hot potato in a world restless for more. Science was blasting off, giving mankind new knowledge and comforts – what else was to be had? Darwin's unique theory of man's origins appealed to those tired of being pushed around by established religion. In Darwin's world, God was conspicuously absent and little more than a fairy tale. All things evolved by natural selection acting on undirected, random processes and there was no 'design' beyond the survival of the fittest.

A forbidden freedom was sniffed in the air. No God meant no sin, which meant no judgment, which meant no hell, which meant 'do what thou wilt shall be the whole of the law' since heaven was empty. The inception of reasoned science in Galileo's day and its

---

[3] **Dembski, W A & Sean McDowell** *Understanding Intelligent Design,* Harvest House, 2008, Josh McDowell foreword, p.11

appalling treatment by the Papal fist probably assured the Holy See would get its comeuppance one day, yet Darwin's book achieved something else. It birthed a challenge to matters which for centuries had been taken for granted. That the Earth was young. That God made it and saw it was good. That sin entered the world with Adam and Eve and began the process of decay. That the world was destroyed in a global flood, following which eight people survived and repopulated the Earth.

In kindergarten I had a toy ark and a selection of animals to put inside before giving it a whirl in the pool. Sunday School reinforced the Bible's view of my origins and I was captivated by the imagery. Then years later I was taught evolution by Dr Brian Tricker at Charterhouse and all that changed. It says something of Tricker's personal worldview that when his cat got flattened by a car one day, we dissected what was left of the poor creature in our next biology class. I remember being amazed the man could be so *practical* about losing the sort of pet some people treat as a child, but Tricker's view was that one man's two-dimensional feline was another's anatomical prospect. Later I would study biology, geology, anthropology and embryology and, you name it, get an 'A'. And straight after that, it was through the cloisters to Lenny Morrison's theology sessions in C Block to tank up on God. If anyone felt at odds with the paradox, it wasn't discussed at the time. If you wanted Oxford, you didn't ask those questions. Unbeknownst to me at the time, my future wife, Samantha, was undergoing a similar experience at a convent in Sittingbourne. The nuns were teaching both evolution and creation to their impressionable charges and the students went along with it all.

Then one day out of the blue I became bothered. Science was supposed to be empirical, testable and demonstrable but I'd found a hole big enough to drive a Mac truck into. Tricker's evolution denied the existence of purpose in the universe and substituted design with bare chance and necessity. Fair enough. For this, evolution requires an ancient Earth and billions of years. It denies design and replaces it with man's haphazard ascent from the brute. Evolution denies the immortality of the soul and, in so doing, implies the beckoning of a mindless oblivion after a pointless life.

But the sheer uselessness of that program was not what bothered me. It was the population. The world was just celebrating the birth of its five billionth soul. I walked out of maths one morning and ran the numbers during tea-break. If mankind had been climbing Darwin's tree for the thick end of three million years (standard evolutionary theory), we have a problem. Where was everyone? My calculations revealed that a population of 5 billion was consistent with mankind being in the procreation business for around 4,500 years from two common ancestors, give or take a plague or war or three. All right, I'll give you 10,000 years. The point is, the aggregate population derived over a million years of constant sex would be unthinkably ridiculous.

What was going on? Were we wiped out? Evolution holds no truck with catastrophism except for one life extinction event '65 million years ago' when the dinosaurs supposedly got theirs from an asteroid. Geologist Dr John Morris remarks:

"Observation of Earth's population and population growth supports a young Earth…. Starting one million years ago, with a growth rate of 0.002% and a present population of six billion, can you guess how many people would have lived and died throughout history? …There should be 10^{8600} people alive today. That's 10 with 8600 zeros following it. …The number is so large it is meaningless, and it's approximately the number which could just fit inside the volume of the entire Earth! If all these people lived and died, where are their bones? Why are human bones so scarce?"[4]

Whoops.

To his credit while out collecting ants one day, Brian Tricker admitted evolution had never been proven fact but he hung his hat

---

[4] **Morris, John** *The Young Earth,* Master Books, 1994, pp.70-71

(and salary) on it anyway. Evolution was a belief system and a good one, he explained. Ah, but a belief system's a religion, countered I. Wasn't that why Darwiniacs behaved with all the ardour of the Spanish Inquisition whenever challenged? Tricker was about to say something when some ants got into his shoes and we broke off the chat.

The following day, I was reading a magazine in which a scientist was stating that people who reject evolution are delusionally afflicted, even dangerous. Strange. You don't find scientists defending chemotherapy with quite the same fervour. I went digging. In fact, I spent most of the weekend in Charterhouse's library which is extensive, and the single hole I found in evolution rapidly grew into a whole cheeseboard.

Why should any of this matter? Because evolution underpins all science and not an inconsiderable chunk of modern civilisation. What we believe of our origins. What we take as the truth. You might be different but I hate being lied to. Evolution's the reason we use drugs instead of nutrition and continue to fail with cancer and other diseases. Evolution justifies the mass killing of the unborn with abortion - after all, it's not human yet. Evolution justified who lived and who died in the Nazi death camps. Stalin's evolutionary beliefs resulted in the slaughter of the entire Polish officer corps and millions of the dictator's own countrymen, never mind the enemy. Today, evolution underpins geology, physics, chemistry, astronomy, anthropology, biology, psychiatry, eugenics and racism. When questioned, the high priests of evolution have always failed to come up with the wafers. In fact, something called 'confirmation bias' is used to ward off detractors in the first place so the argument never gets going. Why are you QUESTIONING me? Do you have a DEGREE? Evolution is FACT like gravity! THAT'S IT! CASE CLOSED! They just say it.

Evolution determines our worldview and how we behave. Whether we kill. Whether morality exists and where it comes from.

Whether we save the weak or let them go tumble in the great wash-tub of natural selection. No-one's ever seen evolution in action. We've never seen whales become cows or dinosaurs become birds. I'm a farmer's boy and I'll tell you for nothing, you can plant all the beans you want and you'll not get one sheep. And monkeys became men? Why Charlie, do you mean blacks did not evolve as far as the whites? The full title of Darwin's *magnum opus* is an embarrassment. *On The Origin of Species by Means of Natural Selection, or the Preservation of Favoured Races in the Struggle for Life.* Did you know that Marx and Engels admired Darwin's book to such an extent that they used it as the basis for Communism? More about that later.

In a passing sop to the nervous, evolution is described to this day as 'consensus science', which is rich given that consensus is politics not science. Sure, if you don't know in science you can move to belief, but belief, alas, is not science it's faith, so that makes evolution a religion. And from what Stalin, Hitler, Mao and Pol Pot did with it, a rather lethal religion at that.

As for evolutionary science – *what science?* Dr Vij Sodera writes:

"Look at a speck of dust on the table in front of you. Given the timespan of a few billion years, is it possible for such a particle, being composed only of simple molecules, to re-arrange its structure, to join with other simple particles and to acquire consciousness – ultimately to peer down on another dust particle and to contemplate its origins? Yet inherent in the theory of evolution by natural selection is the assumption that not only is this possible, but that it actually happened."[5]

And as we'll see, not a shred of evidence to back it all up. They just *believe* it. If you want to *believe* grandpappy was an orangutan, you have a perfect right to believe that, but don't call it science unless you come up with a monkey-man. And don't point at 'specimens' in the Natural History Museum on Cromwell Road

---

[5] **Sodera**, **V** *One Small Speck to Man*, Vij Sodera Productions, Bognor Regis, UK, 2003

either. The ones they have in there were all made out the back to show what early man *may* have looked like. The 'real' ones they tried to convince us with have all been exposed as frauds. More about that later too.

It's straightforward. If you want to convince me *scientifically* that rats turned into bats, then show me a rat-bat. In his day, Darwin was aware the fossil record was coming up short but believed future finds would eventually vindicate him. Good for you, Charlie, only they haven't. But that doesn't stop evolutionists *believing*. Through the glossy pages of *National Geographic, Omni* and *Time* – in museums, news reports, in science courses taught in schools and universities across the world – evolution is still packaged to look like science and sold to the world as fact. As we'll see, evolution is a laughable cry from fact. Millions believe in evolution today simply because it is all they have ever heard. I'm like an elkhound with a string of sausages over stuff like this.

Of course there's a wider revolution underway. Call it what you want: Science versus religion. Liberal versus conservative. *Guardian* versus *Mail*. God versus Satan. The real control is in the information. What do you *believe*, and on what do you base those *beliefs?* Faith? Science? Myth? Anything you want that doesn't challenge your lifestyle? Personally, I think the intelligent design guys like Dembski, Behe, Missler and Meyer are being far too nice to the quacks, and for that matter to those Supreme Court judges in America who actually thought posting the Ten Commandments in the classroom was going to give the kiddies brain damage. The reality is, not long after they took the Ten Commandments out of America's schools, they had to put the metal detectors in. More children today are on psychiatric medication in the US than ever before because they've started asking questions like "What's the point?" "Why bother when life ultimately sucks?" "What if the Hokey Cokey really *is* what it's all about?"

What we're *not* being told is the one thing that can and will change everything for science and for us. I don't want to convince you, I want you to make up your own mind, or what's left of it, based on the evidence. Life *does* matter, especially *your* life, and the universe is taking notes whether we like it or not. *Origins* is less about religion than science, it's how we've been snowed, what's been withheld from us, and the jaw-dropping evidence uncovered in the last ten years which has started to change everything.

I think Darwin would have approved. As we'll see, Candid Charlie was quite willing to admit his shortcomings, which is more than can be said for the zealots who carry his banner today. In fact, I'll bet Charlie, wherever he is now, is probably still asking those same four questions:

Who am I?

Where did I come from?

What am I doing here?

And where am I going now this life is over?

Perhaps he now knows.

- Part 1 -

Rubbish science

THE GREAT DEBATE

"How fortunate for those in power that the people never think."
- Adolf Hitler

One would imagine a concept having such far-reaching ramifications as evolution would have solid foundations based in the sciences, but you would be wrong. What bothered me at Charterhouse was the default attitude of 'We'd better believe in monkeys or, God, what's left is religion!' Why were they so afraid to go where the evidence led them? Today I still glaze over every time Michael Hanlon rabbits on about mankind's forthcoming 'quantum' leap into the future, which turns out to be cloning sheep, GM soy, or an impressively huge waste of money called the Large Hadron Collider. Here's the really interesting question. What if the next boggling leap in scientific endeavour was the ultimate discovery? That the universe, Earth and man show unmistakable evidence of design? That we're not alone? Such notions already intrigue us, as exemplified by the Search for Extraterrestrial Life (SETI) programs and popularity of Hollywood films such as *Knowing, ET, Close Encounters* and *Contact*. The conclusion, it seems, is that many of us are up for just about any alien as our progenitor – even a Sigourney Weaver one – so long as it's not the God Alien.

The religion of evolution

HS Lipson, Professor of Physics at Manchester University:

"Darwin's book, *On the Origin of Species,* was published in 1859. It is perhaps the most influential book that has ever been published, because it was read by scientist and non-scientist alike, and it aroused violent controversy. Religious people disliked it because it appeared to dispense with God; scientists liked it because it seemed to solve the most important problem in the universe – the existence of living matter. In fact, evolution became in a sense a scientific religion; almost all scientists have accepted it and many are prepared to 'bend' their observations to fit in with it."[6]

Professor GA Kerkut, Department of Physiology and Biochemistry at Southampton University, UK, puts it this way:

"It is therefore a matter of faith on the part of the biologist that biogenesis did occur and he can choose whatever method of biogenesis happens to suit him personally; the evidence for what did happen is not available." [7]

Mary Midgley, former Senior Lecturer in Philosophy at England's Newcastle University, writes:

"In our own culture, where many people officially have no religion at all, and those who have can chop and change, new faiths have much more scope and can become more distinctive. They are hungrily seized on by people whose lives lack meaning. When this happens, there arise at once, unofficially and spontaneously, many elements which we think of as characteristically religious. We begin, for instance, to find priesthoods, prophecies devotion, bigotry, exaltation, heresy-hunting and sectarianism, ritual sacrifice, fanaticism, notions of sin, absolution and salvation, and the confident promise of a heaven in the future. ... Marxism and evolutionism, the two great secular faiths of our day, display all these religious-looking features. They have also, like the great religions and unlike more casual local faiths, large-scale, ambitious systems of thought, designed to articulate, defend and justify their ideas - in short, ideologies."[8]

Marjorie Grene, Professor Emeritus of Philosophy at the University of California, Davis, agrees:

"It is as a religion of science that Darwinism chiefly held, and holds men's minds. The derivation of life, of man, of man's deepest hopes and highest achievements, from the external and indirect determination of

---

[6] **Lipson, HS** "A Physicist Looks at Evolution", *Physics Bulletin,* vol.31, 1980, p.138

[7] **Kerkut, GA** *Implications of Evolution*, Pergamon Press, London, 1960, p.150

[8] **Midgley M** *Evolution as a Religion: Strange Hopes and Stranger Fears,* Methuen, London, 1986, p.15

small chance errors, appears as the very keystone of the naturalistic universe. And the defence of natural selection appears, therefore, as the defence of their integrity, the independence, the dignity of science itself."[9]

When a scientist tells you about something he has never seen, such as evolution or the Big Bang, he is giving you a theory or a belief. When he insists on teaching you this belief as fact, he is now a priest pushing a religion. Evolution is a religion that is being advanced in our schools and society today with a fervour and zeal more pronounced than ever in decades past. From the *National Geographic* to *Omni* to David Attenborough's wildlife programs to the works of Richard Dawkins, this religion of entrenched error is being compelled upon us, right down to the furry toy dinosaur our child picks up in the store with the label coming out of its rear end: "Millions of years ago...."

Richard Dawkins is perhaps evolution's most high-profile spokesperson today. Author of the bestselling *The God Delusion*, Professor Dawkins is completely secure in his faith:

"Evolution is a fact. It's a fact which is established as securely, essentially, as any other fact that we have in science."[10]

But Alister McGrath, Professor of Historical Theology at Dawkins' Oxford University, demurs:

"The God Delusion has established Dawkins as the world's most high-profile atheist polemicist, who directs a withering criticism against every form of religion. He is out to convert his readers. 'If this book works as I intend, religious leaders who open it will be atheists when they put it down.' Not that he thinks that this is particularly likely; after all, he suggests, 'dyed-in-the-wool faith-heads are immune to argument.'

Yet the fact that Dawkins has penned a 400-page book declaring that God is a delusion is itself highly significant. *Why is such a book still necessary?* Religion was meant to have disappeared years ago. For more than a century, leading sociologists, anthropologists and psychologists have

---

[9] **Grene M** "The Faith of Darwinism", *Encounter*, Vol. 74, November 1959, p.48
[10] *Expelled – No Intelligence Allowed*, Premise Media Corporation, 2008

declared that their children would see the dawn of a new era in which the 'God delusion' would be left behind for good. Back in the 1960's, we were told that religion was fading away, to be replaced by a secular world."[11]

The reason Dawkins wrote his book is because thinking people are still asking questions. *The God Delusion* comes across as much more a defence of Richard's own beliefs than it does a swingeing assault on the enemy. No one likes their religion challenged and Dawkins is no different. Shoring up the crumbling dyke, however, has proved no easy matter. As we'll see, many evolutionists will admit in frank moments that their own religion has not a shred of testable proof to vindicate it, so someone is wrong. Here's Darwin:

"For I am well aware that scarcely a single point is discussed in this volume [*On the Origin of Species*] on which facts cannot be adduced, often leading to conclusions directly opposite to those at which I have arrived. A fair result can be obtained only by fully stating and balancing the facts and arguments on both side of each question; and this here is impossible."[12]

People are free, of course, to believe what they want. Where the line must be drawn is when tax dollars/pounds are being used to teach evolution *as fact* to kids, thereby promoting deceit, infidelity, crime, a lack of moral character and atheism. Those in turn who believe religion is the root of all evil cannot afford to view their own beliefs in the same light. It's the old 'My God is better than your God' routine even if your God is no God at all. Christianity has certainly killed in the past but *which* Christianity? It's noteworthy that few bother to reconcile the complete absence of Christian jihad in the teachings of the New Testament with the atrocities the Papal 'Christians' carried out during the Crusades and Inquisition, and Protestants would do after the Reformation.

---

[11] **McGrath, A** *The Dawkins Delusion*, SPCK, London, 2007

[12] **Darwin, Charles** Introduction to *On the Origin of Species*, p.2. Also quoted in *Washington Times*, 8th February 1984

Recently, Channel 4 showed a series entitled *The History of Christianity*. Each episode was hosted by a different celebrity. In the entire series, only Michael Portillo briefly mentioned that no-one who claims to place their eternal trust in the Jesus of the New Testament and follow his ways could commit the kinds of acts many have claimed 'for Christ's sake' down through the ages.

A quick glance at history's slaughtometer reveals that pagan Rome was mild in comparison to the genocide committed by the popes. But even the Vatican must take second seat to the deadliest religion of all – neo-Darwinian atheism – which has butchered more for the sake of its belief in the past 150 years than the dead of all previous wars combined. Historical figures and religious commentators of the past were not slow to learn the lessons we seem incapable of learning today. To them the progression was clear. From evolution to humanism (atheism) to socialism, Marxism, totalitarianism, Nazism and their antithetical positions to Biblical Christianity, in contradistinction to *'Holy War'* Christianity, the counterfeit:

"The law of Christ is incompatible with the law of evolution…. Nay, the two laws are at war with each other," says Sir Arthur Keith in *Evolution and Ethics.*

"I myself have little doubt that in England it was long-age uniformitarian geology and the theory of evolution that changed us from a Christian to a pagan nation." - F Sherwood Taylor, *Geology Changes - The Outlook,* Curator of the Museum of the History of Science, Oxford, England

"Martin Lingis is probably right in saying that 'more cases of loss of religious faith are to be traced to the theory of evolution... than to anything else.'" - Huston Smith, *Evolution & Evolutionism,* July 1982, p.755

"Humanists regard the Universe as self-existing and not created." – Humanist Manifesto, 1933, tenet 1

"Education is thus a most powerful ally of humanism. What can a theistic Sunday school's meeting for an hour once a week and teaching only a fraction of the children do to stem the tide of the five-day program of humanistic teaching?" – *Humanism: A New Religion,* 1930

"Give me your four-year-olds, and in a generation I will build a socialist state." – Vladimir Lenin

"Our enemy is not those with guns but missionaries with Bibles." - Jiang Zhernin, head of the Communist Party, Peoples Republic of China

"Socialism is the gospel of envy, the creed of ignorance, and the philosophy of failure." — Winston Churchill

But let us take pause. Are we being unfair to those who believe evolution in all good conscience? Most evolutionists are not *bad* people. If evolution *is* wrong, isn't it all just fanciful fun or is there something more sinister going on? We can best answer these questions by examining the worldviews held by the creationist and evolutionist.

World View - Evolution

With Darwinian evolution, *the origin of life* is never explained, for Darwin's theory begins with the first cell. The rest of what happened must be inferred.

"Evolution is unproved and unprovable. We believe it only because the only alternative is special creation, and that is unthinkable," writes Sir Arthur Keith in the forward to the 100th anniversary edition of Charles Darwin's *On the Origin of Species,* 1959

"In recent years several authors have written popular books on human origins which were based more on fantasy and subjectivity than on fact and objectivity. At the moment, science cannot offer a full answer on the origin of humanity...." – Dr Robert Martin, Senior Research Fellow, Zoological Fellow, Zoological Society of London

Today's evolution story goes like this. Man is nothing but a primordial pollywog that accidentally washed up on a beach 4 million years ago – some say 2 million – pick your pollywog. We then began the agonisingly slow process of evolving into the splendid creatures we are today in spite of the Second Law of Thermodynamics, one of science's most basic laws, which states that as time passes, matter and energy become more random and disorganised. Nevertheless, what a journey it's been, according to 19th century thinkers Charles Lyell (inventor of the Geologic Column) and Charles Darwin. During the evolutionary process, we started as inanimate, 'dead' matter. Somehow we found the spark of life (no small matter), became a germ which became a fish, an amphibian, a reptile, a bird, an orangutan and finally a fully paid-up member of *homo sapiens* with his two-jointed finger hovering over the nuclear trigger, threatening to start the whole tedious process all over again.

In evolution, there are no rules, no catastrophism, just 'survival of the fittest', for which natural selection is co-opted – that all things come about through undirected processes via the survival of *unobserved* 'beneficial' mutations. Some evolutionists argue that there exists a loosely defined unwritten moral code based on 'Mother Nature' that somehow binds the whole machine together. One hears this term used constantly in news bulletins and press reports.

Though 'neo-Darwinists'[13] have expanded Charlie's original work into a veritable sheetwork of cause and effect over the past century, sometimes even the faithful blush:

---

[13] Neo-Darwinism is the modern evolutionary synthesis of evolution acting on random variations melded with genetics. It's the idea that genetic mutations caused by translation errors within the cell result in variations within the genus, upon which natural selection then works its magic. The problem with this theory is that natural selection always *reduces* genetic information.

"The evolutionary trees that adorn our textbooks have data only at the tips and nodes of their branches; the rest is inference, however reasonable, not the evidence of fossils." – Stephen Jay Gould, "Evolution's Erratic Pace", Harvard University, May 1977

"I fully agree with your comments on the lack of evolutionary transitions in my book. If I knew of any, fossil or living, I would certainly have included them. I will lay it on the line — there is not one such fossil." – Dr Colin Paterson, Senior Palaeontologist, British Museum of Natural History, in correspondence to Luther Sunderland quoted in the latter's *Darwin's Enigma,* 1988, p.89

"All those trees of life with their branches of our ancestors? That's a lot of nonsense." – British anthropologist, Mary Leakey, quoted in Associated Press, 10th December 1996, the day after her death.

Loren Eiseley, Professor of Anthropology, University of Pennsylvania:

"With the failure of these many efforts [to explain the origin of life], science was left in the somewhat embarrassing position of having to postulate theories of living origins which it could not demonstrate. After having chided the theologian for his reliance on myth and miracle, science found itself in the unenviable position of having to create a mythology of its own: namely, the assumption that what, after long effort, could not be proved to take place today had, in truth, taken place in the primeval past."[14]

Palaeontologist Niles Eldredge writes:

"No wonder palaeontologists shied away from evolution for so long. It never seemed to happen. Assiduous collecting up cliff faces yields zigzags, minor oscillations, and the very occasional slight accumulations of change – over millions of years, at a rate too slow to account for all the prodigious change that has occurred in evolutionary history. When we do see the introduction of evolutionary novelty, it usually shows up with a bang, often with no firm evidence that the fossils did not evolve elsewhere! Evolution cannot forever be going somewhere else. Yet that's

---

[14] **Eiseley LC** *The Immense Journey,* Vintage, New York, NY, 1957, p.199

how the fossil record has struck many a forlorn palaeontologist looking to learn something from evolution."[15]

Aside from neo-Darwinists' attempts to hijack science in support of their beliefs, evolution has, and continues to spawn far more tragic, sociological effects. The belief that man is not answerable to any higher power often unchains him from moral rectitude. All the genocidal monsters of the past one hundred years have been Darwin fanatics. The disgraceful acts of Mao, Pot, Marx, Lenin, Milosevic, Stalin and Hitler will be examined later. We think we've learned the lessons, yet today's religion of evolution extends into environmental fundamentalism, in which it is no longer enough to place your newspaper and plastic into separate containers, *you* are the problem. From evolution teaching that we are nothing special in the pantheon of our fellow creatures beyond the (to date unexplained) development of a super-extensive intelligence, environmentalism now teaches that in our role as 'king of animals', all must be done to ensure the propagation of all species, even if that means at the expense of man himself:

"The collective needs of non-human species must take precedence over the needs and desires of humans," says *The Wildlands Project*

"We've got to ride the global-warming issue. Even if the theory of global warming is wrong, we will be doing the right things — in terms of economic policy and environmental policy." – Timothy Wirth, former U.S. Senator (D- Colorado)

"It may not be long before the practice of religion must be regarded as anti-science." – John Maddox, editor of *Nature,* (per *American Spectator,* July 1994)

And from these mainstream sentiments, it's a hop, skip and a jump to:

---

[15] **Eldredge, Niles** *Reinventing Darwin,* Wiley, New York, 1995, p.95

"Isn't the only hope for the planet that the industrialized civilizations collapse? Isn't it our responsibility to bring that about?" – Maurice Strong, Head of 1992 Earth Summit, Rio de Janeiro

"People are the cause of all the problems; we need to get rid of some of them...." – Charles Wurster, Environmental Defense Fund

"The world has cancer, and the cancer is man." – Alan Gregg, *Mankind at the Turning Point*, 1974

"Christianity is our foe. If animals rights is to succeed, we must destroy the Judeo-Christian religious tradition." Peter Singer, Ira W. DeCamp Professor of Bioethics at Princeton University, and laureate professor at the Centre for Applied Philosophy and Public Ethics (CAPPE), University of Melbourne. Professor Singer favours killing babies up to 28 days old.[16]

Prince Philip, Duke of Edinburgh, President of the World Wildlife Fund: "If I could be reincarnated, I would wish to be returned to Earth as a killer virus to lower human population levels."

John J Dunphy in *The Humanist's* prize-winning essay, Jan/Feb 1983: "The battle for humankind's future must be waged and won in the public school classroom by teachers who correctly perceive their role as the proselytizers of a new faith: A religion of humanity... utilizing a classroom instead of a pulpit to carry humanist values into wherever they teach.... The classroom must and will become an arena of conflict between the old and the new—the rotting corpse of Christianity, together with its adjacent evils and misery, and the new faith of humanism...."

Richard Dawkins: "It is absolutely safe to say that if you meet somebody who claims not to believe in evolution, that person is ignorant, stupid or insane (or wicked, but I'd rather not consider that)."[17]

---

[16] Associated Press, 22nd November 1999; See also: www.geocities.com/Athens /Agora/2900/psai.html

[17] **Dawkins R** "Put Your Money on Evolution", Review **of Johanson D & Edey MA** *Blueprints: Solving the Mystery of Evolution,* in *New York Times*, 9th April 1989, sec. 7, p.34

World View - Creation

Creationism is the belief that the universe and man were just that – created, and that the world shows unmistakable evidence of design. 'Young Earth' creationists believe the Earth and universe came into existence around 6,000-7,000 years ago, literally according to the Bible, when man began multiplying from two common human ancestors, born into a civilised state, created along with the flora and fauna by a Designer who had a plan for the work of his hands. In order to safeguard the successful running of his creation, the Designer created rules to be obeyed. The Bible is his story (history) of man and his relationship with the Creator. Catastrophism plays a large part in God's plan. Uniformitarianism, espoused by evolutionists, never has done.

And so we have two widely divergent worldviews – evolution and creation – sometimes combined, always contested. Logic dictates that both cannot be correct. Indeed, in the opinion of many, neither need be correct.

The worldview of the evolutionist can produce a human with a confused and under-developed sense of right and wrong. To the evolutionist, survival is the dominant dynamic to the exclusion of all else because all is chaos and only the strong survive. There is no designer, no moral code or grand plan. Morality is the sentimentality of religion. Communism, Illuminism, Masonry, Hitlerite Fascism and a whole smorgasbord of New Age concepts are all dominated, as we shall see, by the theory of evolution.

The worldview of the creationist is very different. A creationist typically acknowledges a superior power in charge of creation. The creationist recognises that man is part of a higher purpose. Notwithstanding their belief in an ultimate judgment, the true creationist will suppress the urge to kill, maim, commit adultery, lie, cheat or steal because they acknowledge that the laws prohibiting this behaviour are fundamental to the favourable running of the system. The worldview of each produces radically different behaviour towards fellow human beings. For instance, under evolutionist systems the weak are neglected and sometimes murdered (Hitler, Stalin, Mao, Pot, Milosevic). In today's social sphere, evolution underpins Communism, radical women's liberation, racism, environmental fundamentalism, abortion, euthanasia, neo-Nazism, pornography, socialism, humanism, gay rights, atheistic Satanism and New Age religions. On the other hand, false Christian systems kill, but true ones cannot since they adhere to the precepts laid down by Christ in the New Testament for the promise of eternal life.[18]

To believe in evolution is to come under the control of superior and more powerful humans or be the dominant human. One who believes in creation and a Creator comes under the ultimate authority of God, not man, knowing the content of his life will one day be judged. If there is a God who is smart enough to design us, he's smart enough to do what he wants with us. Evolutionists blench at such nostrums and see them as stifling to a 'freely expressive lifestyle'. Since the existing moral code is Judeo-Christian, they rebel against it, though seem less harsh on Muslims because they are frightened of them. It is neither convenient nor expedient for the evolutionist to believe in God. Success is everything to the evolutionist. Materialism is all there ever will be, with technology the capstone of human endeavour. A creationist believes in the power of God to redeem him. Science, or human knowledge, expressed as the religion of humanism, becomes the redeemer of the evolutionist.

In their own day, America's Founding Fathers knew this problem well. Almost all believed *genuine* Biblical morality held the key to the survival of their new nation:

---

[18] For a full exposé of counterfeit Christianity, see **Day, Phillip** *Origins II – Holy War,* Credence, 2009

"It cannot be emphasized too strongly or too often that this great nation was founded not by religionists but by Christians... not on religions but on the Gospel of Jesus Christ." – Patrick Henry

"It is impossible to rightly govern…without God and the Bible." – George Washington

"Good intentions will always be pleaded for every assumption of power... It is hardly too strong to say that the Constitution was made to guard the people against the dangers of good intentions. There are men in all ages who mean to govern well, but they mean to govern. They promise to be good masters, but they mean to be masters." – Daniel Webster

"If we abide by the principles taught in the Bible, our country will go on prospering, but if we neglect its instruction and authority, no man can tell how soon a catastrophe may overcome us, and bury all our glory in profound obscurity." – Daniel Webster

"All the miseries and evils which men suffer from vice, crime, ambition, injustice, oppression, slavery, and war proceed from their despising or neglecting the precepts contained in the Bible." – Noah Webster

The Geologic Column

In the 1830s, Charles Lyell invented the Geologic Column which he believed chronologically tabulated the different eras existing since the formation of the Earth. We know the Geologic Column today as a chart in museums and a school's biology department, which lists eras such as the Cretaceous, Jurassic, Cenozoic and Palaeozoic. The problem is, Lyell's Geologic Column cannot be found anywhere in the world outside of the museum and biology textbook.

Science teacher Kent Hovind watched as his daughter asked an evolutionist one day in a museum how it was that scientists were able to calculate the age of a fossil. The reply was, "By the age of the stratum of rock in which the fossil was discovered." Imagine the poor girl's confusion when, not thirty minutes later, she asked the same man how it was that scientists could calculate the age of a stratum of rock. The reply came, "By the fossils found in the stratum of rock." Yet this advice is accepted today and even charged for. Professor Ronald R West sums up this bizarre anomaly:

> "Contrary to what most scientists write, the fossil record does not support the Darwinian theory of evolution because it is this theory (there are several) which we use to interpret the fossil record. By doing so, we are guilty of circular reasoning if we then say the fossil record supports this theory." [19]

David Berlinski, secular Jewish professor of mathematics and philosophy, who stated his "religious education did not take", writes in his *Commentary,* September 1996, p.28:

> "...There are gaps in the fossil graveyard, places where there should be intermediate forms but where there is nothing whatsoever instead. No palaeontologist writing in English (R. Carroll, 1988), French (J. Chaline, 1983), or German (V. Fahlbusch, 1983), denies that this is so. It is simply a fact. Darwin's theory and the fossil record are in conflict."

Values

Why do we care about what we do to others? Where did morals come from? The fact that we have social values and mores, and have had so from the dawn of recorded history, speaks more to the theory that mankind has chosen, or been instructed to arrange his society thus. As we progress, we'll examine the evidence that mankind has always been in a civilised state (though in some cases not so civilised). Rather than paying lip-service to a convenient 'natural' morality posited by the atheist (which looks suspiciously Judeo-Christian), consider for a moment: Why *not* murder, lie, cheat and steal if it helps you survive? Why not

---

[19] **West, Ronald R** Assistant Professor of Paleobiology at Kansas State University, *Compass,* vol.45, May 1968, p.216

commit adultery and rape if the end justifies the means to create progeny for the survival of your species? Where do you get the notion that it is *wrong* to do this if evolution rules? If man evolved by chance, why do atheists arrange their social structures with design's every detail? Why don't they naturally resort to heinous crimes to survive, as do animals every night on David Attenborough's wildlife programs? Values gainsay the whole concept of random processes, not to mention the survival of the fittest.

Evolution – really?

There are other problems. There is a limit to how far a species can alter, says Australian molecular biologist, Michael Denton:

"The idea of transmutation was rendered even less likely in the eyes of many nineteenth-century typologists by the well-established fact that breeding experiments with domestic animals had for generations revealed a distinct limit beyond which further change became impossible." And, "… As in so many other fields of biology, the search for continuity, for empirical entities to bridge the divisions of nature, proved futile. Instead of revealing a multitude of transitional forms, through which the evolution of the cell might have occurred, molecular biology has served only to emphasize the enormity of the gap."[20]

If evolution is happening all around us, why is it so infuriatingly hard to observe or replicate? Or perhaps, as was reported in the newspapers, evolution has *stopped*….[21]

Simple to complex

And what about this 'simple cell', from which all creatures supposedly evolved in spite of the Second Law of Thermodynamics? In Darwin's day, the limits of science prevented any meaningful studies into the smallest structures, so the idea that

---

[20] **Denton, Michael** *Evolution: A Theory in Crisis,* Adler & Adler, USA, 1986
[21] http://www.timesonline.co.uk/tol/news/uk/science/article4894696.ece

a homogenous glob might be mankind's earliest ancestor – a simple life-form from which extraordinary complexity derived – was accepted with nary a blush, no proof given. Biologist Thomas Huxley, known as 'Darwin's Bulldog', writes:

"Looking back through the prodigious vista of the past, I find no record of the commencement of life, and therefore I am devoid of any means of forming a definite conclusion… but… if it were given to me to look beyond the abyss of geologically recorded time to the still more remote period when the Earth was passing through physical and chemical conditions, which it can no more see again than a man recall his infancy, I should expect to be a witness of the evolution of living protoplasm from not-living matter."[22]

Blithely the assumption is made that living matter evolved from non-living matter. This is no small matter, neither is it science. Where is the proof of the prebiotic soup from which this slime was said to originate? They've looked into the oldest rocks on Earth and found nothing. To Denton this is the deal-breaker:

"The evidence of a prebiotic soup is an absolute prerequisite for the evolutionary emergence of life on Earth, but even if good evidence for the soup had been found, the problem of the origin of life would still be far from solved. The most difficult aspect of the origin of life problems lies not in the origin of the soup, but in the stages leading from the soup to the cell. Between the basic building blocks, amino acids, sugars and other simple organic compounds used in the construction of the cell, and the simplest known types of living systems, there is an immense discontinuity." [23]

Scientists have done their best to come up with an intermediate form between bare chemicals and the living cell. Denton explains why they failed:

---

[22] **Huxley, Thomas** "Biogenesis and Abiogenesis", *Collected Essays of T H Huxley,* (1894) Macmillan and Co, London 1970
[23] Denton, Michael, *Evolution: A Theory in Crisis,* op. cit. p.263

"We now know not only of the existence of a break between the living and non-living world, but also that it represents the most dramatic and fundamental of all the discontinuities of nature. Between a living cell and the most highly ordered non-biological system, such as a crystal or a snowflake, there is a chasm as vast and absolute as it is possible to conceive.

Molecular biology has shown that even the simplest of all living systems on Earth today, bacterial cells, are exceedingly complex objects. Although the tiniest bacterial cells are incredibly small, weighing less than 10^{-12} grams, each is in effect a veritable micro-miniaturized factory containing thousands of exquisitely designed pieces of intricate molecular machinery, made up altogether of one hundred million atoms, far more complicated than any machine built by man and absolutely without parallel in the non-living world."[24]

Michael Behe summarises:

"There is an elephant in the roomful of scientists who are trying to explain the development of life. The elephant is labelled 'intelligent design'. To a person who does not feel obliged to restrict his search to unintelligent causes, the straightforward conclusion is that many biochemical systems are designed. They were designed not by the laws of nature, not by chance or necessity; rather, they were planned. The designer knew what the systems would look like when they were completed, then took steps to bring them about. Life on Earth at its most fundamental level, in its most critical components, is the product of intelligent activity."[25]

---

[24] Denton, Michael, *Evolution: A Theory in Crisis*, op. cit. p.249-250

[25] **Behe, Michael** *Darwin's Black Box*, Simon and Schuster, New York, 1996, p.193

INTELLIGENT DESIGN
Daily Telegraph, 3rd November 2008:

PADDY POWER OFFERS ODDS
OF 4-1 THAT GOD EXISTS

"A bookmaker has slashed its odds on proof being found of God's existence to just 4-1… Initially the odds that proof would be found of God's existence were 20-1, and they lengthened to 33-1 when the multi-billion pound atom smasher was shut down temporarily because of a magnetic failure. But interest in the wager has increased greatly following the recent launch of a campaign to have atheist adverts placed on London buses declaring that "there's probably no God"….

The atheists' planned advertising campaign seems to have renewed the debate in pubs and around office water-coolers as to whether there is a God and we've seen some of that being transferred into bets. However we advise anyone still not sure of God's existence to maybe hedge their bets for now, just in case."

There's a section of the world population today exhibiting a strange schizophrenia. They want to push the bounds of science to know more about the world and its origins, but they are selective about what they want the conclusions to tell them. They don't mind playing god through genetic modification and cloning, yet are uncomfortably aware that they are not the ones creating anything. They put the pieces together in a lab and something else takes over from there. What frightens humanism is the thought of going the next mile for fear of what it will find. Intrinsic in the belief in evolution is the desire to dominate everything from birth to death, or at least have unintelligent causes as the architect. It's about control. Design theory terrifies the humanist because if design is proved, then there's a Designer and man's rule is over. And if a Designer, there's likely accountability. After all, who puts themselves out to design something as unique as the universe and then loses interest in why they did it in the first place?

The proof of the pudding

In evolution chatrooms on the Internet, the fear is evident in the ridicule and fervent denunciations. BeanCounter snorts.

"Scientific causes must have naturalistic explanations!" "Come up with any explanations you like about Earth and man's origins but design is excluded because it is not scientific!"

Biochemist Richard Dickerson, an elected member of the National Academy of Sciences, explains rule number 1 in his profession:

"Operational science takes no position about the existence or non-existence of the supernatural [a Creator]; it only requires that this factor is not to be invoked in scientific explanations. Calling down special-purpose miracles as explanations constitutes a form of intellectual 'cheating'. A chess player is perfectly capable of removing his opponent's king physically from the board and smashing it in the midst of a tournament. But this would not make him a chess champion because the rules had not been followed."[26]

Obviously, Dr Dickerson does take a position. Early writings must be discounted since they invoke a design conclusion, even though….

"…it may be stated categorically that no archaeological discovery has ever controverted a Biblical reference," – Palestinian archaeologist Nelson Gluek in *Rivers in the Desert*, 1959, p.31

Today, intelligent design comes in for a bashing, yet science has used design inference for years as a means of settling truth. Archaeologists like Nelson Gluek exist for no other reason than to dig up artefacts and ponder whether they were formed from

---

[26] **Dickerson, Richard** *Journal of Molecular Evolution,* 34, 277, 1992

natural processes or human design. To biochemist Michael Behe this is standard operating procedure:

"The inference to design can be made with a high degree of confidence even when the designer is very remote. Archaeologists digging for a lost city might come across square stones buried dozens of feet under the earth, with pictures of camels and cats, griffins and dragons. Even if that were all they found, they would conclude that the stones had been designed....

The conclusion that something was designed can be made quite independently of knowledge of the designer. As a matter of procedure, the design must first be apprehended before there can be any further question about the designer. The inference to design can be held with all the firmness that is possible in this world without knowing anything about the designer."[27]

Forensics too is about design. Did the vicar fall or was he pushed? Detectives use design theory to uncover a felon perpetrating fraud on a company. Cryptographers have advanced training in design theory to detect and break enemy codes. And let's not forget that when Jodie Foster's astrophysicist in the movie *Contact* infers alien design in the prime number sequence she's plucked from the ether, evolutionist Carl Sagan, who wrote the book the film was based on, had no problem with any of it so long as it wasn't the God Alien. In fighting for her chance to be the one selected to meet said aliens, Jodie Foster's character interestingly states:

"What is more likely? That an all-powerful, mysterious God created the universe and then decided not to give any proof of His existence, or that He simply does not exist at all?"

In the film, the time machine the scientists have built to visit the aliens with is blown up by – you guessed it – a goggle-eyed religious maniac quoting scripture.

---

[27] Behe, Michael, *Darwin's Black Box,* op. cit. p.197

The big problem for Sagan, Dawkins and the others is, of course, that the world and its wonders *look* designed and this can now be concluded scientifically.

"Biology is the study of complicated things," Dawkins admits, "that give the appearance of having been designed for a purpose."[28]

Yet, as a world humanist authority, he must refute design or be finished professionally. Richard Dawkins is by all means a charming man, yet all too keenly aware he has thrust his colours into the dirt and must fight or fall by his banner. What at first sight appears a rather unscientific position to take has an altogether more interesting explanation. Dawkins is a product of the evolutionary establishment which trained him in Descartian, matter-only biochemistry. Tangible stuff is the only empiricism. Richard Lewontin, Professor of Zoology and Biology at Harvard University, paints the scientific paradox this way:

"Our willingness to accept scientific claims that are against common sense is the key to an understanding of the real struggle between science and the supernatural. We take the side of science in spite of the patent absurdity of some of its constructs, in spite of its failure to fulfill many of its extravagant promises of health and life, in spite of the tolerance of the scientific community for unsubstantiated just-so stories, because we have a prior commitment, a commitment to materialism. It is not that the methods and institutions of science somehow compel us to accept a material explanation of the phenomenal world, but, on the contrary, that we are forced by our *a priori* adherence to material causes to create an apparatus of investigation and a set of concepts that produce material explanations, no matter how counter-intuitive, no matter how mystifying

---

[28] **Dawkins, Richard** *The Blind Watchmaker: Why the Evidence of Evolution Reveals a Universe Without Design,* Penguin Books, London, 1987

to the uninitiated. Moreover, that materialism is absolute, for we cannot allow a Divine Foot in the door."[29]

The problem is, the world is *biophysical*, not biochemical. Biochemical materialism cannot account for a thought, the mind, remote cell communication, values, morals, psychoneuro-immunology, information, placebo, the desire for belief, the origin of conscience, the spirit, soul, Freud's ego or consciousness, the indefinable part of us that departs upon death. Since they cannot account for it, evolutionists mostly ignore it. Dr Bruce Lipton explains:

"In the seventeenth century, René Descartes dismissed the idea that the mind influences the physical character of the body. Descartes' notion was that the physcial body was made out of matter and the mind was made out of an unidentified, but clearly immaterial substance. Because he couldn't identify the nature of the mind, Descartes left behind an irresolvable philosophical conundrum: since only matter can affect matter, how can an immaterial mind be 'connected' to a material body? The non-physical mind envisioned by Descartes was popularly defined as the 'Ghost in the Machine' by Gilbert Ryle fifty years ago in his book, *The Concept of the Mind*. Traditional biomedicine, whose science is based upon a Newtonian matter-only universe, embraced Descartes separation of mind and body. Medically speaking, it would be far easier to fix a mechanical body without having to deal with its meddling 'ghost'."[30]

Which poses a major problem for John Haldane, late Professor of Genetics at London University:

"It seems to me immensely unlikely that mind is a mere by-product of matter. For if my mental processes are determined wholly by the motions of atoms in my brain I have no reason to suppose that my beliefs are true. They may be sound chemically, but that does not make them sound logically. And hence I have no reason for supposing my

---

[29] **Lewontin RC** "Billions and Billions of Demons", Review of **Sagan, Carl** *The Demon-Haunted World: Science as a Candle in the Dark*, New York Review, 9th January 1997

[30] **Lipton, Bruce** *The Biology of Belief*, Elite Books, USA, 2005, pp.124-125

brain to be composed of atoms. In order to escape from this necessity of sawing away the branch on which I am sitting, so to speak, I am compelled to believe that mind is not wholly conditioned by matter."[31]

Richard Dawkins refuses to go where the evidence leads him because he cannot, and so falls foul of the most basic, scientific no-no. He allows his prejudices to dictate his conclusions, driving even his atheist colleagues mad. Alister McGrath, Professor of Theology at Oxford, writes:

"Dawkins is forced to contend with the highly awkward fact that his view that the natural sciences are an intellectual superhighway to atheism is rejected by most scientists, irrespective of their religious views. Most unbelieving scientists of my acquaintance are atheists on grounds other than their science; they bring those assumptions *to* their science, rather than basing them *on* their science. Indeed, if my own personal conversations with scientists are anything to go by, some of Dawkins' most vociferous critics within their number are actually atheists. His petulant, dogmatic insistence that all 'real' scientists ought to be atheists has met with fierce resistance from precisely the community that he believes should be his fiercest and most loyal supporter. Dawkins clearly has no mandate to speak for the scientific community at this point on this topic."[32]

Dawkins' hypocrisy is no more noteworthy than that of the religious bigots he condemns who once hounded Copernicus. For two thousand years the top minds believed they were looking at design because the world *looked* designed. Today, the new information sciences have put the cat among the pigeons. Out goes 'If it looks like a duck, walks like a duck and quacks like a duck, it's a duck', to be replaced by scientific methodology which can really bang in the tent-pegs. And just as Darwin proposed his theory at a time when the modern tools of science were unavailable to unhorse

---

[31] **Haldane JBS** "When I Am Dead", in *Possible Worlds: And Other Essays*, Chatto and Windus, London, 1932, p.209
[32] McGrath, A, *The Dawkins Delusion*, op. cit. p.21

him, Dawkins is in a much more invidious position. Stuffed so far down the evolution rabbit-hole now, he must come out, teeth bared and snapping, or vanish. Personally, I would not be disappointed if Dawkins continued to dig.

Religious nuts

A significant chunk of the scientific community is waking up to the evolution versus intelligent design (ID) argument, and many of them don't want to. Others are excited that measurable design might herald the quantum leap in science everyone's been looking for, except that it leads to the God Alien. Others tenaciously hold the Biblical view of man's origins for no other reason than that the 'young Earth' has never been scientifically debunked. Dr D Russell Humphries, a nuclear physicist who works at Sandia National Laboratories, states:

"Using a simple statistical approach, I would conservatively estimate that in the United States alone there are 10,000 practising professional scientists who openly believe in a six-day, recent creation."[33]

But the bonfires have been lit for the heretics. In his documentary *Expelled, No Intelligence Allowed*, Ben Stein interviews several top scientists who have felt the hot singe of the secular Inquisition. After Professor Caroline Crocker mentioned intelligent design in her cell biology class at George Mason University (*'Think. Learn. Succeed'*), she was disciplined by her supervisor and lost her job at semester's end for 'teaching creationism'. Prof. Crocker laments:

"Whenever I was interviewed for a job, I would usually be offered it on the spot. Since this has happened, and since people can Google my

---

[33] www.answersingenesis.org/home/area/bios/default.asp.
A comprehensive list and biographies of some of these are listed on the *Answers in Genesis* website.

name, I'm finding that when I send my credentials, I do get interviews – many interviews – but I never get offered a job."[34]

When neurosurgeon Michael Egnor MD, Professor of State University of New York Stony Brook, wrote a paper for high school students, in which he declared that studying Darwinism was not necessary for doctors to practise medicine, the execution was swift.

"A lot of people on a lot of blogs called me unprintable names that were printed. There were a lot of very nasty comments. Other people suggested that people call the university I worked at, suggesting perhaps it's time for me to retire. I realised that when I went public with my doubts about the inadequacy of Darwin's theory that I would incur criticism. What has amazed me is the viciousness and the baseness of it."[35]

Astronomer Dr Guillermo Gonzalez of Iowa State University enjoyed an unimpeachable career, during which he discovered several planets. Upon publishing his book, *The Privileged Planet*, in which he argued that the universe shows unmistakable evidence of design, his application for continued tenure was declined.

"People really get emotional about this," rues Dr Gonzalez. "Whenever you say 'Intelligent Design' in a room full of academics, them's fighting words!"[36]

Donald Gould, former editor of *New Scientist*, writes:

"The scientific establishment bears a grisly resemblance to the Spanish Inquisition. Either you accept the rules and attitudes and beliefs promulgated by the 'papacy' (for which read, perhaps, the Royal Society or the Royal College of Physicians), or face a dreadful retribution. We will not actually burn you at the stake, because that sanction, unhappily, is

---

[34] *Expelled – No Intelligence Allowed,* Premise Media Corporation, op. cit.
[35] Ibid.
[36] Ibid.

now no longer available under our milksop laws. But we will make damned sure that you are a dead duck in our trade."[37]

Burn in Hell

When the boot is on the other foot, the feelings on both sides are revealed. Wildlife veteran Sir David Attenborough complains that:

"Christian viewers have told him to 'burn in hell' because of his views on evolution. The 82-year-old broadcaster says his accusers, from the more fundamentalist wings of Christianity, have attacked him in hate mail for not giving credit to God in his wildlife programs. Talking to *Radio Times*, he said:

"They always mean beautiful things like hummingbirds. I always reply by saying that I think of a little child in East Africa with a worm burrowing through his eyeball. The worm cannot live in any other way, except by burrowing through eyeballs. I find that hard to reconcile with the notion of a divine and benevolent creator."[38]

And so the argument rages. And the crocodile only survives by surging out of the waterhole and snagging the antelope. Yet the more savaging the debate engenders, the more proof we have that beliefs are shaping the arguments, not science. But we *can* observe with our eyes and draw sensible conclusions, and a group of eminent scientists has been doing just that since the mid-eighties.

Today, Seattle's Discovery Institute is viewed by Darwinists as the viper's nest of intelligent design, 'which sucks in money from wealthy religious investors to produce a sanitised, quasi-scientific creationism for the schools'. On the other side, ID scientists view themselves as legitimate enquirers of scientific evidence which cannot be explained by the standard model. If it leads to a design

---

[37] **Gould D** "Letting poetry loose in the laboratory", *New Scientist*, 29th August 1992, p.51
[38] www.dailymail.co.uk/news/article-1127826/My-vicious-hate-mail-ordeal-Attenborough-evolutionist.html

inference, so be it. That's how cryptography, forensics and fraud detection work. What's so different about origins science?

With all the accusations of religious bias, however, it goes unsaid that every branch of science over the past 400 years was founded by creationists and, most noteworthy, not a single useful advancement in science has emerged through the study of evolution. Darwinists level recriminations against others, yet theirs is a fear of asking just three simple questions. Is there empirical evidence for design in the world? How can we tell? And how do we quantify design?

Evidence of design - irreducible complexity

Dr Wernher von Braun, designer of the Nazi V2 combat rocket and father of America's manned space program, stated:

"One cannot be exposed to the law and order of the universe without concluding that there must be design and purpose behind it all.... To be forced to believe only one conclusion— that everything in the universe happened by chance—would violate the very objectivity of science itself.... They [evolutionists] challenge science to prove the non-existence of God. But must we really light a candle to see the sun? It is in scientific honesty that I endorse the presentation of alternative theories for the origin of the universe, life and man in the science classroom. It would be an error to overlook the possibility that the universe was planned rather than happened by chance."[39]

Must all be there

A mousetrap contains a handful of components which, when arranged a certain way, provide the mousetrap's function of killing a mouse. No-one has a problem believing the mousetrap had a designer and that the bits go together in a certain order. Many over the years have sought to improve it, but the fact that we still have

---

[39] **Hovind, K** *Creation seminars series*, www.drdino.com

the same old mousetrap down at the hardware store means that no-one came up with a better one.

Notice the five components to the mousetrap are essential and cannot be reduced further and still retain function. *There is no functional precursor system.* If any one of the parts is removed, you do not catch four-fifths of the mice, you lose complete function. Thus the system is said by design theorists to be 'irreducibly complex' and evidence for design. A mousetrap cannot have evolved because there is no working precursor system from which natural selection could select a beneficial mutation.

Another point made by biochemist Michael Behe is that the components alone are not enough to cause a mousetrap to function. The mousetrap has to be assembled. The components must be made of a material conducive to anticipated forces. The tolerances must be correct.

"If the base were made out of paper, for example, the trap would fall apart. If the hammer were too heavy, it would break the spring. If the spring were too loose, it would not move the hammer. If the holding bar were too short, it would not reach the catch…"[40]

Minimal function of a system, Behe contends, is vital for the process of natural selection to occur. Since irreducibly complex systems have no working precursors by dint of their make-up, they cannot have evolved.

How do we detect design?

Mathematician Dr William A Dembski has shown that design can be measured using a set of clearly defined protocols he names 'the explanatory filter'. Firstly, he reasons that the origins of observed phenomena in the universe can be explained by any one of three causes:

1) Chance

---

[40] Behe, Michael, *Darwin's Black Box,* op. cit. p.45

2) Necessity (the result of natural laws)

3) Design

The more complex the working system, the less chance it derived by chance:

"To see the connection between complexity and probability, consider a combination lock. The more possible combinations of the lock, the more complex the mechanism, and correspondingly the more improbable the mechanism can be opened by chance.... Complexity and probability therefore vary inversely: the greater the complexity, the smaller the probability. Thus to determine whether something is sufficiently complex to warrant a design inference is to determine whether it has sufficiently small probability."[41]

Dembski sets the Universal Probability Bound at 1×10^{150}. Beyond these odds, an event occurring by chance is so improbable, it can be scientifically discounted. Most scientists don't argue with this. They do argue, however, when William Williams' calculations for a whole raft of Earthly phenomena occurring 'by chance' demonstrate that when the chance probabilities are calculated for just for a handful, Dembski's threshold is rapidly exceeded. And there are literally dozens of examples to choose from, as we shall see.

Dembski cites the example of a rat being made to navigate a maze. If the maze only involves two right turns before the exit, chance figures prominently in the rat being able to escape its confines. If the maze requires twenty or so 'choices' to escape, then a rat negotiating the puzzle successfully will lead one to surmise intelligence on behalf of the rat (the ability to make choices and memorise). This is the protocol sometimes used in such rat experiments.

---

[41] **Dembski William A** *The Third Mode of Explanation,* The Proceedings of the Wethersfield Institute, 1999. Published in *Science and Evidence for Design in the Universe,* Ignatius Press, San Francisco, 2000

Specificity

The next marker Dembski requires is independent specificity. This means agreeing on a specification in advance, which we know for sure has been constructed using intelligence. Language is a good example. Imagine we came across the following Scrabble letters spilled on a beach.

HEOUTESELOTAPHRIAMFN

The above sequence appears random and does not conform to any prior specification, at least not in the English language. If a monkey prints out the above on a typewriter, we would not confer advanced linguistics on the simian – he just pounded the keys and got fed up. If we came upon these Scrabble letters in the sand, there's something else we can infer. Because the letters are scrambled and not laid out in a line, we have no problem inferring chance. The basic specification for the English language is that letters are laid out next to each other, aligned to a base. Even if they are found as above, this does not necessarily infer design. Natural laws, such as those governing the tides, may have conspired to arrange them in a line. It's thin but it could happen. Notice the longer the sentence, the greater the complexity and the less probable the phenomenon occurred by chance. So how did the letters get there? Perhaps someone was carrying Scrabble letters along the beach and a few slipped out and fell onto the sand.

Next day, you walk your dog along the same beach and find, to your surprise, the letters have been lined up to spell:

THEHOUSESOFPARLIAMENT

There's still a chance this could have happened by accident, albeit 1 chance in 26^{21}, times the odds of each letter aligning to a base. But you are an evolutionist so you're used to long shots, and besides, you're well short of Dembski's 10^{150} threshold. The following day, throwing Fido the stick, you return to find gaps have been put between some of the letters to form

THE HOUSES OF PARLIAMENT

This increases the plausibility of design but again is not conclusive. This is a relatively simple system – three or four turns in the maze – so you're not yet uncorking the Bollinger. The following morning you find the same letters are there, only this time they have re-arranged themselves to form:

LOONIES FAR UP THE THAMES

Now you're suspicious. Why? This looks like design but you are an evolutionist so you swallow hard and work out the numbers. 26^{21} x 26^{21} before you add in the odds of the letters being aligned to a base with the right gaps. Perhaps you're also unsettled that the second phrase seems not only a cynical commentary on the first, but information is being conveyed in the words; namely, *there are loonies far up the Thames.* Not only that, the letters are made of hard plastic, not paper or grass, which could infer intent to avoid damage by the tide. Someone wants you to have this information and the medium (plastic) has been chosen (design). The next day, you return and the letters have shifted again:

THE SHAMEFUL OPERATIONS

Further multiplication ensues. The odds are by this time so long, you decide intelligent design is the most likely explanation. Someone's playing Scrabble anagrams on the beach. Also, the three phrases taken together appear to convey contextual information, perhaps even humour - another sign of design. What are the chances natural processes such as the wind or tide could have had a hand in this?

Rock on

At Mount Rushmore, near Keystone, South Dakota, thousands of tourists arrive each year to study a rocky anomaly. Faces have been carved into the mountainside which, using an independent, predetermined specification of what a human face looks like, leads us to believe intelligence was behind the carved portraits of four of America's presidents. On the other hand, if you were one of Carl Sagan's aliens visiting the planet and did not know Mount Rushmore from a natural feature, you may note that the contours of the faces are anomalous, as are the rock formations around them. Yet you have studied man from your spaceship for some time now and watched his TV transmissions, so you possess a predetermined specificity on what the human face looks like, with which you conclude that intelligence is at work in the construction of the rock-face anomaly. Archaeologists use this technique to decipher a lump of natural rock from a genuine arrowhead or a fossil. William Dembski posits another angle.

"The principle characteristic of intelligent agency is choice…. For an intelligent agency to act is therefore to choose from a range of competing possibilities…. Intelligent agency always entails discrimination, choosing certain things, ruling out others." [42]

This is a simplification of the ingenious diagnostic Dembski gives to determine whether design is at work rather than chance or necessity. Professor Stephen C Meyer explains:

"Chance best explains events of small or intermediate probability; necessity (or physical/chemical law) best explains events of high probability; and intelligent design best explains small probability events that also manifest specificity (of function, for example)…. When events

---

[42] Dembski William A, *The Third Mode of Explanation,* op. cit. p.41

are both highly improbable and specified (by an independent pattern), we can reliably detect the activity of intelligent agents."[43]

[43] Ibid. p.55

THE MACRO UNIVERSE

Evidence of design in large structures

"The Cosmos is all that is or ever was or ever will be…"

– Carl Sagan[44]

Is Earth's place in the universe significant? Do studies reveal anything of Earth's uniqueness, or do we inhabit just one planet among millions or billions of other worlds that could host life? Most of what a citizen knows of the universe comes through school and college education as well as TV documentaries and magazines with an evolutionary bias. But if we pause and ponder for a moment as I did at Charterhouse, an altogether more intriguing picture emerges.

It is evident that we are inside the workings of a cosmic machine that operates flawlessly according to the known and yet to be discovered laws of science, yet the sheer size of the universe boggles the mind. On 5th September 1977, when the unmanned spacecraft Voyager was launched on a mission to examine Jupiter and Saturn, few could imagine the insights the probe would provide on its lonely trip into the unknown. The most poignant moment was when the 1500 lb craft completed its assignments and rotated to photograph us for the last time before heading off into the dark. Among the pictures sent back to Earth was one iconic print of a belt of light with a tiny, almost invisible pale blue dot suspended in the centre. Atheist Carl Sagan was unimpressed:

"Because of the reflection of sunlight, the Earth seems to be sitting in a beam of light, as if there were some significance to this small world. But it's just an accident of geometry and optics. Look again at that dot. That's here. That's home. That's us. Our posterings, our imagined self-importance, the delusion that we have some privileged position in the

---

[44] **Sagan, Carl** *Cosmos,* Macdonald, London, 1981, p.4

universe, are challenged by this point of pale light. Our planet is a lonely speck in the great enveloping cosmic dark."[45]

Copernicus's discovery of the sol-centric solar system developed over the following centuries into what has come to be known as the Copernican Principle. This holds that the Earth is not unique, the universe does not have us in mind, and we have no preferred place in the cosmos. We are just one insignificant planet in an enormous universe of other planets and stars. This position is widely accepted in science and taught in schools and universities today, yet a growing body of scientists has begun to question Earth's 'mediocrity' precisely because our planet's very existence is such a surprise.

After *Star Trek*, we've come to assume that the universe is in the habitable-planet-making business. Donald Brownlee, professor of astronomy at UC Berkeley and principal investigator on the NASA Stardust mission, disagrees.

"The entire universe is highly hostile to life. If you compare all the known places in the universe, none of them compares to Earth. We live in a very special environment that provides what we need; provides air, food, stable conditions, so the Earth is almost like a giant organism in which its systems are interacting in a way that allows animals to survive. The real question is why did this happen? Is it just a matter of luck or not?"[46]

In his book, *Rare Earth: Why Complex Life is Uncommon in the Universe*, Brownlee makes the point that while single cell organisms may well survive on other planets, the precise conditions required to support *complex* life-forms such as humans and animals remain unique to Earth.[47] In this respect, we won the

---

[45] **Sagan, Carl** *Pale Blue Dot*, Ballantine Books Inc, 1997

[46] *The Privileged Planet* documentary, www.illustramedia.com

[47] **Ward, Peter & Donald Brownlee** *Rare Earth: Why Complex Life is Uncommon in the Universe*, Springer, 2009

cosmic lottery and Earth is a lucky planet. But does *luck* have anything to do with it?

Big space

In the early half of the 20th century, astronomer Edwin Hubble laid bare the enormity of the universe from the Mount Wilson Observatory above Los Angeles, California. For the first time, galaxies by the thousand were seen comprising billions of stars with astonishing variety, *and they were rushing away,* which meant the universe had to have had a beginning (a Big Bang). And there was our Earth in the middle of it all, or maybe on the edge. Nothing special. A pale blue dot. The ultimate vindication of the Copernican Principle which paved the way for stellar evolution and the search for extraterrestrial life.

There had to be more of us out there.

Does the observable evidence vindicate the Copernican Principle? Can we know for sure that we have no special place or purpose in the vastness of space? Can science, by extrapolating the number of planets around innumerable stars across countless galaxies, conclude that countless planets like Earth hosting innumerable life-forms *must* exist?

Programs like *Star Trek, Star Wars, ET* and *Contact* explore these themes in the realm of science fiction. Real scientific projects such as SETI, the Search for Extraterrestrial Intelligence, base their work on the premise that there is intelligent life out there, and radio dishes around the world monitor electromagnetic emissions from distant stars for signs of ET intelligence. To date there has not been any official contact with extraterrestrial life, at least so far as the News at Ten and SETI are concerned. The meaningless static returning to Earth's radio arrays bears witness to an alien species that either is not talking, or does not exist in the first place.

But while the notion that we live in a universe brimming with life is still good box-office today, the Copernican Principle has hit the skids due to recent discoveries in the information sciences and astronomy. These can be summarised as the Anthropic Principle - the most exciting scientific breakthrough you won't be reading in your newspapers any time soon.

Chance, really?

The Privileged Planet by Jay Richards and Guillermo Gonzalez opens up the idea that Earth's existence is remarkable, not least from the standpoint of being so scientifically unexpected. The Anthropic Principle holds that for life to be possible, a multitude of finely calibrated constants and ratios must exist. What are the chances any one of these happened by chance? And if so, by what processes? The Big Bang? We will see in a minute that an explosion does not pass muster. All explosions are destructive and undo cohesion. From the forces operating within an atom to the laws governing gravity, the tides and the planets, the surprise of the sheer *ordered* nature of the universe should bring us up short. The further miracle of Earth's existence is reflected in the many finely tuned conditions that must exist for the planet, let alone humankind to survive.

Total eclipse

Dr Guillermo Gonzalez was an astrobiologist at Iowa State University and member of NASA's astrobiology program. He began his career believing there to be other civilisations amid galaxies teeming with life. One event he later witnessed planted doubt in his mind for the first time. On 24th October 1995, Gonzalez saw a total eclipse of the sun in Northern India. As the moon passed across the face of the sun, Gonzalez experienced the marvel felt by many of his peers in the centuries before – that for a total eclipse to be possible, the sun, moon and Earth have to be aligned precisely in such a way that the moon's diameter perfectly eclipses the sun. Science just accepts that this happens without considering the odds. What are the chances that our moon appears the same size as the sun from the Earth? Is it mere coincidence that the sun is 400 times bigger than the moon yet 400 times further away?

The size of the moon and its orbit are finely calibrated to stabilise the orbit of the Earth at 23.5%. If the moon were a little further in, the tides would swamp the continents. A little further out and the Earth would wander off-orbit. Another coincidence? If the sun were smaller or larger, the circumstellar habitable zone of our solar system would change, and if Earth did not move with it, no life would be possible. Yet here we are.

The Flash Spectrum

A total eclipse leaves a tiny disc around the edge of the phenomenon in the 51 seconds of totality, during which electromagnetic emissions from the sun's chromosphere can be observed without blinding the viewer. This unique opportunity is *only* afforded by the precise dimensions of the sun and moon. A percentage or two difference in measurement either way and stellar astrophysics would never have left the stables. As it is, studying the sun's chromosphere during a total eclipse gave us the electromagnetic spectrum, and from that we can deduce how other stars and planets work. We are creatures of discovery!

A study of the electromagnetic band given off by our sun's chromosphere – the Flash Spectrum – reveals another miracle. Namely that within the vast band of solar radiation emitted by our sun, which ranges from gamma through x-ray to ultraviolet to infrared, microwave and radio, there exists an impossibly narrow zone of visible light in the middle, by which all things live and can be seen. This visible spectrum comprises only *1 trillion of a trillionth* of the entire range of the universe's electromagnetic emissions. And imagine that this just so happens to be the light spectrum our sun emits in abundance, which can penetrate our wafer-thin atmosphere in precise amounts to be used by plants, animals and humans for life.

"It's a surprise," says Gonzalez. "It's something you wouldn't expect just chance to produce. Why would the universe be such that those places that are most habitable also offer the best opportunity for scientific discovery?"[48]

It just so happens that Earth is in the optimal position in the solar system from which to observe a total eclipse. Gonzalez made a study of the other planets and moons in our system and found that the best place to observe a total solar eclipse is from the surface of the only planet which hosts complex life capable of observing and remarking on it! Of the 70-odd planets and moons (excluding Earth), only seven have atmospheres, all opaque, to whom the universe is invisible and unknown. Only Earth has a special, low-carbon, transparent atmosphere which, apart from hosting just the right chemical mix to allow life to flourish on the surface (coincidence), enables observers on the planet to gaze through its sheen into the universe beyond (more coincidence). This facility is also only made possible *due to the Earth's precise positioning* in the Milky Way galaxy – as it happens, in the galactic habitable zone between two spiral arms from which is afforded a dust-free view into deep space. What luck!

Other anthropic factors

Atmosphere: Earth is the only planet found so far with liquid water in abundance, critical for the sustenance of life and the accurate regulation of the surface temperature of the planet. The oxygen-nitrogen mix of the atmosphere is precisely right for carbon-based life-forms to thrive. It just so happens also that our paper thin atmosphere provides climate with which to water plants and humans.

---

[48] *The Privileged Planet* documentary, www.illustramedia.com

Distance from parent star: Earth's distance from its parent star is finely calibrated and critical. 5% closer and the atmosphere would be boiled off in the heat and Earth's rotation halted. Half the planet would roast while the other half remained in perpetual darkness and ice. 20% further away and the oceans would freeze.

In *The Privileged Planet,* Richards and Gonzalez cite the opening requirements for Planet Earth to be habitable:

- Earth has to lie within the galactic habitable zone
- It has to orbit a special type of star, in this case a main sequence G2 dwarf star
- It has to be protected by gas giant planets capable of drawing away comets
- It must exist within the circumstellar (solar) habitable zone
- It must have a nearly circular orbit
- It must host an oxygen-rich atmosphere
- The planet must have the correct mass
- Must be a terrestrial planet
- Must be orbited by a large moon
- Have a thin enough crust to host plate tectonics which recycle carbon, mix elements and release heat from within
- Must have the correct ratio of liquid water to continents
- Must have a moderate rate of rotation[49]

Yet here we are, all perfectly done, completely by chance. Despite his evolutionary stance, co-discoverer of DNA, Francis Crick, is not so certain:

"An honest man, armed with all the knowledge available to us now, could only state that in some sense, the origin of life appears at the

---

[49] Ibid.

moment to be almost a miracle, so many are the conditions which would have had to have been satisfied to get it going."[50]

Fading attraction: Then there's the Earth's magnetic field which, it so happens, is just right, generated from the rotating molten iron core of the planet. The field acts as a protective shield around the Earth to ward off solar radiation which would otherwise kill us. If the size of the Earth were smaller, the magnetic field would be weaker and the solar winds would strip off the atmosphere, transforming our planet into a barren rock. Any stronger and the magnetic field would kill all life on Earth.

The weak nuclear force, the strong nuclear force, Boltzmann's Constant, proton and electron mass, atomic mass, speed of light, gravity, Planck's Constant, the list goes on. All these factors have to be present and fine-tuned at precisely the same time and place for life to be possible on Earth, or anywhere else for that matter. And then there's the surprise part, say Gonzalez and Richards:

"The same narrow circumstances that allow us to exist also provide us with the best overall setting for making scientific discoveries."[51]

Why would we ever develop the skill to discover Planck's Constant when this is surplus to the requirements of Darwinian evolution? It's a skill we do not need and yet we have it. Dembski and McDowell write:

"Einstein once remarked that the most incomprehensible thing about the world is that it is comprehensible. In fact, he saw the world's comprehensibility as a miracle (his word) that the increase in scientific knowledge constantly reinforced. Nature is not the confusing world of Alice in Wonderland but an orderly place that our minds seem ideally suited to understand. This is one of the great questions confronting the scientist: Why is the world ordered and what is the origin of that order? If

[50] **Crick, F** *Life Itself: Its Origin and Nature,* Simon and Schuster, New York, 1981, p.88
[51] **Richards, Jay W and Guillermo Gonzalez** *The Privileged Planet,* Regnery Pub, 2004

the world evolved without a guiding intelligence, why should we be able to understand it at all? If the human mind evolved for the sake of survival, why should it be trusted?"[52]

The authors go on to quote Templeton Prize-winning physicist Paul Davies:

"Science is based on the assumption that the universe is thoroughly rational and logical at every level. Atheists claim that the laws [of nature] exist reasonlessly and that the universe is ultimately absurd. As a scientist I find this hard to accept. There must be an unchanging, rational ground in which the logical, orderly nature of the universe is rooted."[53]

Gravity, magnetism, chemistry, biophysics and astronomy all owe their persuasion to natural laws, minutely calibrated. If designed, they are the product of an infinite mind. William Williams reviews the complexity of these systems:

"The Earth turns over noiselessly every 24 hours, carrying on its bosom, at the rate of 1000 mph, at dizzy heights, a most tenuous atmosphere, without a rustle…. The Earth with its satellite is travelling around the sun at the rate of 18.5 miles a second – 75 times as fast as a cannon ball – bearing a load of 6,000,000,000,000,000,000,000 tons, and arriving at a given point in its orbit on exact time every tropical year. It has arrived so promptly on time following its eliptical course and at such a rate that the radius vector, a line from the sun to the Earth, passes over equal areas in equal times, furnishing each moment an abtruse problem difficult for a scholar to solve. The orbit is so vast that it varies from a straight line but 4 inches in 666 miles, the distance from Philadelphia to Chicago."[54]

Every raindrop that falls. The dynamics of a storm. Countless chemical reactions occurring in our bodies every second. The human body in all its function. The bumble bee. The mosquito. No-

---

[52] Dembski, W A & Sean McDowell, *Understanding Intelligent Design,* op. cit. p.32

[53] Ibid.

[54] **Williams, William** *The Evolution of Man Scientifically Disproved*, Bibliobazaar, 2007

one doubts the laws which govern them flawlessly operate, but whose laws? Where did they come from? And what keeps them in place?

The Big Bang

For centuries, men held to the Bible's view of our origins. Today, scientists are going back to those early accounts because they contain observations that can be verified scientifically. Most notable is the Bible's assertion of a young universe, in spite of the critics.

From Bishop James Ussher's literal take on Biblical chronology, Creation occurs around 4004BC. Earth's special place in the cosmos is gleaned in the very first verse of Genesis which declares, "**In the beginning, God created the heavens and the Earth.**" (Gen 1:1) Of all the heavenly bodies created, Earth alone is singled out for special mention. Some believe this is Earth's story from man's point of view, yet the Bible makes it clear it is man's story from the Designer's point of view. Some believe there was a pre-Adamic race existing prior to Genesis 1:1 which was annihilated. Nothing in subsequent scripture confirms this.

For evolutionists, the most likely scenario for Earth's creation is not 'God', but that matter coalesced into a ball of energy the size of a dot and then exploded in a 'Big Bang' (creation!). All galaxies were formed from this primordial detonation along with our own solar system, the planets and Earth. Here is the standard school textbook explanation with this writer's italics:

"How was the universe born and how will it end? Most astronomers *believe* that about 18 to 20 billion years ago all the matter in the universe was concentrated into one very dense, very hot region that *may have* been smaller than a period [full-stop] on this page. *For some unknown reason*, this region exploded. This explosion is called the Big Bang."[55] This will

---

[55] **Prentice Hall** *General Science*, 1992, p.61

allegedly re-occur as the universe remakes itself: "In a closed universe, a big bang *may* occur once every 80 to 100 billion years."[56]

Another book your child is taught states:

"In the realm of the universe, nothing really means nothing. Not only matter and energy would disappear, but also space and time. However, physicists theorize that from a state of nothingness the universe began in a gigantic explosion about 16.5 billion years ago. This theory of the origin of the universe is called the Big Bang."[57]

At least one or two people are blushing. This from *Discovery* magazine:

"The universe burst into something from absolutely nothing – zero, nada. And as it got bigger, it became filled with even more stuff that came from absolutely nowhere. How is that possible? Ask Alan Guth. His theory of inflation helps explain everything."[58]

But Alan Guth hasn't a clue. "The observable universe could have evolved from an infinitesimal region. It's then tempting to go one step further and speculate that the entire universe evolved from literally nothing."[59]

So originally there was nothing, then it exploded. Kent Hovind is outraged. "We all came from a dot and the dot came from nothing? And they call that science and put it in a science journal?"[60]

Conservation of angular momentum

Firstly, nothing that explodes goes from simple to complex, the reverse is always observed. If I crash a million cars into a million walls, I'll never make a better one. Secondly, Hovind contends that if everything originated from a spinning dot which exploded, then all the bits flying off should be rotating in the same direction,

---

[56] **Prentice Hall** *Earth Science,* 1999, p.63

[57] **Harcourt Brace Jovanovich** *General Science,* 1989, p.362

[58] "Where Did Everything Come From?" *Discover,* April 2002

[59] **Guth Alan & P Steinhardt** *Scientific American,* May 1984, p.128

[60] Hovind, Kent, *Creation seminar series,* op. cit.

according to the law of Conservation of Angular Momentum. They do not. Venus, Uranus and possibly Pluto rotate backwards from the six other planets. 8 out of the 91 moons rotate backwards. Jupiter, Saturn and Neptune have moons orbiting in both directions.[61]

Today, the modern version of the nebular hypothesis is taught in colleges and universities, known as the Solar Nebular Disk Model. The original thesis was derived by 17th century mystic Emmanuel Swedenborg, who alleged it had been given to him in a séance. The theory goes that at some point our sun exploded material outwards and the debris became the planets of our solar system. This is flatly rejected by most scientists, says Missler:

"The sun contains 99.86% of all the mass of the solar system, yet the sun contains only 1.9% of the angular momentum. The nine planets contain 98.1%.(This was known at the time of Laplace a century ago). There is no plausible explanation that would support a solar origin of the planets. James Jeans (1877-1946) pointed out that the outer planets are far larger than the inner ones. Jupiter is 5,750 as massive as Mercury, 2958 as massive as Mars, etc. This is also a difficulty with current theories."[62]

Why are the nine planets in our solar system so different in character if they all came from the sun? Why are the larger ones further away from the sun? Chuck Missler wants to know why Mars and Earth have identical spin-axis tilts (23.5⁰). Also why the orbital mechanics of three pairs of planets in our system are so strikingly similar. Mars and Earth, Saturn and Jupiter, and Neptune and Uranus all have spin-rates which are within 3% of their partner.[63]

---

[61] *Astronomical Almanac*, US Government Printing Office, Washington DC, 1989. p.E88

[62] www.khouse.org

[63] Ibid.

In a news item entitled *Goofy Galaxy Spins in Wrong Direction,* CNN reports:

"A galaxy captured by the camera of the Hubble Space Telescope seems to be rotating in the direction opposite of what it should, astonished astronomers announced this week."[64]

And H Reeves, a well known evolutionist solar-system scientist, writes:

"This [angular momentum] would have caused the sun to spin very rapidly. Actually, our sun spins very slowly, while the planets move very rapidly around the sun. In fact, although the sun has over 99% of the mass of the solar system, it has only 2% of the angular momentum. This pattern is directly opposite to the pattern predicted for the nebular hypothesis."[65]

Stuart Ross Taylor has no idea either: "The ultimate origin of the solar system's angular momentum remains obscure."[66]

No-one knows how stars form. Not even *Science* magazine has a good theory on how to compress matter into a star.

"The silent embarrassment of modern astrophysics is that we don't know how even a single one of these stars managed to form."[67]

Science News writes: "…no-one has unambiguously observed material falling into an embryonic star, which should be happening if the star is still truly forming. And no-one has caught a molecular cloud in the act of collapsing."[68]

---

[64] *CNN,* 11th February 2002

[65] **Reeves, H** *The Origin of the Solar System,* John Wiley and Sons, New York, 1978, p.9

[66] **Taylor, Stuart Ross** *Solar System Evolution: A New Perspective,* Cambridge University Press, 1992, p.53

[67] **Harwit, Martin** *Science,* vol. 231, 7th March 1986, pp.1201-1202

[68] **Peterson, Ivan** "The Winds of Starbirth", *Science News,* vol. 137, 30th June 1990, p.409

American astronomer Fred Lawrence Whipple states: "Precisely how a section of an interstellar cloud collapses gravitationally into a star – a double or multiple star, or a solar system – is still a challenging theoretical problem…. Astonomers have yet to find an interstellar cloud in the actual process of collapse." [69]

Of course, the Big Bang theory fails to answer the questions of where matter originally came from and who/what provided the energy for it to bang and organise. The Big Bang is taught today as fact, yet the only fact about the Big Bang is that no-one saw it bang, so it's a theory. A belief system. A religion.

Celebrated astronomer and cosmologist Sir Fred Hoyle states: "I have little hesitation in saying that a sickly pall now hangs over the Big Bang Theory."[70]

Charlie Campbell writes: "There are only three options for the existence of the universe. One, that it has always been. Two, that it came into being by itself. Three, that it was created. The first option, that the universe is eternal, has been utterly rejected by the scientific community. The motion of the galaxies, the background radiation echo, and other evidences all overwhelmingly point to the fact that the universe sprang into existence at a particular point in time, something scientists call the Big Bang. Option two, that the universe created itself, is philosophically impossible. Of course, before the universe existed it would not have been around to do the creating. Obviously, a non-existent universe could not have done anything! It did not exist. We all know that nothing cannot do anything. Nothing is nothing. It (if we could even call nothing an it!) cannot see, smell, act, think, or create. So option one and two can be thrown out on scientific and philosophical grounds. Option three, that something or someone outside of the universe created the universe, is the only reasonable option."[71]

---

[69] **Wipple, Fred L** *The Mystery of Comets,* Cambridge University Press, 1985, p.211, 213

[70] **Hoyle, Fred** "The Big Bang Theory Under Attack" *Science Digest,* vol 92, May 1984, p.84

[71] www.alwaysbeready.com

Kent Hovind has four possible ways the universe could have arrived: [72]

1) Infinite Creation:

The universe, matter and life have always existed but probably in different forms of matter throughout the aeons, i.e. galaxies formed through super-hot, gaseous clusters, suns evolved, etc. This doctrine holds that energy and matter have always existed in the cosmos, but perhaps not always in the form we see today.

2) Natural Generation (evolution):

The universe and earth came into being through an initial natural, generative process and life evolved thereafter.

3) Supra-Natural Generation (creation):

The universe, earth, life and all matter came into being through a process that was not 'natural' as science defines it today, which ended at the conclusion of the creation process. All matter, including vegetation, animals and man came into being during this creative process.

4) Nihilism:

The universe, earth, life and matter never existed at all.

Re-examine to ensure all eventualities are catered for. Under current rules, the above arguments can all be considered by science with the exception of Point #3, which is discounted because it raises design implications.

Point #1, Infinite Creation (Infinite Gradualism), posits that our existence is on-going, having arrived by a process of gradual evolution over billions or trillions of years. Point #1 holds that there

---

[72] www.drdino.com

was never a point of creation, either through a Big Bang or otherwise. It states that matter has always existed.

The problem with this belief, which became popular in the '60s as Darwinism grew holes, is that it contravenes the Second Law. Everyone knows the universe is 'rushing away' and breaking down. Entropy or decay kills our bodies and dissolves them, erodes cars and buildings, destroys nature and geological formations. The Second Law states that energy is becoming more random and disorganised as time passes, not the opposite. We may burn petrol in our cars, converting that energy into carbon monoxide and other gases, but we will not in a million years be able to get the petrol back into the tank once it has combusted.

If matter has been around forever, albeit in different forms, why has it not totally disorganised long before now, leaving us with a universe of random particles with no cohesion or organisation? How can Point #1, even from a scientific standpoint, be valid when it contravenes the most basic scientific laws?

Hubble's motion of the galaxies implies a finite start to the universe. Astronomer Stephen Hawking of Cambridge University agrees:

"Almost everyone believes that the universe, and time itself, had a beginning."[73]

Point #2, Natural Generation, states that there was an inception point, or Big Bang, which brought matter into being from nothing through 'natural' processes. The universe literally made itself. Life then evolved over millions of years into the nature we recognise today. This view, held by evolutionary science, contravenes not only the Law of Entropy, but also the First Law of Thermodynamics – the Law of Conservation. Nothing cannot

---

[73] **Hawking, S and R Penrose** *The Nature of Space and Time,* Princeton University Press, 1996, p.20

create nothing. A non-existent universe cannot create itself if it does not exist.

Matter cannot be created or destroyed. Ice, as a solid, can be melted into a liquid or sublimated into gas but the same amount of energy will always exist. The Law of Conservation states that there is a finite amount of energy or matter in the universe. Proof of this is acknowledged since we have never seen matter created out of nothing through a natural process, nor have we ever been able to destroy energy without transmuting it into another form. Yet incredibly, after spending thousands of pounds being educated into dumbness at top educational establishments, scientists happily accept that matter came from nowhere naturally, and energy is becoming more organised as time goes by (evolution), despite all indication to the contrary.

Dr Vernon McGee maintains that believing complex humanity somehow evolved from a 'Big Bang' is about as ludicrous as maintaining that the dictionary came into existence after a big explosion in a print shop. Point #2 (evolution) is a philosophical, logical and scientific impossibility. And evolution does not answer the basic question of where matter came from. More importantly, where did the information come from to organise it so precisely? Engineering scientist Chuck Missler states that the evolutionist cannot account for the origin of life because he cannot account for the origin of *information*.[74]

Point #4 is when science throws up its hands and passes the whole question over to the philosopher. It states that we never got here at all. Nihilism co-opts the phrase: "If a tree falls in a forest and is not heard, did it make a sound?" How are you defining 'sound'? As a wave, or as something that has to be heard? What is sound? A wave. Are waves generated whether we hear them or

---

[74] www.khouse.org

not? Of course. Do the black crows of England fall silent whenever I go on holiday? I wish.

Point #3 remains. It states in scientific vernacular:

> That the universe, the Earth, life and all matter came into existence through supernatural agency (non-natural means) by means of a process that was initiated for a limited period

> That at some time after it began, this supernatural, creative process stopped and entropy began

> That all matter and energy in the universe is disorganising, according to the Second Law of Thermodynamics

Irish churchman Bishop Ussher formulated his famous chronology of the world based on the time-frames in the Bible. Interestingly, the following were almost unanimously endorsed by scientists through the ages until Charles Lyell and the Industrial Revolution:

- **CREATION**: Approx. 6,000-7,000 years ago (4004BC)
- **GLOBAL INUNDATION** (the Flood): Approx. 5,000-4,400 years ago (approx. 2345BC)

In the documentary, *The Privileged Planet*, Jay Richards says:

"The founders of modern science like Copernicus and Keppler and Galileo and Newton himself believed that the universe was the product of a mind, that it was intelligible to beings like ourselves because the universe itself was the product of an intelligent being."[75]

Dr Gonzalez believes that, "There's something about the universe that can't be simply explained by the impersonal forces of nature and atoms colliding. So you have to reach for something beyond the universe to try to account for it."[76]

---

[75] *The Privileged Planet* documentary, op. cit.
[76] Ibid.

What actually happened? No-one knows because no-one was there. Any explanation for the universe's origins can only be theory, so the Genesis account is as valid as any other if it fits with what we're finding. We can infer that if the universe is expanding, it had to have started from somewhere. Let's examine other factors which gainsay an ancient universe.

Magnetic field half-life

National Geographic writes: "Earth's magnetic field is fading. Today it is about 10 percent weaker than it was when German mathematician Carl Friedrich Gauss started keeping tabs on it in 1845, scientists say.... Not surprisingly, Hollywood has already seized on this new twist in the natural-disaster genre. Last year Tinseltown released *The Core*, a film in which the collapse of Earth's magnetic field leads to massive electrical storms, blasts of solar radiation, and birds incapable of navigation."[77]

An obvious geochronometer of the planet can be seen in the decay of the Earth's magnetic field. The field is dipolar and forms a protective shield around us. Without this, life could not exist. Space junk and the sun's radiation would impact the planet with nothing to stop them, generating carbon-14 in the outer atmosphere, which would vary according to the changing strength of the magnetic field. Scientists state that the strength of Earth's field halves every 1,400 years. Since 1829, this phenomenon has been measured and the results extrapolated. In 1835, the Magnetic Moment was calculated at 8.558 amp-meter^2 x 10^{22}. By 1935, it was down to 8.088. By 1965, 8.017. When plotted, the data form a curve. This means that in 600AD, the field was twice as strong as it is today. In 800BC, the field was four times as strong. In 2200 BC, eight times more powerful, and so on.

---

[77] "Earth's Magnetic Field is Fading", *National Geographic News,* 9th September 2004

Dr John Morris explains that the decay of the Earth's magnetic field sets a time limit on the age of the planet:

"If the Earth's magnetic field intensity had been twice as strong every 1,400 years as you go back in time, that would mean only 100,000 years ago, the magnetic field would have been incredibly strong, comparable to that of a neutron star. The heat generated by resistance to the electrical currents in the molten core, sufficiently strong to produce such a large magnetic field, would have dire consequences. Dr Thomas Barnes, Emeritus Professor of Physics at the University of Texas, speculated that in the not-too-distant past, life would have been nearly impossible and some 20,000 years ago, the Earth's internal structure would have been disrupted by the heat produced."[78]

The estimate is that the Earth could not be more than 20,000 years old since the field would have been an estimated 18,000 gauss - so strong that the huge electrical conductivity produced by the interaction of Earth's magnetic field with its core would have rendered the planet white-hot.[79] Some evolutionists refute this by saying that the magnetic field is undergoing reversals. There have never been any reversals observed or measured. Rocks from the mid-Atlantic ridge showing 'reverse polarity' could equally have been flipped over in a cataclysm, as we shall see. The mid-Atlantic ridge is a mess.

Round and round

The rotational speed of the Earth demonstrates the young age of our planet. Earth's rotation is slowing down due to the entropic factor and also progresses through a half-life. The Royal Greenwich Observatory adds a 'leap second' every now and then to compensate for this.[80] This means our planet used to be rotating faster. This fact sets a limit on the age of the Earth. If the world is

---

[78] Morris John D, *The Young Earth*, op. cit. p.75
[79] Hovind, Kent, *Creation seminar series*, op. cit.
[80] www.greenwichmeantime.com/info/leap-second.htm

only 6,000-7,000 years old, there is no problem accommodating a slightly faster rotation five thousand years ago. Noah's day would have been about twenty minutes shorter than our own, says Hovind. If scientists wish to convince us that the Earth is billions of years old, they do so in ignorance of the variance in our planet's rotational speed.

Space dust

Meteorites are constantly bombarding the Earth, millions each day. Most are burnt up in the atmospheric interface and fall as dust to the planet's surface.[81] Space is full of dust, as evidenced by the return of orbiting spacecraft whose portholes have been pitted and scored with the passage of dust at high speeds.

The moon gathers this dust as it passes through space. It has been calculated that 40 million tons of space dust a year falls onto Earth, mostly in the form of nickel, iron and other compounds.[82] When American scientists prepared the Apollo moon-shot in the 1960s, scientists had to calculate the dust accumulation on the moon to obtain a picture of the landing surface awaiting their spacecraft. They calculated the dust accumulation rate on the moon's surface to be one inch every 10,000 years. Based on their belief in evolution, the longevity of the planets and that the moon was supposedly 4.5 billion years old, some of the most learned men on the planet surmised there would be 54 feet of dust on the moon (brought down from a whopping 150 feet). For this reason the Lunar Landing Module was constructed with the stalky legs and ground-plates.

On July 20th 1969, America landed on it. Neil Armstrong said his famous line: "One small step for man; one giant leap for

---

[81] www.khouse.org

[82] **Leinert C & E Gruen** "Interplanetary Dust", *Physics and Chemistry in Space*, Springer-Verlag, 1990, pp. 204-275

mankind," then made this comment in front of millions on TV: "It's solid."

Notice the importance of communicating this piece of information to Mission Control as soon as possible. Of course it was solid. There was only three-quarters of an inch of dust on the moon. The sticklers calculate that this places the age of the moon at around 7,000 years according to the scientists' own methodology. These scientists were also bothered by the rarity of nickel on Earth. Where was all the nickel that had fallen over the eons? The problem with the dust influx theory, says Hovind, is that the rate at which the Earth is bombarded varies enormously. The fact remains, though, that there should be more nickel if the Earth were ancient, and a lot more dust on that 'four-billion-year-old' moon.

Comets

Scientists will tell you some comets originated from subsequent stellar explosions after the Big Bang. There are problems with the ages given, the most obvious being that comets are dirty, super-cold snowballs which lose matter constantly (the tail) as they fly through space. You cannot keep losing material or no more comets. The fact that we still have comets argues that they are no more than a few thousand years old. Can a comet fly for millions of years and keep losing material? No. Scientists try to get around this by saying comets are regularly spawned by the Oort Cloud, yet no-one's ever seen the Oort Cloud, much less observed any 'spawning' in action. Even astronomer and author Carl Sagan states:

"Many scientific papers are written each year about the Oort Cloud, its properties, its origin, its evolution. Yet there is not one shred of direct, observational evidence for its existence."[83]

---

[83] **Sagan, C & Ann Druyan** *Comet*, Headline Book Publishing, 1997, p.148

British astronomer RA Lyttleton forms the obvious conclusion that "Probably no short-period comet can survive more than about 10,000 years."[84]

Saturn's rings

The planets in our solar system appear not to be billions of years old. The seismic volatility of some and their active atmospheres demonstrate these to be young and still cooling off. For instance, the particles in Saturn's rings are still separating according to the Poynting-Robertson Effect, indicating they are still stabilising. Do you think *National Geographic* would have us believe that these planets have been cooling off for billions of years? According to a literal interpretation of the Ussher Chronology, our solar system is 6,000-7,000 years old at the outside (Gen 1:16).

The disappearing Moon

Kent Hovind reports that every year the moon moves further away from the Earth. It's only a foot or two each year and nothing to worry about but the moon's definitely off. This means that in times past, the moon used to be closer. The further back in time we go, the closer the moon comes to the Earth. The moon's departure may be logarithmic, but the important fact is that it sets an outside limit to the age of our planet. The moon cannot be billions of years old. A million years ago, imagine what the moon would be doing to the tides.

Anthropics, anthropics….

As the evolutionist would have man's existence begging at the judgment bar of chance, how could so many variables making life possible all have been so minutely orchestrated in the fashion we see today? Scientists estimate that at least one hundred anthropic

---

[84] **Lyttleton, RA** *Mysteries of the Solar System*, Clarendon Press, Oxford, 1968

indicators need to be present for complex life to be possible anywhere in the universe. A further thirty are required for life to be possible on any given planet. And just having the conditions in place is no guarantee that life itself will come into being on its own from inorganic matter.

Dr Chuck Missler points out, for example, that if the axial tilt of the Earth were greater, the surface temperatures would be too great and life could not exist. If the atmospheric electric discharge rate were greater, there would be too much fire destruction on our planet and life could not exist. A little less and there would be inadequate nitrogen fixing in the soil. The thickness of the Earth's crust, the planet's reflectivity (albedo), the Earth's gravitational interaction with the moon, the distance from our parent star, our surface gravity, the planet's oxygen-to-nitrogen ratio, the planet's level of seismic activity – all these factors, to name but a few, have to be precisely and minutely calibrated for life to stand a chance.[85]

Professor Stephen C Meyer is director of the Discovery Institute's Center for the Renewal of Science and Culture. He writes:

"Imagine that you are a cosmic explorer who has just stumbled into the control room of the whole universe. There you discover an elaborate 'universe-creating machine' with rows and rows of dials, each with many possible settings. As you investigate, you learn that each dial represents some particular parameter that has to be calibrated with a precise value in order to create a universe in which life can exist. One dial represents the possible settings for the strong nuclear force, one for the gravitational constant, one for Planck's constant, one for the ratio of the neutron mass to the proton mass, one for the strength of electromagnetic attraction, and so on. As you, the cosmic explorer, examine the dials, you find that they could easily have been turned to different settings. Moreover, you determine by careful calculation that if any of the dial settings were even slightly altered, life would cease to exist. Yet for some reason, each dial is

---

[85] **Missler, Chuck** *Beyond Coincidence,* Koinonia House, PO Box D, Coeur D'Alene, ID, 83816, USA. www.khouse.org

set at just the exact value necessary to keep the universe running. What do you infer about the origin of these finely tuned dial settings?"[86]

The cumulative odds of such details occurring by chance make a mockery of any school of evolutionary thought, and have led many to conclude that design is the simplest explanation. Meyer quotes physicist John Polkinghorne:

"We are living in an age where there is a great revival of natural theology taking place. That revival of natural theology is taking place not on the whole among theologians who have lost their nerve in that area, but among the scientists."[87]

And this from Fred Hoyle, the late mathematician, physicist and Professor of Astronomy at Cambridge:

"I have always thought it curious that, while most scientists claim to eschew religion, it actually dominates their thoughts more than it does the clergy."[88]

Many universes

But the evolutionists aren't finished yet. They come up with tortuous scenarios to assign necessity (natural laws) or chance to account for everything. Here are some of the excuses:

- Since mankind and the world are obviously here, the fine tuning required for our existence needs no explanation ('the weak anthropic principle')
- Natural laws can explain everything
- There are an infinite number of universes operating over an infinite period of time, so sooner or later one will pop up with the right settings

---

[86] Behe, Michael, Dembski, William A, Meyer, Stephen C, *Science and Evidence for Design in the Universe,* op. cit. p.55-56

[87] Ibid. p.65-66

[88] **Hoyle, F** "The Universe: Past and Present Reflections", *Annual Review of Astronomy and Astrophysics,* Vol. 20, 1982, pp.1-35, p.23

Notice the degree to which the most likely conclusion is studiously avoided, namely, that all the settings were *deliberately* calibrated for life to exist. This conclusion is immediately rejected because it posits a non-naturalistic and thus 'non-scientific' conclusion. So Charles Darwin could not have designed *On the Origin of Species,* but a billion monkeys did, on a billion typewriters, and took billions of years to do it. Meyer agrees that evolutionists are dodging the issue:

"Though we humans should not be surprised to find ourselves living in a universe suited for life (by definition), we ought to be surprised to learn that the conditions necessary for life are so vastly improbable."[89]

Why *shouldn't* we want to explain it?

Because it takes us somewhere we don't wish to go?

The excuse that 'natural laws can explain everything' is done to death *ab initio* since the minutely calibrated physical constants of the Earth and universe are themselves specific parts of the natural laws of nature and cannot have been created by them! Moreover, the fact that these precise calibrations are a component of these laws demands explanation in itself. British physicist Paul Davies remarks:

"The impression of design is overwhelming." And that the laws of physics "seem themselves to be the product of exceedingly ingenious design."[90]

Isaac Newton realised the law of gravity alone did not account for the initial, perfect positioning of the planets in our solar system:

"Though these bodies may indeed persevere in their orbits by the mere laws of gravity, yet they could by no means have at first derived the regular position of the orbits themselves from those laws.... [Thus] this

---

90 **Davies, Paul** *The Cosmic Blueprint,* Simon and Schuster, New York, 1988

most beautiful system of the sun, planets and comets could only proceed from the counsel and dominion of an intelligent and powerful being."[91]

Prof. Meyer points out the utter absurdity of believing any of the anthropic settings could have been contrived by natural laws:

"Natural laws by definition describe phenomena that conform to regular or repetitive patterns. Yet the idiosyncratic values of the physical constants and initial conditions of the universe constitute a highly irregular and non-repetitive ensemble. It seems unlikely, therefore, that any law could explain why all the fundamental constants have exactly the values they do – why, for example, the gravitational constant should have exactly the value of 6.67×10^{-11} Newton-meters^2 per kilogram^2 and the permittivity constant in Coulombs law the value of 8.85×10^{-12} Coulombs^2 per Newton-meter^2, and the electron charge constant of 6.63×10^{-34} Joules-seconds, and so on. These values specify a highly complex array. As a group, they do not seem to exhibit a regular pattern that could in principle be subsumed or explained by natural law."[92]

The third argument, namely that an infinite number of universes constantly popping up will eventually produce one worthy of life, requires no further disbelief. There is no scientific evidence for any universes other than our own, which should end the debate but sadly it doesn't. Very well. How are these 'other' universes being created? What is the design, form and evidence of the existence of such a universe-generating machine? What/who made the original universe-generating machine? As universes go, they have to subscribe to the same natural laws as the one we are living in to produce life like the Earth we're living on, so we're back to the anthropic argument, only this time with odds of each dial being calibrated correctly multiplied to an infinitesimal power – for eternity. Professor Meyer concludes

---

[91] **Newton, Isaac** *Mathematical Principles of Natural Philosophy,* University of California Press, 1978, pp.543-544

[92] Behe, Michael, Dembski, William A, Meyer, Stephen C, *Science and Evidence for Design in the Universe,* op. cit. p.60

"That some scientists dignify the many-worlds hypothesis with serious discussion may speak more to an unimpeachable commitment to naturalistic philosophy than to any compelling merit for the idea itself."[93]

And so....

Kent Hovind sums up the questions:

- Where did the space for the universe come from?
- Where did matter come from?
- Where did the laws of the universe come from?
- How did matter get so perfectly organised?
- Where did the energy come from to do all the organising?
- With whom did the first cell capable of sexual reproduction reproduce?
- Why would any plant or animal want to reproduce more of its kind since this would only make more mouths to feed and decrease the chances of survival?
- When, where, why and how did life come from dead matter?
- When, where, why and how did man evolve feelings? Love, mercy, guilt, etc., would never evolve in the theory of evolution.
- Could it be that people accept evolution because of some of the following factors:
A. It is all they have been taught?
B. They like the freedom from a God (no moral absolutes, etc.)?
C. They are bound to support the theory for fear of losing their jobs or status or grade point average?
D. They are too proud to admit they are wrong?

When someone tells you about something for which they have no proof, they are asking you to take it on faith. Believing a frog

---

[93] Ibid. p.65

can turn into a prince over millions of years with no proof is not science. Real science pushes the envelope without fear or favour of where the evidence leads. And where might that be? After all those space probes and *Star Trek* films and *Pioneer 10*s blasting off with plaques aboard bearing information of life on Earth for the benefit of some slaver-jawed alien,[94] what are we really frightened of finding?

That we're *not* alone?

[94] http://en.wikipedia.org/wiki/Pioneer_plaque

THE EARTHLY REALM
Evidence of design on our planet

"I do not know what I may appear to the world. But to myself, I seem to have only been like a boy playing on the sea shore, diverting myself, now and then, in finding a smoother pebble or prettier shell than the ordinary, while the great ocean of truth lay all undiscovered before me."
– Isaac Newton

In 1831, Charles Darwin set sail as part of a research expedition to the Galapagos Islands in the eastern Pacific. Charlie at the time was a young man just 22 years old. He spent a month studying the incredible diversity of life he found there, and the notes and specimens he brought back with him helped form his future theory of how he believed all life-forms originated.

The eventual publication of his book, *On The Origin of Species by Means of Natural Selection, or the Preservation of Favoured Races in the Struggle for Life* changed Western culture forever. Darwin's theory took the world from believing that the Earth and everything therein had been the product of some supreme design to suggesting that all life came from natural selection acting on random variations which assured the survival of the fittest. Through his study of finches on the Galapagos, it seemed evident to Charlie that those with longer beaks enjoyed a functional advantage over others which were not able successfully to crack the hard casings of seeds found during the drought season. The environment therefore forced a change in the finch population and favoured those which were able to access the food source.

Then Charlie wondered whether all creatures had not themselves evolved from purely undirected processes over vast periods of time without any intelligence to organise them. And that being the case, dare one not ask whether all creatures and flora themselves could have come from a single common, primordial ancestor?

It was an elegant thought. The world may *look* designed but perhaps it just *looked* that way. Darwin knew the evolutionary argument hung on many factors coming together in the right order at the same time and in the same place. On occasion he voiced his reticence:

"If it could be demonstrated that any complex organ existed which could not possibly have been formed by numerous, successive, slight modifications, my theory would absolutely break down."[95]

Well, it has, Charlie. An elephant, cheetah, cuttlefish, mosquito and hummingbird have design written into their anatomy, character, lifestyle and 'instincts'. These are just a few of the animals which have been programmed with *information* in a specific way - we'll examine examples in a minute. What is the source of this information, which could not have evolved as a 'shared mind'? What compels a baby to breastfeed immediately after birth? Why suck on the breast and not the big toe? Creatures know instinctively how to behave, and when you examine their feeding patterns, many use systems which are irreducibly complex and defy evolution. Yet Charlie was right in one area. Paul Nelson, philosopher of biology, explains:

"Natural selection is a real process, and it works well for explaining certain limited kinds of variations, small scale change, and we have lots of examples of that, in fact. Where it doesn't work well is explaining what Darwin thought it could, namely the real complexity of life. You've got the finch beak, and then you've got the finch itself. A minor change in the structure of the beak versus the origin of the organism itself. These are different scales of phenomena, these are different kinds of problems. And the important problem for biology is to understand where natural selection works and where it doesn't, and why there's a difference."[96]

---

[95] **Darwin, Charles** *Origin of Species,* 6th ed, New York University Press, p.154
[96] *Unlocking the Mystery of Life,* Illustra Media, www.illustramedia.com

The peppered moth experiment is cited when proof of evolution is called for. Wikipedia provides the standard excursion:

"The evolution of the peppered moth over the last two hundred years has been studied in detail. Originally, the vast majority of peppered moths had light coloration, which effectively camouflaged them against the light-colored trees and lichens upon which they rested. However, due to widespread pollution during the Industrial Revolution in England, many of the lichens died out, and the trees which peppered moths rested on became blackened by soot, causing most of the light-colored moths, or typica, to die off due to predation. At the same time, the dark-colored, or melanic, moths, carbonaria, flourished because of their ability to hide on the darkened trees."[97]

This is not evolution but natural selection. For what it's worth, this example was disproved decades ago since peppered moths do not hang out on tree-trunks anyway but up in the foliage, yet this is still cited as an example of evolution in textbooks. How boring. The moths did not morph into giraffes. The dark moths fared badly prior to the Industrial Revolution because they allegedly showed up against the lighter trunks and were fair game. Then along came the smokestacks of the 19th century and the roles were reversed. Now the lighter moths showed up against the sooty trunks and were easy meat for predators.

So what? Not one hippo out of the entire process. At no time did the moths grow appendages, change into other animals or other such nonsense. Biochemist Michael Behe quotes researchers Ho and Saunders:

"It is now approximately half a century since the neo-Darwinian synthesis was formulated. A great deal of research has been carried on within the paradigm it defines. Yet the successes of the theory are limited to the minutiae of evolution, such as the adaptive change in the coloration of moths; while it has remarkably little to say on the questions

---

[97] http://en.wikipedia.org/wiki/Peppered_moth

which interest us most, such as how there came to be moths in the first place."[98]

Returning to the premise of irreducible complexity, what are the first things we note about Earth's bounty?

- There is a huge variety of animal, bird, fish and insect species
- Each precisely fits into its environment in terms of how it eats, reproduces and survives
- Each appears finished and fully functional

Honest anthropologists will admit that all the mammals appear in the fossil record suddenly and 'finished'. If they evolved, there should be billions of transitional forms, yet they have found *not one*. Many creatures exhibit features of lifestyle, feeding or reproductive habits which are irreducibly complex, meaning they could not have evolved from a non-functioning precursor through natural selection. Bear in mind that any feature which survives natural selection must be of benefit to the organism or it is not selected. And in the case where a creature must rely on a complex series of actions for its survival, there can be no evolution if all parts of the system are not together at the same time and place for the creature's survival to be possible. The logical conclusion is that the system is born finished and irreducibly complex.

Intellectual levels of the genus

If we all started from the same bacteria, how is it that man was the only animal which evolved so inordinately further in intelligence than any other life-form? It has been demonstrated that man has easily 10 million times the reasoning power over the closest, smartest animal, and many more times the degree of conscience. This was reasoned by Romanes, a disciple of Darwin's.

---

[98] **Ho, MW & P Saunders** "Beyond Neo-Darwinism – An Epigenetic Approach to Evolution", *Journal of Theoretical Biology*, 78,589 1979

Why then don't we have dogs that do calculus? Why do budgies not muscle ahead and place sell orders on the stock markets? Why has not one rhino written a more arresting soliloquy than Shakespeare? What professional bulldozer of arrogance can possibly persuade grown students with a straight face that man *alone* has crossed the measureless chasm to higher-bound intelligence, far ahead of all others put together, by blind, random chance?

Only one species with language. Only one species that understands the concept of the past and can plan for the future. Only one species that marvels at art and beauty, creates music, and is drawn to a Creator. *Only one species alone* made it out of 1,000,000 species of insects, 20,000 species of fish, 350,000 plant species of incredible variety, 9,000 species of bird, and 5,400 species of mammal, from rabbits to rhinos. Why don't we have some of our smart, near relative, gorilla-kin beating us at chess and chiding us in iambic pentameters, as evolution, mathematical probability and sound reason should have it?

"That's it, Day! To the Headmaster's study this instant!"

The human missing link frauds

Several specimens have been presented to the public as man's 'missing link' between the simian and the human. These have been exposed either as frauds or mere human or animal remains. But it begs the question: Why do evolutionists have such a tough time finding human transitional forms? Thousands of animals have been found grouped together at Dinosaur Monument, Vernal, Utah. In Siberia, thousands of woolly mammoths are found frozen in the ice standing up, a few with food still in their mouths and stomachs. Near Lyons, France, the skeletons of 200,000 prehistoric horses are scattered about. In Monrovia, the remains of mammoths abound in such numbers that, according to Ales Hrdlicka of the Smithsonian Institution, *"there are enough mammoth teeth to fill a small sized hall."* Yet we are supposed to believe that millions and millions of humans evolved from apes when nothing approaching even one complete monkey-man skeleton has been found to redeem the theory. Why? I have my own theory, heuristically derived. There are no missing links because there was never any evolution. This has not stopped scientists dredging up bones, giving them impressively deceiving Latin names, and attempting to convince us that the evidence for evolution is pure gold.

Pithecanthropus Erectus (Java Man): Found by Dr Eugene Dubois in river sands, 40 feet down. A few bones, some ape, some human were scattered across 50 feet, no two joined together. Said to have existed over 400,000 years ago (sometimes 750,000 years - take your pick), the impressive sounding *Pithecanthropus* is nothing more than a modern ape combined with a modern human, with a skilful artist to make deceiving drawings for the museums. Before he died, Dubois came clean and confessed that two human skulls had also been found at the site and that the skull fragment had belonged to a gibbon.[99] Yet Java Man is still presented to the world today as a *bona fide* human missing link. Is this science?

Ramapithecus: A supposed missing link made up from a fragment of jaw and a few teeth, lovingly drawn by an enterprising artist to resemble early man. Dr Pilbeam of the Yale-Harvard Peabody Museum, who originally declared to the world that *Ramapithecus* was a missing link, subsequently retracted his statement. Later he stated that this creature was not evolving into a human at all but was probably an orangutan or similar.

'Lucy': Discovered by Dr Donald C Johanson, Director of the Institute for Human Origins. This three-and-a-half foot chimpanzee skeleton has also been sold to the world as a human transitional form. After studying his find, Johanson claimed that Lucy, although markedly chimpanzee, walked upright like a human

---

[99] **Jeremiah Films** *The Evolution Conspiracy*, Hemet, CA, USA

some three million years ago. Today the pigmy chimp walks upright like a human, so this proves nothing. Moreover, the knee joint causing all the controversy was found by Johanson a mile away from the other bones and 200 feet further down. Kent Hovind wants to know how fast that train was going when it hit Lucy.

Piltdown Man: A human skull was made to fit an orangutan jaw and the teeth filed to suit. The composite skull was then stained with potassium dichromate to age it. Piltdown Man was later exposed as a fraud to the dismay of many, who so wanted Piltdown Man to be the long-sought-after vindication for their elusive religion.

Neanderthal Man: Modern-looking humans found in Neanderthal Valley in Germany. A few specimens were found to be stooped over. Later, scientists from the John Hopkins University conducted tests on the creatures and proved these were ordinary humans suffering from a Vitamin D deficiency condition such as rickets. These have now been reclassified as *homo sapiens.*

Nebraska Man: Consists of a single tooth. Pictures were drawn depicting this as an ape evolving into a human. Later the tooth was found to have come from an extinct pig.

US News and World Report, 4th December 1995, writes: "Researchers suggest that virtually all modern men—99.9% of them, says one scientist—are closely related genetically and share genes with one male ancestor, dubbed 'Y-chromosome Adam.' "We are finding that humans have very, very shallow genetic roots which go back very recently to one ancestor… that indicates that there was an origin in a specific location on the globe, and then it spread out from there."

Time magazine, 7th November 1977, states: "Still doubts about the sequence about man's emergence remain. Scientists concede that their most cherished theories are based on embarrassingly few fossil fragments and that huge gaps exist in the fossil record."

No new species and the nature principle

Evolution is refuted with nature's oft proven law that 'like produces like'. No one has ever witnessed the formation of a new species from another, yet we are daily instructed that this is scientific fact. Despite scientists now being aware that the genetic code prevents development of different species from a parent genus, neo-Darwinists still teach that some 3,000,000 species of plants and animals developed from a common ancestor pollywog in an approximate 60,000,000-year time-frame. That being the case, states William Williams, we find that 524,288 species would had to have originated within the last 3,000,000 years. As this is a geometrical gradation, 2097 species must have appeared in the past 6,000 years, an average of one new species of creature every three years. How many new species have actually been observed evolving from another in the last two hundred years, Williams asks. 1,000? 500? 50? 10? Not one.[100]

David B Kitts, Ph.D of the School of Geology and Geophysics at the University of Oklahoma, defends his belief this way: "Evolution, at least in the sense that Darwin speaks of it, cannot be detected within the lifetime of a single observer."[101]

How convenient. And why do we still have 'simple' life-forms? We'll find out in the next chapter that there is no such thing as a 'simple' life-form. Was the amoeba too lazy to evolve? Was it too much like hard work for a piece of pond grease to become an ostrich? Why, if evolution is true, do we still have 'simple' life-forms at all? Or do we have selective evolution occurring here? Even Darwin remarks,

---

[100] **Williams, William** *The Evolution of Man Scientifically Disproved,* Bibliobazaar, 2007
[101] **Kitts, David B** *Evolution,* 'Paleontology and Evolutionary Theory', vol.28, Sept 1974, p.466

"In spite of all the efforts of trained observers, not one change of species into another is on record."

It is true that many varieties and thoroughbreds have been bred by man over the years, expanding the range of the genus, but this is worlds apart from alleging that species sub-divide and self-create new species through 'beneficial mutations' – that unobserved oxymoron. Science repeatedly demonstrates that mutations are never beneficial but always detrimental to the genus. No lower forms have ever been observed developing into higher forms. We have small dogs and big dogs, but these are still dogs unchanged from the dawn of dogs. No rats ever became swans. Which vegetables on my plate ever grew gills and swam? The fact is, history and archaeology hold not a single scrap of evidence in support of evolution. If this theory is science, where is the science?

Ore and Coyne write:

"We conclude — unexpectedly — that there is little evidence for the neo-Darwinian view: its theoretical foundations and the experimental evidence supporting it are weak." [102]

Darwin's contemporary, the eminent English biologist Professor William Bateson, remarked,

"It is impossible for scientists any longer to agree with Darwin's theory of the origin of species. No explanation whatever has been offered to account for the fact that, after forty years, no evidence has been discovered to verify his genesis of species."

And Darwin himself:

"As by this theory innumerable transitional forms must have existed, why do we not find them embedded in countless numbers in the crust of the earth? The number of intermediate links between all living and extinct species must have been inconceivably great!"

---

[102] **Ore, H A & J A Coyne** *American Naturalist*, 1992, p.726

And: "If my theory be true, numberless intermediate varieties… must assuredly have existed…." [103]

Monkey business

Alfred McCann tells us man has 12 ribs, the gibbon and chimp 13. Man has 12 dorsal vertebrae, the chimp and gorilla 13, the gibbon 14. There are great differences in the shape of the skull, femur, the cervical vertebrae above the scapula and the liver between the simian and human. Man has fingerprints to aid in identification, monkeys have straight lines on their fingers but whorls on their palms.[104]

Man buries his dead, monkeys do not. Man knows how to use the resources of the Earth, such as coal, to warm himself. A lump of coal is nothing to a monkey. Williams makes the point that all the precious metals, minerals, oil and gas, secreted away in the depths of the Earth, are only of value to man. What use are they to the brute?

"God foresaw the marvellous inventions of the present and the future and provided the means ages ahead of time. The universe is crowded so full of design, that there is no room for chance or natural selection."[105]

While we're on God, was the writer of Genesis guessing when he stated that every living creature would bring forth after its kind? Why would he even say such a thing unless this was information that was revealed to him? In a following chapter, we'll examine statements the Bible makes which are scientifically correct centuries before man came into such knowledge. The Creation account in Genesis contains thirteen steps which are described in the correct order geologically, logically and have been proven archeologically. The odds of the writer getting these steps in the

---

[103] **Darwin, Charles** *On the Origin of Species,* 1859, p.211
[104] **McCann, Alfred** *God - or Gorilla?* Devin-Adair Co, New York, 1922
[105] Williams, William, *The Evolution of Man Scientifically Disproved,* op. cit. p.28

correct order by chance are calculated at *one chance in six trillion.*
Can we really look ourselves in the mirror and dismiss all such
facts as lucky guesses when the odds of any one being correct by
chance are longer than Pinocchio's nose?

That blessed beetle...

The Australian bombardier beetle is one of the Waterloos
between creationists and evolutionists over its defence mechanism.
The insect produces hydroquinones and hydrogen peroxide which
are pooled in a common reservoir within the beetle's body. When
Bomby is threatened, this mixture is pressured into a thick-walled
reaction-chamber within its body, where the enzyme catalase
triggers an exothermic reaction. The result is water, the skin-irritant
quinone and lots of heat. The solution rises to boiling point and
about 20% of it vaporises into steam as it is shot from a revolvable
turret in the beetle's rear-end to scald its enemies. Jeffrey Dean and
colleagues summarise:

> "The defense spray of the bombardier beetle *Stenaptinus insignis* is
> ejected in quick pulses (at about 500 pulses per second) rather than a
> continuous stream.... The ejection system of the beetle shows basic
> similarity to the pulse jet propulsion mechanism of the German V-1
> 'buzz' bomb of World War 2.... The abdominal tip acts as a revolvable
> turret that enables the beetles to aim the spray in all directions.... We
> report here that the bombardier beetle spray is emitted not as a
> continuous stream but as a pulsed jet, in analogy with fluid delivery
> systems known from technology but not from animal glands."[106]

Time magazine, which adopts an evolutionary stance, reports:
"[The beetle's] defense system is extraordinarily intricate, a cross between
tear gas and a tommy gun. When the beetle senses danger, it internally
mixes enzymes contained in one body chamber with concentrated

---

[106] **Dean, Jeffrey and Daniel J Aneshansley, Harold E Edgerton, and Thomas
Eisner** "Defensive Spray of the Bombardier Beetle: A Biological Pulse Jet," *Science*,
248:1219-1221, 8th June 1990

solutions of some rather harmless compounds, hydrogen peroxide and hydroquinones, confined to a second chamber. This generates a noxious spray of caustic benzoquinones, which explode from its body at a boiling 212°F. What is more, the fluid is pumped through twin rear nozzles, which can be rotated like a B-17's gun turret, to hit a hungry ant or frog with bull's-eye accuracy."[107]

Is Bomby's defence system irreducibly complex and therefore evidence of design? Biochemist Michael Behe chastises creationists for coming up with bogus science, and evolutionists for not coming up with transitional forms. Evolutionist www.talkorigins.org has Mark Isaak attempting to explain fifteen stages through which the beetle must have evolved to arrive at today's weaponry. It's a hopelessly ponderous exercise, presumably carried out because the case cannot go unanswered. The point is: a) how did Bomby defend himself during the millions of years it took for natural selection acting on random variations to come up with his cannon? And b), when attacked, timing is everything to the beetle. How could natural selection be plausible with Bomby blowing his rear-end off in the bushes for a thousand millennia while coming to grips with less beneficial mutations?

The logical conclusion is that Bomby has always been Bomby. Behe contends that no scientific evidence has been produced by Dawkins to prove his version of events. Charles Darwin, candid as always, writes:

"If it could be demonstrated that any complex organ existed which could not possibly have been formed by numerous, successive, slight modifications, my theory would absolutely break down."[108]

The eyes have it

Charlie also said: "To suppose that the eye with all its inimitable contrivances for adjusting the focus to different distances, for admitting

---

[107] "Drafting the Bombardier Beetle," *Time*, 25th February 1985, p.70
[108] **Darwin, Charles** *Origin of Species*, 6th ed, New York University Press, p.154

different amounts of light, and for the correction of spherical and chromatic aberration, could have been formed by natural selection seems, I frankly confess, absurd in the highest degree."[109]

Is the human eye irreducibly complex? Not necessarily. You can see without a lens (not brilliantly), but you cannot see without a retina. Did the eye evolve by chance? The Hon. William J Bryan writes:

"The evolutionist guesses that there was a time when eyes were unknown – that is a necessary part of the hypothesis.... Some say a freckle appeared upon the skin of an animal that had no eyes. This piece of pigment or freckle converged the rays of the sun upon that spot, and when the little animal felt the heat on that spot, it turned the spot to the sun to get more heat. This increased heat irritated the skin – so the evolutionists guess – and a nerve came there and out of the nerve an eye. Can you beat it? But this only accounts for one eye; there must have been another piece of pigment or freckle soon afterward, and just in the right place in order to give the animal two eyes."[110]

Then how did this species reproduce this anomaly? And since the eye is a universal possession among most living things, how long did it take to develop? How did each eye develop on each creature *where* it did? What are the statistical chances of the second eye developing identically and in the mirror location? Why are the eyes located either side of the nose on the majority of creatures? It would be stupefying enough for one eye to develop by itself, but *two?* And at a location on the body most suited to observation?

Why don't we have one eye on our arm and another on our buttocks? Did all our forebears who developed perfect eyes in these 'wrong' locations die out because they couldn't tell their rear ends from their elbows? Where are their dead bodies? According to evolution and Darwin himself, there must have been millions and millions of transitional forms. *We have found not one.*

---

[109] Ibid. p.167
[110] **Bryan, William J** *In His Image,* Kessinger Publishing, 2004, p.97

William Williams points out that the odds of this happening 'by accident' are risible. If one calculates the area of the human body occupied by the eyes and ears, it is possible to calculate the odds of these organs developing at these locations by chance as .000,000,000,001:

> "The two eyes and two ears have but one chance out of a trillion or a million million to be located where they are. The location of the mouth, the nose and every organ of the body diminishes this probability a thousand-fold. We are speaking mildly when we say that this calculation proves that the evolution of the body, by chance or natural selection, has not one chance in a million to be true."[111]

Now what about eyelids and their blinking function? What about eyebrows forming where they are? And why did we evolve eyebrows in any case? They don't serve any useful function. The mathematical odds of all these processes forming at random multiplied together do fierce violence to Dembski's chance threshold, 'beyond which appeals to chance become unreasonable on the cosmic scale'. Then we must have the mouth, nose, legs, arms and fingers all developing where they should, and in the mirror locations where required…. The Hon. W J Bryan sighs:

> "According to the evolutionist, there was a time when animals had no legs, and so legs came by accident. How? Well, the guess is that a little animal was wiggling along on its belly one day when it discovered a wart – it just happened so – and it was in the right place to be used to aid it in locomotion; so it came to depend on the wart, and use finally developed it into a leg. And then another wart, and another leg, at the proper time – by accident – and accidentally in the proper place. Is it not astonishing that any person intelligent enough to teach school would talk such tommyrot to students, and look serious while doing so?"[112]

Williams too has his claws out: "Darwin has used phrases of doubt 800 times in his two principle works. The whole theory is based

---

[111] Williams, William, *The Evolution of Man Scientifically Disproved,* op. cit. p.54
[112] Ibid. p.98

upon guesses and suppositions. Let us suppose that each guess is 95% certain, which is far higher than the average or any. The compound probability would equal .95 raised to the 800th power, which would be .000,000,000,000,000,006,281, which means there are six chances out of a quintillion that evolution is true. Since not all these 800 suppositions are dependent upon each other, we are willing to multiply this result by 10,000,000,000 which still shows that the theory has less than one chance in a million to be true."[113]

Darwin on another occasion states, "The belief that an organ so perfect as the eye could have been formed by natural selection is more than enough to stagger anyone."

Not part of the script

Dr Jobe Martin is a former member of the United States Air Force who served the president's detail on board Air Force One during the Johnson administration. Martin later went on to qualify as a dentist and become a biology major. One day he was challenged by two of his students over his Darwinian views. Unable to dispute their arguments, Dr Martin went on to study the animal and marine kingdom with special attention to creatures hosting features which could not have evolved through natural selection. His DVD series, *Incredible Creatures Which Defy Evolution,* is popular with many today because the research challenges the viewer to observe and conclude. Some of his examples are among the following.

Pacific golden plover

Nothing about this creature is routine. The bird weighs half a pound and is around the size of a dove. It usually lays four eggs and after the hatchlings are born, the parents clear off to Hawaii for the winter, leaving their babies behind. This is an 88-hour, non-stop

---

[113] Williams, William, *The Evolution of Man Scientifically Disproved,* op. cit. pp.54-55

flight that takes three days and four nights sleeping on the wing, preparation for which entails the bird increasing its weight by 70 grams. The energy burn-rate during the flight, however, is 1 gram of fat per one hour's flight, leaving the plover well short of its target. At which point the hapless, *non-swimming* bird should plunge from the sky to its death in the ocean and no more be seen.

It doesn't. The plover flies with other plovers and changes place in the formation by rotation to lessen wind-drag. Thus the plover burns less energy and successfully reaches its destination with milligrams of fuel to spare.

How does this creature navigate to Hawaii in the first place? What manual does it use to calculate how much fuel to take onboard? Alaska to Hawaii is no garden jaunt. Just one degree off and you're shark biscuit. What navigational aids does the bird use? What about side-winds, head-winds, tail-winds and storms – how are these compensated for *even when the bird is asleep on the wing?* Scientists have no idea how the plover does it but it does. And those chicks left behind in Alaska will tank themselves up with the required 70g before setting off on their own 88-hour beano, *never having done it before.* No compass. No GPS. Not one Michelin Guide between the lot of them.

How could this bird have *evolved* such navigation? Perhaps the Pacific is littered with unknown corpses of millions of transitional plovers, all of whom perished trying to evolve a navigation system for Hawaii. If so, why do we still have Pacific golden plovers?[114]

Homing pigeon

The same with the homing pigeon. These can fly thousands of miles from a point of release almost anywhere in the world, and

---

[114] **Martin Jobe and David Hames** *Incredible Creatures that Defy Evolution,* www.explorationfilms.com

return to the home loft unerringly.[115] Upon release, they circle for a while to gain their bearings before setting off. Some scientists think the pigeon uses a 'map and compass' system, which appears to be orientated by the sun and Earth's magnetic field. Studies show that if released at night, or if the magnetic field around the coup is disrupted, the pigeon's homing ability is compromised. How could such a system evolve? Natural selection cannot select from a non-functioning precursor. What did the pigeons use for navigation before that? A torch?

Wasps and hornets

The *Daily Mail* writes:

"You don't need a pest expert to tell you how a wasp can destroy the mood at your barbecue. But they could help you with planning dates to avoid them. According to a study, wasps are at their most annoying in British gardens during the last few days of July - so watch out this week….

Homeowners should not try to remove a wasp or hornet nest themselves. Hornet colonies reach their peak population in late summer and can contain 700 large, angry insects. Wasp nests are even larger - and can contain up to 10,000 insects. The creatures can mobilise the entire nest to sting in defence of an attack….

Killing a hornet near its nest can also be dangerous. The insects release a distress pheromone that could trigger an attack from the whole colony. Traces of the chemical left behind on clothes can provoke an angry reaction much later in the day."[116]

And sure enough, the following day:

"A grandfather has died after being attacked by a swarm of wasps. George Moody, 64, accidentally disturbed a nest as he walked with a friend in the countryside near his home. He is believed to have suffered a fatal allergic reaction when he was stung dozens of times. Wasp experts

---

[115] **Levi, Wendell** *The Pigeon,* Sumter, SC: Levi Publishing Co, Inc, 1977, p.62.
[116] *Daily Mail,* 28th July 2009, p.3

say that when angry, the insects release pheromones which encourage other members of the nest to join in an attack. The number of wasps in each colony increases at the height of summer, reaching as many as 10,000 per nest."[117]

Where does this programming come from? What did the hornets and wasps use to defend themselves with during the hundreds of thousands of years it took for this co-ordinated attack strategy to evolve?

Dragonflies

In the larval stage, dragonflies feed on tadpoles. When a tadpole is attacked, it releases a signal to warn other tadpoles to change their colour and escape. When the dragonfly sprouts wings, it has four of them on its back in two sets of two. The insect can fly forwards, backwards and even bank in a turn, revealing complexity in how the wings work aerodynamically. The wings are wafer thin but veined to provide maximum flexibility and strength. How did the dragonfly survive before all these structures and skills were in place? Where are the fossilised remains of its transitional forms? Perhaps the dragonfly looks finished because it is.

Here's another thing:

"They are the size of a tiny paper aeroplane. And faced with the underside of a shoe, or the maritime storms of the Indian Ocean, they are about as robust as one. So the fact that this small, delicate species of dragonfly commutes an amazing 12,000 miles every year is no mean feat.

According to new research by British naturalist Charles Anderson, the *Pantala flavescens* species migrates farther than any other insect, even though it is barely 5cm long and boasts flimsy 8cm wings…. Incredibly, these bold little insects migrate at an altitude of 1,000m, double the height of the world's tallest building, the Taipei 101 tower, in the Taiwanese capital. They also cleverly take advantage of the prevailing winds of the so-called Intertropical Convergence Zone….

---

[117] Ibid, 29th July 2009

102

They begin their epic journey every August, flying from southern India, via the Maldives and the Seychelles, to Mozambique on the east coast of Africa. They complete their voyage in December - before flying back again. Not a bad summer holiday, if you can get it."[118]

Whales

The largest creatures ever to live on Earth dwell in the ocean but are air-breathing mammals. No recovered dinosaur remains even approach the size of the largest blue whales found, which can weigh up to 300,000 lbs and measure over 110 feet in length. Their tongue can weigh as much as an elephant and when fully extended, the blue whale's mouth can hold up to 90 tonnes of food.

Blue whales feed almost exclusively on krill, a small shrimp-like crustacean abundant in the oceans. The feeding pattern is unique. To sustain its daily requirement of around 1.5 million calories, the blue whale feeds only in areas with maximum krill. The whale dives down and releases a ring of bubbles which rise and form a 'net' for the krill, which flee from the bubbles into the centre of the ring. The whale has trapped its prey with nothing but bubbles! The great beast then rises up through the centre of the ring with its mouth open and gulps down the krill. And anything else, such as squid, which happens to be caught up with the prey.

The flippers contain blood vessels close to the surface which act as a cooling system, regulating the inner temperature of this creature. Blue whale vocalisations are intricate and, according to *Richardson et al*, used for perhaps six functions:

- Maintenance of inter-individual distance
- Species and individual recognition
- Contextual information transmission (e.g., feeding, alarm, courtship)
- Maintenance of social organization (e.g., contact calls between females and males)

---

[118] Ibid, 22nd July 2009

- Location of topographic features
- Location of prey resources[119]

If evolution is ongoing, why does the whale seem finished and uniquely suited to its environment? How did it evolve its navigation, feeding and calling skills? What are the odds of all the components of the blue whale coming together by accident? And then the cheetah? And the kangaroo?

Sparrows

Sparrows are an every-day wonder most fail to recognise. They are so manoeuvrable, they can fly through a tree and not hit a thing. The sparrow looks finished; so finished, in fact, that it can be found in diverse lcations around the world, adapted to its environment. *Adaptation not evolution.* The sparrow can make minute adjustments in flight by flaring and rotating its primary feathers to suit. How long did it take to get that right? Dr Jobe Martin:

"Evolution teaches that feathers came from scales because birds came from reptiles. But [feathers have] no muscles, no folicle, the whole works peels off, there's no relationship there. If [birds] came from reptiles, you would expect their bones to be like reptile bones. They're nothing like reptile bones. They have little air-pockets through them. They can even carry air in their bones like lungs. Their bones are lightweight and made for flying…. A sparrow's heart is so efficient it can beat up to 760 beats per minute. It has a very short digestive system with concentrated digestive juices because you can't have a whole lot of weight on the bird or it won't fly. So it has to eat and then digest it quickly, and then get rid of its waste. All that had to be figured out and thought

---

[119] National Marine Fisheries Service (2002). "Endangered Species Act - Section 7 Consultation Biological Opinion", www.nmfs.noaa.gov/prot_res/readingrm/ESAsec7/7pr_surtass-2020529.pdf

through in the design of the bird, just as in the design of the firefly and the design of the dragonfly."[120]

And the design of the Corvette. Designers can recognise a designed system in the same way a florist knows a rose. They have a nose for it. A designed system works a certain way. It's put together in a certain order so the different stages of construction logically proceed to the next step. The other choice is random processes acting over infinity, and then you have to come up with the transitory bits as proof if you want to punt it as science.

Sparrows lay their eggs so they are unencumbered with extra weight. Fur begins to fall off the lower chest to expose skin which the bird holds in contact with the egg. This 'brooding spot' develops great sensitivity during this phase. A communication transmits between the bird and egg via the brooding spot, so if there is a temperature or moisture variance, the sparrow can adjust its position to suit the egg. This is design. You don't get a sparrow to do this by mistake. Ornithologist Dr Russ DeFusco gives another example:

"Penguins actually incubate eggs on the top of their feet. They put the egg on their feet so they can keep it off the ice and snow. And then they fold a patch of belly skin and feathers over the egg and completely encase it on top of their feet. But it's a very sophisticated mechanism for keeping the temperature under direct control for the developing embryo in the egg."[121]

Dr Martin: "How would that evolve? If you did not have that in the bird with the very first egg the bird laid, that egg would just sit there and die. This comes back to the irreducible complexity idea. All the parts have to be there from the very beginning or you don't have the creature. If you

---

[120] Martin Jobe and David Hames, *Incredible Creatures that Defy Evolution*, op. cit.
[121] Ibid.

don't have the brooding spot, you don't have the eggs. If you don't have the ability to make the egg, you're not going to fly."[122]

Other examples of animals with irreducibly complex systems include the elephant, hippo, bee, hummingbird, dog, horse, penguin, fly, cuttlefish – the list is extensive. On the bottom of rivers and creeks in western America you will find the lampsillis mussel. This creature reproduces by pushing some its soft tissue out to form what looks like a struggling minnow on its shell, complete with 'eyes'. A certain type of bass or trout is attracted to the wriggling prey and comes down to investigate. At precisely the moment the fish lunges for the bait, the mussel explodes its larvae and eggs into the bass's mouth, where they get caught in the gills and attach as parasites. Here they feed on the blood of the host fish until large enough to detach and fall to the bottom to grow.

How does a mussel evolve *that* reproductive strategy? How does it know to form the right bait, or even which fish will be interested? Where does it get the information to know how to mimic the movements of that fish's bait in the first place? And at what point did it learn precisely the right instant to explode its larvae and eggs into the fish's mouth?

Some evolutionists come clean

Plants: "...As yet, we have not been able to trace the phylogenetic history of a single group of modern plants from its beginning to the present."[123] – Professor Chester A Arnold, Professor of Botany and Curator of Fossil Plants, University of Michigan

"I still think that, to the unprejudiced, the fossil record of plants is in favour of special creation.... Can you imagine how an orchid, a duckweed, and a palm have come from the same ancestry, and have we any evidence

---

[122] Ibid.
[123] **Arnold, Prof Chester A** *An Introduction to Paleobotany*, McGraw-Hill, New York, 1947, p.7

106

for this assumption? The evolutionist must be prepared with an answer, but I think that most would break down before an inquisition. Textbooks hoodwink."[124] – Professor E J H Corner, Professor of Tropical Botany, Cambridge University, England

Fishes: "The geological record has so far provided no evidence as to the origin of the fishes...."[125] – JR Norman, Assistant Keeper, Department of Zoology, British Museum of Natural History, London

Amphibians: "...None of the known fishes is thought to be directly ancestral to the earliest land vertebrates. Most of them lived after the first amphibians appeared, and those that came before show no evidence of developing the stout limbs and robs that characterized the primitive tetrapods... Since the fossil material provides no evidence of other aspects of the transformation from fish to tetrapod, palaeontologists have had to speculate how legs and aerial breathing evolved..."[126] – Barbara J Stahl, St Anselm's College, USA

Birds: "The [evolutionary] origin of birds is largely a matter of deduction. There is no fossil evidence of the stages through which the remarkable change from reptile to bird was achieved."[127] – W E Swinton, British Museum of Natural History, London

"The problem [of how feathers evolved from scales] has been set aside, not for want of interest, but for lack of evidence. No fossil structure transitional between scale and feather is known, and recent investigators are unwilling to found a theory on pure speculation [they are?]. It seems, from the complex construction of feathers, that their evolution from reptilian scales would have required an immense period of

---

[124] **Corner, EJH** *Contemporary Botanical Thought,* Oliver and Boyd, for the Botanical Society of Edinburgh, 1961, p.97
[125] Quoted in **Greenwood, PH** *A History of Fishes,* British Museum of Natural History, London, 1975, p.343
[126] **Stahl, Barbara J** *Problems in Evolution,* McGraw-Hill, New York, 1974, pp.148 & 195
[127] Quoted in **Marshall, AJ** *Biology and Comparative Physiology of Birds,* vol.1, Academic Press, New York, 1960, p.1

time and involved a series of intermediate structures. So far, the fossil record does not bear out that supposition." – Barbara J Stahl, St Anselm's College, USA

Mammals: "Each species of mammal-like reptile that has been found appears suddenly in the fossil record and is not preceded by the species that is directly ancestral to it..."[128] – Tom Kemp, Curator of Zoological Collections at the Oxford University Museum, England

Barbara J Stahl states, "Because of the nature of the fossil evidence, palaeontologists have been forced to reconstruct the first two-thirds of mammalian history in great part on the basis of tooth morphology." [129]

Man: "In spite of recent findings, the time and place of origin of order primates remains shrouded in mystery."[130] – Elwyn L Simons, Department of Geology and Geophysics, Yale University

"Amid the bewildering array of early fossil hominoids, is there one whose morphology makes it as man's hominid ancestor? If the factor of genetic variability is considered, the answer appears to be no."[131] – Professor Robert B Eckhardt, Human genetics and Anthropology, Pennsylvania State University, USA

"Modern apes, for instance, seem to have sprung out of nowhere. They have no yesterday, no fossil record. And the true origin of modern humans – of upright, naked, tool-making, big-brained beings – is, if we are to be honest with ourselves, an equally mysterious matter."[132] – Dr Lyall Watson, anthropologist

"The problem with a lot of anthropologists is that they want so much to find a hominid that any scrap of bone becomes a hominid bone." – Dr Tim White, anthropologist, University of California Berkeley

---

[128] *New Scientist*, vol.92, 4th March 1982, p.583
[129] Stahl, Barbara, *Problems in Evolution,* op. cit.
[130] *Annals New York Academy of Sciences,* vol.167, 1969, p.319
[131] *Scientific American*, vol.226(1), January 1972, p.94
[132] **Watson, L** *Science Digest*, vol.90, May 1982, p.44

It's in the stones

Another Earthly realm rich in mystery is geology. Dr Robert Gentry's work on the existence of billions of tiny radioactive polonium haloes in granites reveals that granites had to have been formed instantly and formed cold for these haloes to have been captured before decaying in 1/64th of a second.[133] Predictably Dr Gentry's work has not been well received by the establishment:

"Basically, what happened is that we posted ten papers outlining fatal flaws in the Big Bang theory on the arXiv, an internet service hosted at the time by Los Alamos National Laboratory. The arXiv distributes physics papers worldwide, and we had previously posted papers there with no problem. This time, when those in charge of the arXiv discovered that our papers very clearly outlined the fallacies of the Big Bang and were supportive of a model of the universe that harmonizes with Genesis, the papers were removed. After we posted them again, they were removed a second time and our password was revoked."[134]

Dr John Morris and his father have compiled geological data on the errors of radiometric dating and what the rocks are really telling us. The Earth is young, they assert, and the evidence is everywhere. In *The Young Earth,* Dr Morris Jr explains the unproven assumptions which lead scientists to choose the dating system most likely to give the desired result. Baffled by science, the public accepts it all. Evolution is the only explanation for our origins, we are told. Radiometrics is the glory of rock dating, *National Geographic* says so.[135]

But by far the most dramatic geological arguments lie in the evidence of the Noahic Flood and its aftermath. Such a subject deserves a chapter of its own which we'll come to later. For now, let us move on to examine another universe which holds within it such wonders to discover. For if you think the universe, stars and

---

[133] www.halos.com
[134] Ibid.
[135] Morris, John D, *The Young Earth,* op. cit.

the Earth might be miracles, what happens on the most minute scale possible will not fail to astound you.

THE MICRO UNIVERSE

Evidence of design in micro structures

"I sometimes wonder why anybody talks about anything else, because this is the most interesting topic there is. Where do we come from? How did we get here? What brought us into existence? What is our relationship to reality as a whole?" – **Phillip Johnson, Professor of Law, University of California, Berkeley**[136]

After World War 2, the cell began to be unlocked with the advancement in technology unavailable in Darwin's day. What confronted scientists down the new electron microscope was not Charlie's homogenous glob of protoplasm, but a miniaturised city of untold complexity containing molecular machines performing numerous tasks. Professor of Biochemistry, Michael Behe, writes:

"At the very basis of life where molecules and cells run the show, we've discovered machines, literally molecular machines… There are little molecular trucks that carry supplies from one end of the cell to the other. There are machines which capture the energy from sunlight and turn it into usable energy…. When we look at these machines, we ask ourselves, where do they come from? And the standard answer – Darwinian evolution – is very inadequate in my view."[137]

The flagellum, for example, which drives the E. Coli bacterium, is essentially an outboard motor. The design comprises a hook with filament or propeller rotating up to 100,000 rpm, a rotor, stator, drive shaft, U-joint, bushings and engine casing (inner and outer membranes). Its assembly defies any notion of a functional precursor in the evolutionary process. If just one of 40 structural components of the engine is missing, it does not work and the bacterium dies. How could the flagellum have evolved? It would had to have worked from the very first bacterium for natural

---

[136] *Unlocking the Mystery of Life*, Illustra Media, op. cit.
[137] Ibid.

selection to become possible thereafter. The system is said by Michael Behe to be irreducibly complex. Evolutionary biology has to explain how the bacterial flagellum came into being gradually when no advantage or function could be enjoyed until the last of some forty components was installed.

How was this machine built in the first place? Studies of the bacterial flagellum reveal that the parts have to be assembled *in a certain order,* as with a car engine. Chemicals cannot do this, there has to be information orchestrating the construction. Molecular machines construct the bacterial flagellum in the correct order for it to work. If one piece is mislaid or put in the wrong place, the engine won't work, so the system is irreducibly complex. And the machines which make the flagella are in turn made by other machines, which are themselves constructed by further systems which are also irreducibly complex. Such mind-boggling complexity 'goes all the way down' and has led to an organised re-think into how life is possible. Darwin seemed to anticipate the problem when he wrote,

"If it could be demonstrated that any complex organ existed which could not possibly have been formed by numerous, successive, slight modifications, my theory would absolutely break down."[138]

Intelligent design – information

Even supposing some spark of lightning triggered chemicals to evolve into an upward cycle of growth billions of years ago, how could they organise in so precise a fashion? An evolutionist would say, "Because of natural laws!" then decline to relate what those laws are, where they came from or what organised them and why. Take a look at the elements listed in rows on the periodic table with their sequential atomic numbers – that's order.

---

[138] Darwin, Charles, *Origin of Species,* op. cit. p.154

As far as organisational intelligence goes, if you wish to build a house and Homebase delivers the bricks, that's all you get – a pile of bricks. Gravity will cause the bricks to fall from the back of the truck but it won't build you your house. Natural laws work predictably, which is why they're called laws. Intelligence and design, on the other hand, are by nature anomalous and required to build the dwelling, one brick upon another, into the finished home. Where does the intelligence and design input come from to fashion the 'simple cell', which, now we can stare into its wonders with technology unavailable in Darwin's day, turns out, alas, not to be so simple after all?

Behe writes:

"The discovery of the Lilliputian world had begun, overturning settled notions of what living things are. Charles Singer, the historian of science, noted that 'the infinite complexity of living things thus revealed was as philosophically disturbing as the ordered majesty of the astronomical world which Galileo had unveiled to the previous generation….' In other words, sometimes the new [ideas] demand that we revise all our theories. In such cases, great unwillingness can arise."[139]

The 'simple' cell - DNA

Even the simplest cells are now known to be unbelievably complex. Biochemists have tabulated their components – mitochondria, nucleus, rough endoplasmic reticulum, Golgi apparatus, cytoskeleton, smooth endoplasmic reticulum, proteins, fats, enzymes, minerals, and so on – but not the *biophysical* aspects the cell, which include the information required to assemble and replicate the cell, not to mention the bizarre property of one cell being able to communicate with others over distance.[140] Chuck Missler writes:

---

[139] Behe, Michael, *Darwin's Black Box*, op. cit. p.9
[140] **Stone, Robert B** *The Secret Life of Your Cells*, Whitford Press, 1989

"The 'simple cell' turns out to be a miniaturized city of unparalleled complexity and adaptive design, including automated assembly plants and processing units featuring robot machines (protein molecules with as many as 3,000 atoms each in three-dimensional configurations), manufacturing hundreds of thousands of specific types of products. The system design exploits artificial languages and decoding systems, memory banks for information storage, elegant control systems regulating the automated assembly of components, error correction techniques and proof-reading devices for quality control."[141]

Biochemist Michael Behe is the author of *Darwin's Black Box*. He explains the reason behind his choice of title:

"*Black box* is a whimsical term for a device that does something, but whose inner workings are mysterious – sometimes because the workings can't be seen, and sometimes because they just aren't comprehensible. Computers are a good example of a black box. Most of us use these marvellous machines without the vaguest idea of how they work, processing words or plotting graphs or playing games in contented ignorance of what is going on underneath the outer case. Even if we were to remove the cover, though, few of us could make heads or tails of the jumble of pieces inside. There is no simple, observable connection between the parts of the computer and the things that it does….

Imagine that a computer with a long-lasting battery was transported back in time… to King Arthur's court. How would people of that era react to a computer in action? Most would be in awe, but with luck someone might want to understand the thing. Someone might notice that letters appeared on the screen as he or she touched the keys. Some combinations of letters – corresponding to computer commands – might make the screen change; after a while, many commands would be figured out. Our medieval Englishman might believe they had unlocked the secrets of the computer. But eventually someone would remove the cover and gaze on the computer's inner workings. Suddenly the theory of 'how

[141] **Missler, Chuck** *In the Beginning, there was Information,* audio presentation supplementary notes, Koinonia House, www.khouse.org

a computer works' would be revealed as profoundly naïve. The black box that had been slowly decoded would have exposed another black box."[142]

This is what confronted scientists after World War 2, following the invention of the electron microscope. Different levels of multi-layered reality were peeled back to reveal a far deeper, astonishing order. That the cell could have come about by complete chance has been described as 'the wild, abandoned guess of the simpleton', yet the notion is daily maintained. And while this cell is supposedly evolving, all other specific design attributes in the universe must be coming together in like random fashion, all within 5×10^{17} seconds (the evolutionist's age of the universe), and, as it so happens, just *work*.

"What are the forces that control the twisting and folding of molecules into complex shapes?" biophysicist F Weinhold wants to know. "Don't look for the answers in your organic chemistry textbook."[143]

At the base of the cell's intelligence is Francis Crick's deoxyribonucleic acid template, DNA, a design marvel insurmountable for the atheist. Dr Jerry Bergman, professor of science at Northwest College, Archibold, Ohio, describes some informational aspects of DNA which have so boggled scientists:

"At the moment of conception, a fertilized human egg is about the size of a pinhead. Yet it contains information equivalent to about six billion 'chemical letters'. This is enough information to fill 1,000 books, 500 pages thick with print so small you would need a microscope to read it! If all the chemical 'letters' in the human body were printed in books, it is estimated they would fill the Grand Canyon fifty times!

This vast amount of information is stored in our bodies' cells in DNA molecules and is coded by four bases – adenine, thymine, guanine and cytosine (A, T, G and C). The key to the coding of DNA is in the grouping of these bases into sets that are further sequenced to form the

---

[142] Behe, Michael, *Darwin's Black Box*, op. cit. pp.6,7
[143] Lipton, Bruce, *The Biology of Belief*, op. cit. p.111

20 common amino acids. Together, these genetic codes form the physical foundation of all life.

We've all been exposed to the basic concepts of DNA and its double-helix structure in our high school biology classes. Perhaps you remember being taught that cells divide through the 'unzipping' and subsequent replication of the double helix. In all likelihood, though, the incredible evidence of design in this process was not discussed."[144]

Missler argues that "an elegant design is more than the parts themselves; it involves information. It requires information input external to the design itself – and the deliberate involvement of a designer. The Darwinians cannot explain the origin of life because they cannot explain the origin of information. The technology that provides language – semantics and syntax, for example – is quite distinct from the technology of the ink and paper it may be written on. The physical features of the circuits in a computer provide no clue about the design of the software that resides within it."[145]

Dr Bruce Lipton writes: "Multicellular organisms can survive with far fewer genes than scientists once thought because the same gene products (protein) are used for a variety of functions. This is similar to using the twenty-six letters of the alphabet to construct every word in our language."[146]

Mark Ludwig writes: "E. Coli is one of the simplest living organisms. As of today the only thing simpler is a virus and they need the inside of a cell to live. E. Coli has a DNA molecule which is about 4,000,000 nucleotides long. Each of these four million sites is occupied by one of four different nucleotides. So, the probability of creating it at random from the right bases is 1 in $4^{4,000,000} = 1$ in $10^{3,000,000}$. Putting every atom in the universe to work synthesizing molecules wouldn't even put a dent in this number. Evolutionists suggest with the redundancy of the genetic code we could shrink this number down to $10^{2,300,000}$. After this, the number may be able to be shrunk more but most scientists believe

---

[144] *Creation Ex Nihilo Technical Journal*, PO Box 6302, Acacia Ridge D.C., Queensland, 4110, Australia

[145] Missler, Chuck, op. cit. pp.9-10

[146] Lipton, Bruce, *The Biology of Belief,* op. cit. p.106

that the number would also get much bigger as we begin to factor in different types of chemical bonds and isomers of the nucleic acids, all of which must be in just the right order for the molecules to work as they are supposed to."[147]

And then there's the amoeba. And then the squirrel. And then the clown. Sheep just so happen to give us the wool we need for clothes, bees give us honey, cows milk and leather, and an abundance of vegetables and fruits adorn our salads in breathtaking variety. *Quelle chance!* And then we have to allow the evolutionist the luxury of enough time for this random series of miracles to be achieved for all other species developing elsewhere in the world. When one hears a scientist claiming the universe is 17 billion years old, that seems a lot of time for evolution to smoke up its charm. But 17 billion years is only 5×10^{17} seconds. Conclusion? Evolution is not possible because there is not even close to enough time to form, *by random processes and from a common ancestor,* 1,000,000 species of insects in all their multiplicity, 20,000 species of fish in all their size and assortment, over 350,000 plant species of incredible variety, 9,000 species of bird from the minute to the magnificent, and 5,400 species of mammal, from rabbits to rhinos – and man.

Back to Scrabble on the beach. DNA contains information made up of the four bases, A, C, G and T, to synthesise proteins. The combinations of these bases must be exact to manufacture the proteins required. This is called sequence specificity. Any combinations of these letters won't work any more than they will in Scrabble. For us to understand the English language at all, we have to agree that 'cat' refers to the black thing with four legs that sometimes doubles as a mousetrap. 'Cat' to an Eskimo means nothing. We have agreed in advance what the letters CAT represent so when they pop up, we have common ground, or

[147] **Ludwig, Mark** *Artificial Life and Evolution,* American Eagle Press, 1993

specificity. Conclusion? Intelligence produces information and communicates it by language. If you find evidence of information, there is intelligence behind it.

Chemical evolution

How could life have come about from non-living matter? Though Darwin's theory begins with the first cell, Charlie steers clear of the thorny question of how we came to life in the first place. Getting to the first protein by chance is no small potatoes, says molecular biologist Michael Denton:

"The evidence of a prebiotic soup is an absolute prerequisite for the evolutionary emergence of life on Earth, but even if good evidence for the soup had been found, the problem of the origin of life would still be far from solved. The most difficult aspect of the origin of life problems lies not in the origin of the soup, but in the stages leading from the soup to the cell. Between the basic building blocks, amino acids, sugars and other simple organic compounds used in the construction of the cell, and the simplest known types of living systems, there is an immense discontinuity." [148]

A simple protein is comprised of a chain of amino acids, which have folded together into a complex, three-dimensional form to provide function for a task. There are twenty available amino acids to make a protein, and combinations of these are linked into chains sometimes hundreds of units long which, if done correctly, permit the protein to fold itself into a three-dimensional machine which has function to perform a given task. Just jamming any amino acids together will not provide a protein with function. So where does the information come from to assemble such a machine?

DNA, of course. Its four-letter coding along the double helix provides all the instructions required for the duplication and precise sequencing of amino acids into proteins. But what is the

---

[148] Denton, Michael, *Evolution: A Theory in Crisis,* op. cit. p.263

source of the genetic information in DNA? Darwinism has no answer to life except that it happened by chance and, it so happens, *just worked*.

There are 30,000 different proteins comprising unique chains of amino acid combinations. Dr Meyer writes,

"Proteins, like written languages or computer codes, have a high degree of specificity. The function of the whole depends upon the precise arrangement of the individual parts."[149]

American exobiologist Stanley Miller is famous for the Miller-Urey experiment carried out in 1953, in which atmospheric gases were energised by a source such as ultraviolet light to synthesise a few amino acids. This was seen as a great breakthrough for chemical evolution, however it did not produce life and later geological and geochemical evidence revealed that the gases Miller used did not even match the components of what Earth's early atmosphere was thought to have been. Oxygen, for example, would quench Miller's reaction, whereas it is known that early Earth contained abundant oxygen.[150] Today, Miller's experiment still shows up in science textbooks as an example of how early life began, yet even Miller later admitted that his conclusions were invalid.[151] Dr Meyer points out that a few amino acids are a far cry from an organised protein:

"Proteins are really the important molecules in the cell. They are the cell's tool box. They do all the different kinds of jobs. There are some proteins that are enzymes, there are some proteins that send signals, there are some proteins which build structures. Muscles are made of proteins, the cell's skeleton is made of proteins, and each one is very different. They have very specific and complex three-dimensional shapes. When

---

[149] *Unlocking the Mystery of Life,* Illustra Media, op. cit.

[150] "Stanley Lloyd Miller," *Notable Scientists: From 1900 to the Present,* Gale Group, 2001

[151] **Wade, Nicolas** "Stanley Miller, Who Examined Origins of Life, Dies at 77," *The New York Times,* 23rd May 2007

you get the amino acids hooked together, the proteins, because of their mutual chemical interactions, fold up into complex structures…. The great surprise that came upon the scientific community when this was discovered can't be underestimated."[152]

Chemical evolution cannot get out of the starting gate. For these incredibly complex protein structures to come together by mere chance boggles the mind. Further, these structures have to be put together in a precise way or no function can be performed. The shapes these proteins form comes with a lock-and-key fit to interact with other molecules in the cell. The real contention is not getting from chemicals to a handful of amino acids, but getting from amino acids to the first protein.

What impresses even the naysayers is the complex specificity in how these proteins form and engage with other machines in the cell based on the precise configuration of their amino acid chains. This is not something that can be explained by random chemical evolution – there is *information* contained on the DNA strand which determines how each protein is constructed in a highly specific way. Dr Meyer states:

"This is very profoundly against the idea of chance. These things are very precise and specific…. We call this property 'sequence specificity'. This simply means that the sequential arrangement of the parts determines the function of the whole. "[153]

Biologists are soon overwhelmed by the impression of design and uncomfortable questions raised. These do not involve how chemicals came together in a prebiotic soup but "Where does the information on DNA come from in the first place?" Crick remarked:

---

[152] **Meyer, Stephen C** "The Origin of Information" lecture, Koinonia House, www.khouse.org
[153] Ibid.

"Biologists must constantly keep in mind that what they see was not designed but rather evolved."

This did not satisfy British astronomer Sir Fred Hoyle, who originally coined the term 'Big Bang' in his rejection of the theory in 1949:

"The big problem in biology isn't so much the crude fact that a protein consists of a chain of amino acids linked together in a certain way, but that the explicit ordering of the amino acids endows the chain with remarkable properties.... If amino acids were linked at random, there would be a vast number of arrangements that would be useless in serving the purposes of a living cell. When you consider that a typical enzyme has a chain of perhaps 200 links and that there are 20 possibilities for each link, it's easy to see that the number of useless arrangements is enormous.... This is for one enzyme, and there are upwards of 2,000 of them, mainly serving very different purposes. So how did the situation get to where we find it to be?"

Hoyle calculated that the chance of arriving at the correct set of enzymes for even the simplest living cell was in the order of one chance in $10^{40,000}$, more than the number of atoms in the known universe.

"The chance that higher life forms might have emerged in this way is comparable with the chance that a tornado sweeping through a junk-yard might assemble a Boeing 747 from the materials therein... I am at a loss to understand biologists' widespread compulsion to deny what seems to me to be obvious."[154]

And that is...

"Rather than accept the fantastically small probability of life having arisen through the blind forces of nature, it seems better to suppose that the origin of life was a deliberate, intellectual act."[155]

Stephen Meyer states:

---

[154] "Hoyle on Evolution", *Nature,* Vol. 294, 12th November 1981, p.105
[155] **Hoyle, Fred** *The Intelligence Universe*, M Joseph, 1983

"Bill Gates says that DNA is like a software program but much more complex than any we've been able to write. The challenge of the chemical evolutionary theorist is to explain the origin of that biological software without reference to a programmer."[156]

It gets worse. Proteins are formed by the information contained in DNA, yet DNA itself is constructed by proteins using a three-out of-four, error-correcting code. This circularity is analogous to very advanced engineering systems, or complex self-modifying arrays in computer programming, where components are formed by processes which themselves are formed by the components! There has to be a start to the process and something to start it. ID scientists contend that an intelligence does the starting.

Chance probabilities

Meyer explains that for life to come about by evolutionary chance, you first have to get your amino acids linked up. There are 20 proteinaceous amino acids to choose from, and some variation is allowed at certain sites in the chain but the conditions at others are specific. The odds of having the correct amino acids sequenced in a short protein say 100 links long, allowing for variability, is 1 in 10^{25}. When dealing with proteins hundreds of amino acids in length, Dembski's Universal Probability Bound of 1 in 10^{150} is rapidly exceeded, *"beyond which appeals to chance become unreasonable on the cosmic scale,"* says Meyer.

Then there are two kinds of amino acid bonds: peptide and non-peptide bonds. There has to be a peptide bond at every linkage and the odds of this happening correctly by chance on a short protein comprising 100 amino acids is 1 in 2^{99} or 1 in 10^{30}. One non-peptide bond in the linkage and the protein will not fold.

Another probabilistic condition which must be satisfied is that amino acids come in left-handed and right-handed versions,

[156] Meyer, Stephen C, "The Origin of Information" lecture, op. cit.

known as isomers. To build a protein you can only have the left-handed version of the amino acid. One right-handed isomer anywhere in the chain and the protein will not fold and perform its lock-key function. So for our mercifully short protein of 100 amino acids, there's another 1 in 10^{30} chance of this happening by accident, which has to be multiplied by the previous 1 in 10^{55} odds for these two steps to be satisfied through random processes. The odds come out at 1 in 10^{85}.

Now consider that there are thousands of proteins in nature, hundreds in each cell, and trillions of cells comprising a single complex lifeform like a baboon. To put 1 in 10^{85} into perspective, evolutionists themselves theorise that there are only 10^{65} particles in the universe and that the universe has only been in existence for 5×10^{17} seconds. No wonder that 'chance' has been dead as a theory among biologists to explain biogenesis since the mid-1960's. Neither can necessity, or the laws of science, be invoked, since these form predictable rather than anomalous patterns. The conclusion is that you cannot produce *information* without *intelligence*. And that means *a mind*. And that means a *Person*.

Paul Nelson writes:

"Intelligent design leaves evidence of its existence. It's a powerful idea that the universe is rational and comprehensible, underwritten by a supreme intelligence that meant for this world to be understood. It's something that underwrites the program of science because then you can go out and look at the world and the world will make sense. If it's all just a chaotic assemblage, there's no reason to expect any rationality out there, but in fact if it's the product of a mind then science becomes this enormous, wonderful puzzle-solving project in which you can expect to find rationality and beauty and comprehensibility right at the foundation of things."[157]

---

[157] *Unlocking the Mystery of Life*, Illustra Media, op. cit.

Pierre-P Grasse, editor of the 28-volume *Traite de Zoologie,* is a former Chair of Evolution at Sorbonne University and ex-president of the French *Academie des Sciences*. He writes:

"Directed by all-powerful selection, chance becomes a sort of providence, which, under the cover of atheism, is not named but which is secretly worshipped…. To insist, even with Olympian assurance, that life appeared quite by chance and evolved in this fashion, is an unfounded supposition which I believe to be wrong and not in accordance with the facts."[158]

Michael Behe summarises:

"The result of these cumulative efforts to investigate the cell – to investigate life at the molecular level itself – is a loud, clear, piercing cry of 'design!'…. The observation of the intelligent design of life is momentous. The magnitude of the victory, gained at such great cost through sustained effort over the course of decades, would be expected to send the champagne corks flying in labs around the world. This triumph of science should evoke cries of 'Eureka!' from ten thousand throats, should occasion much hand-slapping and high-fiving, and perhaps even be an excuse to take the day off.

But no bottles have been uncorked, no hands slapped. Instead, a curious, embarrassed silence surrounds the stark complexity of the cell. When the subject comes up in public, feet start to shuffle, and breathing gets a bit labored. In private, people are a bit more relaxed; many explicitly admit the obvious but then stare at the ground, shake their heads, and let it go at that."[159]

[158] **Grasse P-P** *Evolution of Living Organisms Evidence for a New Theory of Transformation*, Academic Press, New York, NY, 1977, p.107
[159] Behe, Michael, *Darwin's Black Box,* op. cit. excerpted p.233

THE SEA OF ENERGY

"We are rising to the conviction that we are part of nature, and so a part of God.... That the whole creation is travelling together toward some great end; and that now, after ages of development, we have at length become conscious portions of the great scheme and can co-operate in it with knowledge and with joy." – **British physicist, Sir Oliver Lodge**

"How is it that we know what we know?" – **Lynne McTaggart**

Studies with plants

Cleve Backster's career had been exemplary. The former CIA scientist had pioneered the polygraph 'lie-detector' machine and worked as a guest instructor at the Department of Defense Polygraph School and FBI Academy. That all changed one night in 1966 when Dr Backster discovered that a plant could be measured reacting to his thoughts when connected to a polygraph. If he held the image of burning the plant in his mind, the plant reacted galvanometrically. Yet when the plant was repeatedly threatened with fire but the threat not realised, the plant soon lost interest and failed to react. The plant seemed to know when Backster was faking it. Dr Robert B Stone writes:

> "Accidentally cut your finger and the plants receive signals from the dying cells in the drying blood and there is their reaction in black and white. Do it purposely and the results are not the same." [160]

It was a seminal moment which Backster knew would change everything, and it did. In the ensuing decades he became both pariah and prophet. His conclusions were:

1. A continuum had to exist by which the plant could detect his thoughts. (If so, what was the nature of this field?)

---

[160] Stone, Robert B, *The Secret Life of Your Cells,* op. cit. p.19

2. The plant was interpreting whether his intentions were honest or not. Where was the seat of this discriminatory intelligence?
3. Our thoughts are known!
4. What an observer thinks becomes part of the experiment!

Backster's findings were not enthusiastically received by his peers, notes Stone.

"Confront classic scientists with the fact that the thing needed to make an experiment scientific, namely protocol, is the very thing that makes it unrepeatable, and they throw their hands up in the air."[161]

Further experiments revealed that plants responded with extreme agitation when Backster dumped live brine shrimp into boiling water. After a while, however, the plants got used to the death of the shrimp and tuned into his thoughts instead. Backster also found that the plants adapted to death and only reacted initially to the brine shrimp's demise if healthy brine shrimp were used. Sick brine shrimp did not gain any reaction.

Backster thought of placebo, where a doctor gives a patient a fake pill and, through the extent of belief, the patient can recover. But if the patient knows the pill is a fake, the effect is not observed. Does belief create chemicals which somehow activate the body's healing processes? Science only considers the mind through evolutionary processes. If faith healing did work, it was viewed merely as an evolutionary mechanism to ensure the host's survival, nothing more.

But Backster went on to find a lot more. Distance was no object to 'Primary Perception', as he termed the phenomenon. He could cut off a leaf and wire it up and still get the plant's reaction. He

---

[161] Ibid. p.18

could grind up a leaf and place the electrodes in the powder in another room and get the same reading.

"Equipment was set up and the leaves were to be tested with electrodes. A dish of water and a dish of acetone were placed alongside. If the card turned up was black, the leaf being tested was put in water as a reward. If the card turned up was red, the leaf being tested would be put in acetone – a quick life-terminator. After the second leaf was put into the acetone, all the leaves went into a state of shock or fainting. That is, there would be no reaction on the equipment, neither up nor down, only a straight line."[162]

The plants seemed to possess a reactive defence against trauma from threats remotely derived. Further studies confirmed this. Two plants were placed in a room and six students selected lots from a hat. One of the slips instructed the student to murder a plant. The other students and Backster left the room while the student tore the plant out of its pot and ripped it to sheds. Backster then returned and wired up the remaining plant, the 'witness' to the murder. As each student came in, the plant's reaction was monitored until the murderer entered and the plant's reading went wild.

Why? Because the plant knows the murderer doesn't fake it. Backster's problem was determining what was being measured here. He later came to the same conclusion Sir Oliver Lodge had decades before, and Deepak Chopra would do in the future. That there exists a universal continuum interpenetrating all living things, which is reactive, and here was the proof. The 'field' was discerning, which meant it had intelligence. Deepak Chopra called it 'Thinking No-Stuff'. Oliver Lodge said it was God. All Backster knew was that if he mentioned God to anyone, his scientific career would take on the glide angle of a grand piano. "Naturalistic conclusions are required for everything!"

---

[162] Ibid.

The very concept of what Backster was facing boggled the mind. Dr Stone writes:

"Privacy seemed now to be non-existent. It appears to be an illusion. How can there be privacy if everything is connected through a oneness, a continuum of intelligence, a morphogenetic field, a collective unconscious or anything else you want to call it? Your secret thoughts are communicated to every cell in your body and probably to a larger continuum in space."[163]

Backster found that plants attune themselves to their owner, even over distance. One night, he took an associate home to a surprise party held in the latter's honour. Both men entered to cries of "Surprise!" from the neighbours. When Backster analysed the reactions of the plants in his lab the following day, his journey was laid out, bare for all to see. He had made notes the night before with a chronometer during points in their trip. The precise time they were running for a bus in the Port Authority. Holding the bus door open for someone. Descending into the Lincoln Tunnel. At the exact moment of "Surprise!" the needles careened off the chart miles away, presumably because of Backster's own reaction to the occasion. Backster realised he had established some sort of quantum connection with his plants.

Stone records another Backster experiment, wherein a veteran of the Japanese attack on Pearl Harbour was asked to watch a video, during which his reactions would be monitored. Painstaking preparations were made to ensure there was no interference in the experiment. The veteran was shown part of a program entitled *The World at War* on his own television at home. The film was about the attack on Pearl Harbor by the Japanese. During the clip, there was a close-up of a naval gunner blazing away at enemy aircraft passing overhead. Stone writes:

---

[163] Ibid. p.38

"The TV program, also being recorded in the laboratory, then showed the downing of an aircraft. Instantly, the readout recorded a reaction by the veteran's mouth cells. An enemy plane crashing into the sea caused the tracing to make a violent dip down and then up."

Later, the veteran admitted he had been emotionally stimulated at that point, hence the reaction. The old man's cells had been collected, centrifuged and connected to the monitoring equipment in a lab *seven miles* from his home.[164]

The Zero Point Field

The Descartian/Newton model of a matter-only universe was falling apart. Matter was not separate from mind, it *was* mind. Yet science still had the body divided into parts, with each assigned a medical specialty. Always ignored was the whole person and their unfathomable mind.

Placebo/nocebo: what is the mechanism? Bad news kills yet dogs do not react to bad news and neither do sharks. Apparently only humans have 'evolved' a higher consciousness with which to process and react to 'information'. Which begs the question, how did man evolve inordinately further than any other creature, with a mind capable of self-harm with negative conditioning thereby (nocebo)? Come to think of it, why *do* we question? Anything? *At all?* You cannot stop a three-year-old asking questions as she tries to learn of the world around her.

Lynne McTaggart, an American researcher and author, has been following an exotic line of enquiry into the very building blocks of matter itself. In her book, *The Field,* she comments:

"The most important quality common to all these researchers was a simple willingness to suspend disbelief and remain open to true discovery, even if it meant challenging the existing order of things, alienating colleagues or opening themselves up to censure and

---

[164] Ibid. pp.68-69

professional ruin. To be revolutionary in science is to flirt with professional suicide. The system tends to encourage professionals to carry out experimentation whose purpose is primarily to confirm the existing view of things, or to further develop technology for industry, rather than to serve up true innovation."[165]

Auras and energy fields were being measured around people using Kirlian photography. Was this evidence of Backster's Primary Perception? Did this life-force or ch'i find its origins in some Quantum of Solace? A concept known as the 'Zero Point Field', writes McTaggart, was soon being openly discussed:

"Several thought again about a few equations that had always been subtracted out in quantum physics. These equations stood for the Zero Point Field – an ocean of microscopic vibrations in the space between things. If the Zero Point Field were included in our conception of the most fundamental nature of matter, they realized, the very underpinning of our universe was a heaving sea of energy – one vast quantum field. If this were true, everything would be connected to everything else like some invisible web. They also discovered that we were made of the same basic material. On our most fundamental level, living beings, including human beings, were packets of quantum energy constantly exchanging information with this inexhaustible energy sea…. We literally resonate with our world."[166]

'Thinking no-stuff'

Peter Hudson writes:

"Energy and matter are the same universal substance, simply vibrating at different frequencies. Recent advancements in quantum physics suggest that the universe is made up of 98% energy and only 2% matter, so it is a great puzzle that we seem to focus far too much, and place too much emphasis on the physical and material aspects of our being instead of the energy that created it."[167]

---

[165] **McTaggart, Lynne** *The Field,* Element, 2003, p.16
[166] Ibid. p.XXI - XXII
[167] **Hudson, Peter J** *Where Do We Go From Here?* Mayfair Publishing, 1999, p.8

Scientists tell us our body is made up of atoms. Dr Stuart Crane reminds that an atom has protons, neutrons and electrons. If the nucleus were the size of a pinhead, scientists have calculated that the first electron in the atom would be 50 yards (150 feet) distant. Everything else in the atom to the Descartian biochemist is… nothing. That's all there is to an atom. If we take all the neutrons, electrons and protons of the atoms in your body and bundle them together, you would be about the same size as a tiny speck of pepper, says Dr Crane. You would weigh the same as you do now because all your atomic weight is in the protons, neutrons and electrons. That's all of you that exists – a speck of pepper. The rest of you… isn't.

If you then take that speck of pepper, do you think you could pass it by another speck of pepper within itself, i.e. 150 feet, without encountering any obstruction? A wall is made the same way we are. A wall, according to atomic physics, is basically nothing. There is absolutely no reason why you cannot walk through a wall, according to all the laws of science except one, says Crane. You bump your nose.

Dr Crane makes the point that much science is dishonest because it does not deal with things as they are, it deals with things that work (events that are demonstrable and repeatable).

"The scientist says: "We had 11,000 people all try and walk through a wall and they all ended up bumping their noses. Therefore we conclude that walking through walls can't be done because noses don't go through and that's what has to go through first."[168]

Now quantum physics tells us the Zero Point Field is measurable both in the material and throughout 'the nothing' – Dr Deepak Chopra's 'Thinking No-Stuff'. Scientists in various fields have been working hard on the enigma despite being shunned by their peers. How does the Field work? Is it a medium through

---

[168] **Crane, Dr Stuart** *The Montreal Conferences*, 1976

which all atoms are interconnected, distance no object? All sense something mind-boggling just out of reach. For years, quantum mechanics had been loosening up adherents to 'impossible concepts', such as sub-atomic particles being in two places at the same time, indeed not even existing unless someone observes them! Neuroscientist Karl Pribram was working on the very nature of perception – how we see and think. The nature of reality. Are objects there whether we perceive them or not? Is there a quantum link between all 'matter'?

The future of the Internet, some say, is in 'cloud computing', whereby all storage and major processing tasks are carried out remotely in huge computer centres, leaving the individual's PC unencumbered by data and processing chores. Scientists are wondering whether the Zero Point Field acts in similar fashion as some sort of quantum repository, into which all our cells, including our brains, are plugged for retrieval of memory.

Peter Hudson writes:

"If we could take a look through high magnification at our solid bodies, we would find the so-called solid reality lost to a rapidly vibrating matrix of energy fields. In other words, there is a vast… emptiness within our bodies but within the void, the emptiness, is a considerable, very subtle form of energy which radiates within and around all molecular or cellular matter."[169]

Lynne McTaggart writes:

"The fact that the human body was exchanging information with a mutable field of quantum fluctuation suggested something profound about the world…. If living things boil down to charged particles interacting with a field and sending out and receiving quantum information, where did we end and the rest of the world begin? Where

---

[169] Hudson, Peter J, *Where Do We Go From Here?* op. cit. p.18

was consciousness? Encased inside our bodies or out there in the Field?"[170]

Boundless affinity

Backster found that the field responded to love, which meant that the field was discerning and therefore had intelligence. Marcel Vogel also found this at the IBM Laboratories at Los Gatos, California. He would place three leaves by his bed and upon waking, direct feelings of affection towards the outer leaves while ignoring the middle one. In a few days, the centre leaf had withered while the outer two remained green and pliant.

This is reminiscent of the story of Jesus and his disciples on their way to the temple in Jerusalem. Jesus sees a fig tree nearby has no fruit upon its branches and he curses the tree: **"Let no-one eat fruit from you ever again!"** The following day, when they pass by the same spot, the tree has withered up from the roots. Peter cries, **"Master, behold, the fig tree which thou cursedst is withered away."**

Jesus replies: **"<u>Have faith in God</u> [the field?]. For verily I say unto you, That whosoever shall say unto this mountain, Be thou removed and be thou cast into the sea; <u>and shall not doubt in his heart</u>, but shall believe that those things which he saith shall come to pass; he shall have whatsoever he saith. Therefore I say unto you, What things soever ye desire, when ye pray, <u>believe that ye receive them</u>, and ye shall have them."** (Mark 11:20-24)

A secret?

Rhonda Byrne's bestselling book, *The Secret*, sold millions on the idea of a compliant 'Universe' and how one might milk it. Predictably, the book provoked criticism from Christian groups for portraying God's principles as some sort of celestial Argos catalogue. Christians believe God's Holy Spirit interpenetrates all

---

[170] Ibid. pp.125-126

things and is the giver and taker of life, so Backster's research was warmly received by many religious groups who saw in Primary Perception a convocation with their own beliefs. Backster's work was also acclaimed by New Age groups who related the 'quantum living phenomenon' to GAIA, Mother Earth. McTaggart concludes:

"The existence of the Zero Point Field implied that all matter in the universe was interconnected by waves, which are spread out through time and space and can carry on to infinity, tying one part of the universe to every other part. The idea of the Field might just offer a scientific explanation for many metaphysical notions, such as the Chinese belief in the life-force, or *ch'i*, described in ancient texts as something akin to an energy field. It even echoed the Old Testament's account of God's first dictum: 'Let there be light', out of which matter was created."[171]

"…If all sub-atomic matter in the world is interacting constantly with this ambient ground-state energy field, the sub-atomic waves of the field are constantly imprinting a record of the shape of everything. As the harbinger and imprinter of all wavelengths and all frequencies, the Zero Pint Field is a kind of shadow of the universe for all time, a mirror image and record of everything that ever was."[172]

British biologist Rupert Sheldrake coined the term 'Morphogenetic Field' 'as the subset of morphic fields which influence, and are influenced by living things':

"The term [morphic fields] is more general in its meaning than morphogenetic fields, and includes other kinds of organizing fields in addition to those of morphogenesis; the organizing fields of animal and human behaviour, of social and cultural systems, and of mental activity can all be regarded as morphic fields which contain an inherent memory."[173]

---

[171] McTaggart, Lynne, *The Field,* op. cit. p.29

[172] Ibid. p.32

[173] **Sheldrake, Rupert** *The Presence of the Past,* Inner Traditions Bear and Company, 2000, p.112

Altered states

In *The Biology of Belief,* Dr Bruce Lipton considers the different states of consciousness and what they might mean in the debate. For this, he states, we need an appreciation of the three brains at work in the human condition. The conscious mind (pre-frontal cortex), the subconscious mind (hind brain) and the 'superconscious mind' in the environment – Dr Lipton's term for Backster's Primary Perception, Sheldrake's Morphogenetic Field, Rhine's ESP, GAIA, The Holy Spirit, God, call it what you will.

Interestingly, meditation and prayer are often carried out in the relaxed alpha state of consciousness, in which the brain cycles at around 10Hz. New Age mystics talk of GAIA interconnected in this plane. Shamans and monks chant themselves into a trance for contact with something beyond. Ray Manzarek, of the pop group *The Doors,* relates how Jim Morrison had his band pound him into an altered state with the sound of their instruments:

"He [Morrison] was not a performer, he was not an entertainer, he was not a showman, he was a shaman. He was possessed, man."[174]

In two minds

The two centres of action in the brain are the conscious and subconscious minds. The conscious mind evaluates information and forms conclusions. The subconscious mind, located hind brain, is the stimulus-response master computer that runs everything. It can be programmed through repetition, according to Pavlov, and is enhanced using pleasure or pain (aversion therapy).

By comparison, the conscious mind is slow and deliberate. The subconscious mind reacts blindingly fast in flight-or-flight situations and deals with behavioural patterning and the running of life-systems in the body. Depressed people get sick. Dr Lipton contends that the subconscious mind forms our end of a quantum

---

[174] Schimmel, Joe, *Rock and Roll Sorcerers,* www.goodfight.org

link into the unknown. We not only transmit but receive. This communication is greatly enhanced in the lower states of consciousness experienced in prayer, meditation, trance-states, drug-states and hypnosis. The obvious questions are: What is the nature of what we transmit? What/who is doing the receiving? What is our relationship with what's doing the receiving? How can we know?

Mind control

The Central Intelligence Agency (CIA) was keen to know more, but for other reasons. The Agency's infamous MK-ULTRA and MONARCH programs in the fifties and sixties were spawned out of Josef Mengele's 'research' on his prisoners in Auschwitz using trauma-based mind control techniques. Infliction of torture on a subject was found to produce a breakaway persona or 'alter' which could be programmed and given access codes like a computer file. The idea was to find a way to develop the perfect assassin using buried alters, creating a subject who would assimilate into society and be triggered to kill or maim years later via radio frequency implant or spoken codeword.[175]

Dr Ewen Cameron, erstwhile head of the Canadian, American and World Psychiatric Associations, received millions of dollars from Allen Dulles (CIA) through front organisations such as the Investigation of Human Ecology, over which Cameron presided. Experiments in mind control and euphemistically named 'basic programming' were conducted in Montreal, mostly at McGill University, St Mary's Hospital and Allan Memorial Institute. Cameron pioneered 'psychic driving' (constant auditory repetition), drug-induced coma and the application of electroshock trauma for

---

[175] Chapter 3, part 4: "Supreme Court Dissents Invoke the Nuremberg Code: CIA and DOD Human Subjects Research Scandals." *Advisory Committee on Human Radiation Experiments Final Report*. Retrieved on 24th August 2005. "The CIA program, known principally by the codename MKULTRA, began in 1950"

alter programming. Many victims were drugged and kidnapped under guise of an 'alien abduction' or recruited through medical 'guinea-pig' programs. Cameron has been conveniently left out of most psychiatric journals probably due to MK-ULTRA being publicly exposed in the 1970's through lawsuits filed by Canadian survivors and their families. The CIA and Canadian government settled out of court to avoid being compelled officially to admit any wrongdoing.[176]

Such events seem far-fetched and hard to believe for the man in the street, yet documentation on ULTRA, if not MONARCH and associated operations is extensive and persistent. Over the years, the press has mentioned some aspect of these programs:

- A London *Sunday Times*, Feb 1978, article revealed that in a NATO conference on Stress Reduction, a Navy Lieutenant-Commander Thomas Narut, stationed in Naples, admitted to a training program for killers and assassins
- *New Federalist* journalist Anton Chaitkin asked former CIA Director William Colby directly, "What about MONARCH?" Colby replied angrily, "We stopped that between the late 1960s and the early 1970s."
- *Washington Times*, December 27th 1988 page A-2, author Bill Gertz
- *Defense News*, January 11-17, 1993 page 29, author Barbara Opall
- *Tactical Technology*, February 3rd 1993 pages 1-5 - Russian Technology Used For Mind Control
- *Aviation Week and Space Technology*, May 24th 1993 - Army Prepares For Non-Lethal Combat
- *Aviation Week and Space Technology*, June 7th 1993 - Washington Outlook Still Under Wraps (discusses the use of non-lethal means on David Koresh and his followers)

---

[176] http://en.wikipedia.org/wiki/Donald_Ewen_Cameron

- *Defense Electronics,* July 1993, page 17, author Mark Tapscott - DoD Intel Agencies Look at Russian Mind Control Technology, Claims FBI Considered testing on Koresh
- *Wall Street Journal,* January 4th 1993, pages A-1/4, author Thomas E. Ricks hosts a lengthy article exploring the future battlefield use of non-lethal weapon systems

Conclusion

Quantum physics declares that the fundamental particles of matter are not matter. That sub-atomic particles can be everywhere and nowhere at the same time. Einstein believed that the speed of light set limits on how fast a material entity could travel. Now we learn that space-time is an illusion. Is everything the Field and *of* the Field? Are we as much a part of the Field in death as in life? Yes, say some scientists. When you die, nothing of your spirit/energy in the Field dies. As the Alanis Morrisette song goes: "How about not equating death with stopping?"

Little science on the Field is published in the public press from one month to the next, so the public remains largely unaware of this fascinating subject. The midnight candles are burning in labs across the world, however, attempting to get to the bottom of it all. Some of the work is mundane. Primary Perception may explain the phenomenon of birds and fish changing direction simultaneously; how they avoid bumping into each other. How a species of blind ant can build two pillars of a towering arch, which meet perfectly overhead. How birds navigate vast distances, separately but to the same destination. Why menstrual cycles line up in prisons, convents and schools over time.

The more proofs produced of what the Field is and what it represents, the weirder the picture becomes, especially in its application to theology. Traditional Christian doctrine states that a total belief in communication works through a process called faith. Faith is put to work in love through the Holy Spirit (field), which interpenetrates all things. Faith in God will return to accomplish all that he has purposed to do. God declares that nothing will be withheld from them that they have imagined to do.[177] We have been given free will and the freedom to exercise it, so we are responsible for what we do on Earth. Prayer is held as communication with the Universal Intelligence. Believe and be healed. Believe, and be part of the eternal picture. Doubt, and even a plant will know you are faking it.

That cells respond to belief by the sender is now a fact in the laboratory two millennia years after a carpenter from Nazareth proved the self-same phenomenon in the vineyards of Israel. In the Bible, we find Jesus using quantum language and concepts two thousand years before Karl Pribram and Cleve Backster, even telling his spellbound audiences that the universe is taking notes:

"Every idle word that men shall speak, they shall give account thereof in the day of judgment." (Matt 12:36)

"For there is nothing covered that shall not be revealed; neither hid that shall not be known. Therefore whatsoever ye have spoken in darkness shall be heard in the light; and that which ye have spoken in the ear in closets shall be proclaimed upon the housetops." (Luke 12:2-3)

---

[177] Genesis 11:6

THE MESSAGE SYSTEM

There is a principle which is a bar against all information,
which is proof against all argument,
and which cannot fail to keep man in everlasting ignorance.
That principle is condemnation without investigation.
– William Paley (1743-1805)

If the world and everything within it are designed, that means there's a Designer. This changes everything. Science has no truck with the 'Who' and desires to control discovery. But if there's a Higher Mind, there's a 'Who'. We would want to know something about this Designer, why he made us, what he wants for us, and what he intends for us when our lives are over. Is the Designer a personal or impersonal life-force? At this point, science washes its hands of the whole affair and tosses it over to the philosopher and theologian.

But hold your horses for a moment. When aliens contact Jodie Foster's astrophysicist with intricate blueprints in *Contact*, design is the order of the day in evolutionist Carl Sagan's story. In *Close Encounters*, contact with extraterrestrials is accepted without question to be the purview of design. Ignoring Hollywood's consummate expertise on such matters for a moment, it does beg the questions:

- Why would 'making contact' *not* be science?
- If a Designer made us, has he ever tried contacting us?

Intelligence produces information and communicates it by language. Dr Chuck Missler believes we are solidly in the realm of the information sciences here. If a Designer created us, the Designer possesses the technology to get a message to us. Does such a message exist? And if so, how do we authenticate it? Like the aliens in *Contact*, we would expect to get a message replete with design – after all, we can infer from the evidence that the Designer is a mathematical prodigy. Dr Missler examined whether quantum design could be detected in any of the Earth's great books. Professor M Montiero-Williams, former Boden professor of Sanskrit, spent 42 years studying the religious books of the East. In summing up the wealth of his findings, the latter stated:

"Pile them [the Eastern books], if you will, on the left side of your study table; but place your own Holy Bible on the right side - all by itself, all alone - and with a wide gap between them. For… there is a gulf between it and the so-called sacred books of the East which severs one from the other utterly, hopelessly and forever…. a veritable gulf which cannot be bridged over by any science of religious thought."[178]

Acrostics (ELS)

Religious prejudice or reality? What did these men find? Dr Missler reviewed research carried out on the earliest sources of the Hebrew Torah (the first five books of the Bible), said to have been given by divine revelation to Moses by God. Scientists have found that the Torah contains key numerological signatures, in the form of equidistant letter sequences or acrostics. This in itself should get our attention, though some have argued that such a phenomenon might be expected in any large body of text. However, the fact that these equidistant letter sequences (ELS) occur *with every relevance to the plain text in which they are found* is another matter entirely.

Under 'Bible Code', Wikipedia relates:

"Contemporary discussion and controversy around one specific encryption method began in 1994 when Doron Witztum, Eliyahu Rips and Yoav Rosenberg submitted their paper, "Equidistant Letter Sequences in the Book of Genesis" to the peer-reviewed journal *Statistical Science*.[179] After unexpectedly surviving an unprecedented three rounds of peer review, the paper was published by *Statistical Science* and the 'ELS'

---

[178] **Collett, Sidney** *All About the Bible*, Barbour Publishing, 1989, pp.314-315
[179] **Doron Witztum, Eliyahu Rips, Yoav Rosenberg (1994)** "Equidistant Letter Sequences in the Book of Genesis", *Statistical Science* 9: 429–438

phenomenon was 'presented as a puzzle' to its readership. A storm of controversy immediately ensued."[180]

Of course controversy ensued. "The God Alien makes contact!" In his bestseller, *The Bible Code,* Michael Drosnin believed that the Bible in its original form was an intricate cipher in multi-dimensional arrays, containing the most accurate, detailed descriptions of names, places and events yet to occur. This, he maintained, was ample proof of God's existence. Mr Drosnin has been discounted in science circles as sensationalist, and several collaborators later distanced themselves from his book. A more erudite study was published the same year by Dr Jeffrey Satinover entitled *The Truth Behind the Bible Code.* Dr Satinover concludes that the codes indeed exist and design is afoot.[181]

In the years since, much work has been done to interrogate both Old and New Testaments in their original languages using computers to lay out the text in two- and three-dimensional grids. By employing variable skip sequences, some astonishing information has emerged related to the plain text in which the codes are embedded. For instance, Isaiah 53, one of the key Old Testament chapters predicting the coming of Messiah eight centuries before Christ, contains a range of codes involving names of the protagonists of Christ's ministry. Some examples are: 'The man Herod', 'let him be crucified', 'the disciples mourn', 'Peter', 'Matthew', 'John', 'Caiaphas', 'Nazarene', 'Yeshua is my name', 'Moriah' (Golgotha), 'Shiloh', 'His signature', 'from the atonement Lamb', and so on.

No news, alas, to some rabbis of great learning who view the Torah as not just a reflection of God's Will, *but the very executable for the Creation itself.* The Torah is God on parchment. The scriptures were meticulously copied throughout the ages from one generation

---

[180] http://en.wikipedia.org/wiki/Bible_code#cite_note-WRR-0
[181] **Satinover, Jeffrey** *The Truth Behind the Bible Code,* Sidgwick & Jackson, 1998

to the next, and if an error was made transcribing a scroll, it was removed and immediately destroyed. After all, it was God himself they were copying. Chuck Missler writes:

"There are a number of other incredible discoveries of hidden designs in the Biblical text. Our exploration of the genealogy of Noah in Genesis 5 should be well-known to our readers.[183] The remarkable acrostics on the names of God in the Book of Esther are also well known in the Talmudic literature.[184] Also remarkable are the discoveries of Ivan Panin who, without the aid of a computer, spent 50 years and 43,000 handwritten pages of calculations to give us his incredible discoveries.[185] Perhaps less well known, except to serious students of cryptography, are the encryptions hidden in the texts of both Isaiah and Jeremiah."[186]

Missler reasons that any Designer wishing to authenticate his message to Earth would have done so in such a way as to demonstrate an unequivocally transcendent intelligence. Several methods could be used to get our attention:

- By revealing design in the words and letters passed to us (code)
- By telling us things that had not happened yet (prophecy)
- By revealing advanced knowledge unknown in ancient times only to be discerned in the future (revelation)

What would we expect to hear from an entity existing outside of time – indeed one who *created* time and was powerful enough to make the universe and everything in it? What form would the

---

[183] **Missler, Chuck** Personal UPDATE, February 1996, p.19-23; *Footprints of the Messiah*, p.3; *Flood of Noah*, p.2; *The Christmas Story*, p.13-14; *Countdown to Eternity*, pp.103-106

[184] *Personal UPDATE*, March 1996, pp.5-9; *Beyond Coincidence*, pp.15-21

[185] *Personal UPDATE*, February 1995, pp.12-15; Also, in *Expositional Commentary on Matthew*, vol.3, pp.47-54

[186] **Missler, Chuck** Discussed in *Expositional Commentary on Isaiah*, vol.1, p.15-16; from David Kahn, *The Code Breakers: the Story of Secret Writing*, Macmillan, New York, 1967

message take from a God Alien who made every fish in the ocean and ant in the garden? Would any work originating from the Zero Point Field comprise some quite godlike features? The stakes are high. If one detail contained in the Bible is wrong, then the God of the Bible is not infallible, the book not divinely received, the game is up, and we can relegate God to the garden shed along with Dawkins' fairies. What *has* been found?

Bible science

In Daniel 12, the Hebrew prophet Daniel is given a vision of the last days and then told to **"shut up the words, and seal the book until the time of the end; many shall run to and fro, and knowledge shall increase."** This infers that the prophecy will not be unsealed (understood) until the last days, a time when newfound knowledge will abound. 'Many shall run to and fro' is significant enough to mention and thought to refer to increased commercial travel.

In any case, many scholars have remarked upon the exponential progress in knowledge/science since the 1900's. So steep has this learning curve become that the Sony Corporation states that an estimated 4 exabytes of *unique* information was generated in 2009, more than in the previous 5,000 years.

"The amount of new technical information is doubling every two years. Predictions are that by 2049, a $1,000 computer will exceed the computational capabilities of the entire human species. The top ten jobs for 2010 did not even exist in 2004. We are currently preparing students for jobs that don't yet exist, using technologies that haven't been invented, to solve problems we don't even know are problems yet."[187]

Today, a number of statements in the Bible can be challenged scientifically, such as astronomic data which have only recently been verified.

---

[187] **Sony** *Did You Know?* www.youtube.com/watch?v=cL9Wu2kWwSY

Science has discovered that the stars contained in each of the constellations, Orion and the Pleiades, are not independent of one another but gravitationally bound. The Book of Job, widely regarded as the oldest book in the Bible, was informing readers of this fact thousands of years ago.[188] For two thousand years, it was taught as fact that the world was flat despite Isaiah 40:22, which describes the Earth as a sphere or circle. Astrophysicist Dr Hugh Ross cites other fundamentals which surface in scripture centuries before man realised the implications of what he was reading – ancient explanations of modern-day phenomena with which we are familiar today. Examples of these are:

Conservation of mass and energy: Ecc 1:9; 3:14-15

The water cycle: Ecc 1:7; Isa 55:10

Gravity: Job 26:7; 38:31-33

Effects of emotions on physical health: Prov 16:24; 17:22

Control of contagious diseases: Lev 13:45-46

Importance of sanitation on health: Lev; Num 19; Deut 23:12-13

Light in motion: Job 38:19-20

Sunlight causing wind patterns: Job 38:24

Electricity carrying information: Job 38:35

Winds blowing in cyclones: Ecc 1:6

Blood as the source of life and healing: Lev 17:11

The weight of air: Job 28:25 [189]

Dr Missler lists further examples as:

Modern weapons technology: Matt 24:22

Pathways in the sea: Psa 8:8; Isa 43:16

Medical hygiene: Ex 15:26; Deut 23:12,13

Circumcision: Gen 17:10-12

---

[188] Job 38:31

[189] **Ross, Hugh** *A Scientist's Search For Truth*. www.reasons.org

Weapons of mass destruction: Zech 14:12; Exe 38,39; Matt 24:21-22

Radioactive fallout: Eze 39:11-16

Smart weapons: Jer 50:9

Global TV coverage: Matt 24:15; Rev 11:8-10

Meteorological cycle: Eccl 1:6,7; Job 36:27,28

Electronic funds transfer: Rev 13:17

Round Earth: Job 26:7; Isa 40:22; Luke 17:34-36

Animation: Rev 13:15

Cloning: Daniel 2:43

The language of life, digitally defined: Gen 1:25[190]

The origins of the Bible

So where did our modern Bible come from? Today we see an Old and New Testament. The Old Testament deals with the history of God's holy line from the Creation up to a few hundred years BC. The New Testament comprises, among other books, the four gospels of Jesus, the Acts of the Apostles, the Epistles (a series of letters written to various church groups), and the Revelation of St John the Apostle. Both Old and New Testament writings have been collated into their respective 'canons' or compilations, which are considered inspired and genuine, as opposed to the OT and NT Apochryphas, which are ex-Biblical writings considered flawed.

The scriptures Jesus and the disciples/apostles used comprised the same Old Testament we have today but in its original Hebrew. These writings were divided into the Law (the TORH – first five books of the Bible), The Prophets, the Poetical Books, the Five Rolls and Historical Books. Unusually, the Old Testament 'canon' did

---

[190] **Missler, Chuck** *Technology and the Bible,* supplementary notes, www.khouse.org

not come about until after the destruction of the Second Temple by Titus 37 years after the crucifixion.[191] Josh McDowell explains:

"The Jewish sacrificial system was ended by the destruction of Jerusalem and the temple in 70AD. Even though the Old Testament canon was settled in the Jewish mind long before 70AD, there was a need for something more definitive. The Jews were scattered and they needed to determine which books were the authoritative Word of God because of the many extra-scriptural writings and the decentralization. The Jews became a people of one Book and it was this Book which kept them together. Christianity started to blossom and many writings of the Christians were beginning to be circulated. The Jews needed to expose them vividly and exclude them from their writings and use in the synagogues."[192]

Why were the books of the Old Testament Apocrypha rejected? Unger's Bible Dictionary states that they contain verifiable historical and geographical inaccuracies as well as anachronisms, proving they are not inspired. They promote doctrines at variance with accepted scripture, do not contain the signature of prophecy, and are written in styles dissimilar to traditional scripture.[193] Jesus and the apostles never quoted from them, neither did the Church Fathers and extra-Biblical sources such as Philo or Josephus.

The New Testament canon was compiled along similar lines. The writings must not contradict anything in the Old Testament; must be historically and geographically correct; must not contradict any other writings within the New Testament canon; must be inspired, and must hold Jesus Christ as their supreme authority (a feature known as apostolicity). The writings which fail these standards go into the New Testament Apocrypha. All of

---

[191] From the Hebrew word 'ganeh' and Greek 'Kanon' meaning 'reed' or standard.

[192] **McDowell, Josh** *Evidence That Demands a Verdict*, Here's Life Publishers, 1972, p.30

[193] **Unger, Merrill F** *Unger's Bible Dictionary*, Moody Press, Chicago, 1971, p.70

which begs the question: Who had the final say in determining what was the true word of God in the New Testament?

Constantine's Roman Catholic Church in the 4th century AD. Anathasius of Alexandria provided the earliest list of New Testament books identical to our own around 367AD.[194] Jerome and Augustine confirmed the official canon shortly after.[195] Copies of the gospels had been in circulation within at least one hundred years of the death of Christ. The earliest copy dates from 125AD, within as little as 25 years of the original (40AD – 100AD), according to the best estimates.[196] The conformity of successive texts is impressive, says Josh McDowell:

> "The bibliographical test is an examination of the textual transmission by which documents reach us. In other words, since we do not have the original documents, how reliable are the copies we have in regards to the number of manuscripts and the time interval between the original ['the autograph'] and extant copy?... There are now more than 5,300 known Greek manuscripts of the New Testament. Add over 10,000 Latin Vulgate and at least 9,300 other early versions and we have more than 24,000 manuscript copies of portions of the New Testament in existence today. No other document of antiquity even begins to approach such numbers and attestation. In comparison, the Iliad by Homer is second only with 643 manuscripts that still survive. The first complete preserved text of Homer dates from the 13th century."[197]

Something other-worldly is going on. When we examine the manuscript evidence for, say Caesar's Gallic Wars (composed between 58 and 50BC), or the works of Tacitus or Livy, we find the number of surviving manuscripts (MSS) in low double digits. 9-10 versions of Caesar's Gallic Wars have survived of any worth, and

---

[194] McDowell, Josh, *Evidence That Demands a Verdict,* op. cit. p.37

[195] **Bruce F F** *The Books and the Parchments*, Revell Co, 1963, p.112

[196] For an exhaustive study of this subject, together with sources, **McDowell, Josh** *Evidence That Demands a Verdict*, Here's Life Publishers, 1972

[197] Ibid. p.39; also, **Leach, Charles** *Our Bible. How We Got It*, Moody Press, 1898, p.145

these date from 900 years after the original. Of the 142 books of the Roman history of Livy, only 35 survive, derived from no more than 20 MSS of any quality, the earliest dated in the 4th century.[198] The deciding factors on reliability include: the number of surviving MSS, their condition and readability, their text variance, length of time between the autograph and earliest surviving manuscript. David Holdaway writes:

> "The procedure for assessing the reliability of the New Testament is the same as for any other important ancient document when the original no longer exists. There are three vital factors. First, the bibliographical test – have the original manuscripts been handed down faithfully? Then there is the internal evidence test – what the Gospels tell us about themselves. Finally there is the external evidence test – an examination of other sources that shed light, such as contemporary ancient literature. Following this process, which is the one used to check the authenticity of all ancient writings, we can come to an accurate decision regarding the accuracy of modern belief based upon ancient manuscripts. When we find several copies which are basically similar and fairly near in time to the original author, we are able to build a case for the reliability of their trustworthiness."[199]

No historical scholar would dare quibble over the veracity of the *Annals* of Tacitus, and yet only 20 copies remain, the earliest of which is dated a thousand years after the autograph. How about Herodotus's *History?* Eight copies remain, of which the earliest is dated 1,300 years after the autograph. In comparison, we have 24,633 surviving MSS of the New Testament, of which the earliest is within 100 years of the autograph which makes up the NT books.

Philip Schaff carried out an in-depth comparison between the Greek New Testament texts (the original language of the NT) and the English translations. He concluded that:

---

[198] **Bruce, FF** *The New Testament Documents: Are They Reliable?* Inter-Varsity Press, 1964, pp.16,17

[199] **Holdaway, David** *The Life of Jesus,* Sovereign World Ltd, Tonbridge, UK, 1997, pp.76-77

"…only 400 of the 15,000 variant readings caused doubt about the textual meaning, and only 50 of these were of great significance. Not one of the variations altered an article of faith or a precept of duty which is not abundantly sustained by other and undoubted passages, or by the whole tenor of Scripture teaching."[200]

In other words, what has come down to us in the King James Version is as close to what was originally written as it is possible to get in English. Geisler and Nix believe the sum total of research into New Testament manuscript veracity reveals that:

"…only about one-eighth of all the variants had any weight, as most of them are merely mechanical matters such as spelling or style. Of the whole, then, only about one-sixtieth rise above 'trivialities' or can in any sense be called 'substantial variations'. Mathematically, this would compute to a text that is 98.33 percent pure."[201]

The early Church Fathers quoted so extensively from the New Testament that Sir David Dalrymple and J Harold Greenlee independently calculated that the entire NT canon could be reconstructed from their writings alone bar eleven verses.[202] The 1947-56 discoveries of the Qumran writings ('Dead Sea Scrolls'), dated 2nd century BC, revealed a plethora of copies of non-extant Biblical manuscripts, including an earlier version of the book of Isaiah, which experts examined for textual and theological variance. Garry K Brantley writes:

"Interestingly, when scholars compared the [Masoretic Text - 9th century AD] of Isaiah to the Isaiah scroll of Qumran, the correspondence was astounding. The texts from Qumran proved to be word-for-word identical to our standard Hebrew Bible in more than 95 percent of the

---

[200] McDowell, Josh, *Evidence That Demands a Verdict*, op. cit. p.44; see also **Schaff, Philip** *Companion to the Greek Testament and the English Version*, Harper Brothers, New York, 1883, p.177

[201] **Geisler, Norman L & William E Nix** *A General Introduction to the Bible*, Moody Press, Chicago, 1968, p.365

[202] Per www.khouse.org; **Greenlee, J Harold** *Introduction to New Testament Textual Criticism*, Eerdmans Publishing Co., 1964

text. The 5 percent of variation consisted primarily of obvious slips of the pen and spelling alterations (Archer, 1974, p. 25). Further, there were no major doctrinal differences between the accepted and Qumran texts. This forcibly demonstrates the accuracy with which scribes copied sacred texts, and bolstered our confidence in the Bible's textual integrity (Yamauchi, 1972, p. 130). The Dead Sea Scrolls have increased our confidence that faithful scribal transcription substantially has preserved the original content of Isaiah." [203]

But atheists will never be satisfied. *Daily Mail* columnist Andrew Alexander retorts:

"The sad truth is that Christianity claims to reveal the greatest truth of our existence, yet the Church's attitude to facts has always been remarkably cavalier. You do not need Darwin to show it. Christian scholars acknowledge that of the four evangelists – Matthew, Mark, Luke and John – only the third is a truthful attribution. And he wrote long after Jesus's death, inspired by Paul, who never even met Jesus. Misattributions are not a good start. Then we come to the Virgin Birth tales in Matthew and Luke. The texts have clearly been tampered with later, as Biblical scholars also concede, to produce a miracle. No biography in history has ever started with a lengthy bloodline of a stepfather."[204]

Firstly, Biblical scholars concede no such thing. And Paul said he met Jesus on the road to Damascus and went on years later to die for his faith. Given the Christian murderer Paul/Saul was before his conversion, what would make him do that? Was Paul *mad?* His copious writings, passed down intact, reveal a man of profound learning and humility in inspired control of his senses. Secondly, Andrew Alexander accuses the gospels themselves of being faked for ignominious gain. He does so in breathtaking disregard of the thousands of citizens who saw Jesus personally, knew what he did and said, and survived long enough to pass this information on to others.

---

[203] **Brantley, Garry K** *The Dead Sea Scrolls and Biblical Integrity,* www.apologeticspress.org/articles/266

[204] *Dail Mail,* 5th February 2009

Who cares who wrote the gospels? It was obviously not a point of interest among the writers (except Luke) to identify themselves in their work. Far more interesting is what happens when you lay the gospels on top of one another and align them chronologically. They dovetail into a four-camera-angled view of the life, ministry and death of Jesus of Nazareth, passed down to us intact in the face of insuperable odds. No errors. No contradictions. Now that's inspired.

Thirdly, Alexander mocks the genealogy of Jesus Christ, which significantly opens the New Testament. *"No biography in history has ever started with a lengthy bloodline of a stepfather."* Chuck Missler challenges anyone to construct a genealogy on the basis of God's number (7) with the following attributes in Greek:

"The number of words must be divisible by 7, evenly. The number of letters must also be divisible by 7, evenly. The number of vowels and number of consonants must also be divisible by 7. The number of words that begin with a vowel must be divisible by 7. The number of words that begin with a consonant must be divisible by 7. The number of words that occur more than once must be divisible by 7. Those that occur in more than one form must be divisible by 7. Those that occur in only one form must be divisible by 7. The number of nouns must be divisible by 7. Only 7 words shall not be nouns. The number of names shall be divisible by 7. Only 7 other kinds of nouns are permitted. The number of male names must be divisible by 7. The number of generations shall be divisible by 7 (21)."[205]

But Alexander is not interested. He dismisses with a wave of the hand the painstaking research conducted into the origins and veracity of NT documents over the past century. This includes examined archaeology, manuscript evidence and corroborative verification of the extra-Biblical authors. Some of the atheist researchers caught up in their study were even converted. Alexander cocks a snook at changed lives and withdraws instead

---

[205] **Missler, Chuck** *Cosmic Codes,* vol.2, www.khouse.org

into Darwin, who won't judge him as a writer or sinner because Charlie is dead and still in his grave. Alexander won't even consider the apostles themselves, who had every chance to flee and live out their lives in distant lands, but chose instead the way of the Master. Perhaps they too were mad to die as they did.

Old Earth, young Earth

The Bible asserts that the Designer's creative act took place a mere 6,000-7,000 years ago, making the Earth and man extremely young rather than millions of years old. This was the accepted view of the Church and almost every civilisation up to the mid-1700s. Then came the French Revolution, the rejection of God and arrival of 'philosophical reason' (humanism/atheism). By no coincidence, the first challenges to the young Earth came not from Darwin in England but from intellectuals in France.

Dr Terry Mortensen made the study of this conflict his PhD thesis at Coventry University. He lists the main players who began arguments for an ancient Earth, a position which would later provide fertile soil for the theory Darwin set forth in his *Origins:*

Comte de Buffon (1707-1788). A French naturalist sympathetic to the new Age of Reason. He wrote *Epochs of Nature* in 1778, in which he believed the Earth cooled from a molten state over 78,000 years.

Pierre Laplace (1749-1827). An astronomer who wrote *Exposition of the System of the Universe* in 1796. In this work he surmised that the universe was a great gas cloud which slowly cooled and condensed to become our solar system. This became known as the Nebular Hypothesis and involved long ages.

Jean Lamarck (1744-1829). A naturalist who specialised in shellfish. He wrote *Philosophy of Zoology* in 1809, which proposed that biological evolution took place based on the inheritance of acquired characteristics. The theory was almost universally rejected but was the forerunner to Darwin.

Abraham Werner (1749-1817). A mineralogy professor who taught his students that the sedimentary rocks and layers we see today came about from depositions from a slowly receding global ocean over a million years. Werner did not bother to study the significance of the fossils found in these layers but he was right about 'the ocean'.

James Hutton (1726-1797). A doctor, agriculturalist and geologist. In his *Theory of the Earth* (part 1: 1795, part 2: 1785), he argued that the Earth was caught up in a vast cycle of continents slowly eroding into the oceans. The sea-levels dropped to form new continents which were dried by the heat of the inner Earth and raised. Hutton declared that there was no evidence of a beginning in the rock record, inviting charges of atheism from his contemporaries. He too paid no attention to the fossils.

Georges Cuvier (1769–1832). A comparative anatomist and palaeontologist. In his *Theory of the Earth* (1812), he expounds his idea that over many ages there have been a number of catastrophic floods which produced the fossil record. At least he looked at the fossils and water.

William Smith (1769-1839). A drainage engineer, surveyor and geologist who built roads and railways during the Industrial revolution. Smith became the first to propose that you could date rock layers by the types of fossils found in them.

Charles Lyell (1797-1875). A lawyer and geologist. In his *Principles of Geology* (3 volumes, 1830-1833), he developed uniformitarianism. Lyell declared that any reference to Biblical testimony as an ancient historical source should be ignored.[206] The only valid method of interpretation was to explain everything by present material processes operating at present rates, intensities and frequencies, involving vast ages.

---

[206] **Rudwick MJS** "Charles Lyell Speaks in the Lecture Theatre", *Brit J Hist. Sci.*, IX:2:32 (July 1976), p.150

But, as Dr Vij Sodera points out, you cannot reject a scientific notion just because you dislike it, yet this is exactly what the new science was encouraging under such men.[207] Of the leading voices now shaping the public mind in the new age, some were deists who believed that while a God-force may well have made everything, this occurred in the distant past and God was 'letting Earth get on with it' according to his natural laws. Miracles were therefore out of the question since miracles violated God's natural principles.

Loose canons and diehards

Before long, the pressure was on and leading ministers with an interest in geology began doubting the Bible. Two such influential theologians were William Buckland and Adam Sedgwick. Buckland was Professor of Geology at Oxford University while Sedgwick taught geology at Cambridge. Both were enamoured of 'millions of years' and this became the dominant model from 1840 onwards. Soon others were leading the charge to 'harmonise' the Bible with the new ideology.

Thomas Chalmers (1780-1847), a Presbyterian minister and naturalist, advocated the Gap Theory, wherein he proposed millions of years existed between Genesis 1:1 and 1:2. George Stanley Faber (1773-1854), an Anglican theologian, proposed the Day-Age Theory in 1823, wherein the six days of Creation were long periods of time, despite contradicting the order of creative processes described in the Bible, namely that grass, seeds, fruits and other plants were created a day before the sun, so how could they survive an entire age with no light? The Day-Age Theory won influential adherents like Hugh Miller (1802-1856). By 1850, the Day-Age and Gap Theories were dominating church thought to the detriment of the established Bible account.

---

[207] Sodera, V, *One Small Speck to Man,* op. cit. p.16

John Fleming (1785-1857), a Presbyterian minister and zoologist, further proposed the 'Tranquil Flood' view – that there was indeed a Flood but it did not upset anything and left no traces. John Pye Smith (1774-1851), a Congregational theologian, maintained that the Creation and Flood accounts described in Genesis were only relevant to the Mesopotamian Valley. Before long, an ever growing cohort of liberal theologians were daring to suggest that the Genesis account could be entirely allegorical, and that the whole discussion was irrelevant anyway because that was then and this was now and Jesus was all that mattered.

Opposing the new science were Dr Mortensen's 'scriptural geologists', who maintained Bishop Ussher's 6,000 year-old Earth, Creation occurring on or around 4004BC, and the Flood around 2345BC. Chief among these was George Young (1777-1848), a Presbyterian minister and geologist who graduated from the University of Edinburgh. Young was an accomplished intellectual who studied Hebrew, Greek, Latin and Italian, Arabic, Chaldee and Anglo-Saxon. He wrote 21 books, including three on geology which were ignored. Charles Lyell scorned such men as:

"…wholly destitute of geological knowledge [and unacquainted] with the elements of any one branch of natural history which bears on the science… [They are] incapable of appreciating the force of objections, or of discerning the weight of inductions from numerous physical facts… [instead] they endeavour to point out the accordance of the Mosaic history with phenomena which they have never studied [and] every page of their writings proves their consummate incompetence."[208]

Astronomer Fred Hoyle writes:

"The trouble lay in an unremitting cultural struggle which had developed from 1860 onward between biologists on the one hand and the supporters of old beliefs on the other. The old believers said that rabbits had been created by God using methods too wonderful for us to

---

[208] **Lyell, Charles** "Review of Memoir on the Geology of Central France, by GP Scrope", *Quarterly Review,* vol. XXXVI, no.72 (1827), p.482

comprehend. The new believers said that rabbits had been created from sludge by methods too complex for us to calculate and by methods likely enough involving improbable happenings. Improbable happenings replaced miracles and sludge replaced God, with believers both old and new seeking to cover up their ignorance in clouds of words, but different words. It was over the words that passions raged, passions which continue to rumble on in the modern world, passions that one can read about with hilarious satisfaction in the columns of the weekly science magazine *Nature* and listen to in *basso profundo* pronouncements from learned scientific societies."[209]

The rebellion of ideas, then, into which the young Charles Robert Darwin was thrust and educated. The nineteenth century became the battlefield for the clash of these two titanic worldviews. To this day, many evolutionist Christians believe the debate does not 'hit the Cross', and that faith in Jesus is all that matters, yet they take their faith from the same Bible in which Jesus remarks of Adam and Eve, **"Have you not read that He which made them <u>at the beginning</u>, made them male and female...?"** (Matt 19:4), and **"<u>But from the beginning of the creation</u>, God made them male and female...."** (Mark 10:6). Was Jesus *wrong?*

Charlie was sometimes reticent over the trouble he was causing:

"Often a cold shudder has run through me, and I have asked myself whether I may have not devoted myself to a phantasy."[210]

Darwin's *frisson* may well have been a symptom of the swingeing divine guilt of his age but, unlike the neo-Darwinists who would follow, Darwin at least possessed a measure of honest desire for the truth, albeit uncomfortably aware of the apostasy his life's work was engendering in others.

---

[209] **Hoyle F** *Mathematics of Evolution,* Acorn Enterprises, Memphis, TN, 1999, p.3

[210] **Darwin, Charles** *Life and Letters,* vol.2, p.229, 1887

From infinity and beyond

What does the Designer have to say on such an awesome subject? Can we expect the Message System to stay silent if it is what it says it is? Here follow some interesting verses that prefigure the evolution/creation conflict:

"For in six days the LORD made heaven and earth, the sea, and all that in them is, and rested the seventh day: wherefore the LORD blessed the sabbath day, and hallowed it." (Exo 20:11)

"Knowing this first, that there shall come in the last days scoffers, walking after their own lusts and saying, 'Where is the promise of his coming? For since the fathers fell asleep, all things continue as they were from the beginning of the creation' [uniformitarianism]. For this they willingly are ignorant of, that by the word of God the heavens were of old, and the Earth standing out of the water and in the water, whereby the world that then was, being overflowed with water, perished. But the heavens and the Earth, which now, by the same word, are kept in store, are reserved unto fire against the day of judgment and perdition of ungodly men." (2 Peter 3:3-7)

"In the beginning was the Word, and the Word was with God, and the Word was God. The same was in the beginning with God. All things were made by Him, and without Him was not any thing made that was made. In Him was life, and the life was the light of men. And the light shineth in darkness, and the darkness comprehended it not." (John 1:1-5)

"Saying to a stock [tree], 'Thou art my father'; and to a stone, 'Thou hast brought me forth.' For they have turned their back unto Me, and not their face. But in the time of their trouble they will say, 'Arise, and save us.'" (Jer 2:27)

"For the wrath of God is revealed from heaven against all ungodliness and unrighteousness of men, who hold the truth in unrighteousness. Because that which may be known of God is manifest in them, for God hath shewed it unto them. For the

158

invisible things of Him from the creation of the world are clearly seen, being understood by the things that are made, even His eternal power and Godhead, so that they are without excuse.

Because that, when they knew God, they glorified Him not as God, neither were thankful, but became vain in their imaginations, and their foolish heart was darkened.

Professing themselves to be wise, they became fools, and changed the glory of the incorruptible God into an image made like to corruptible man, and to birds, and four-footed beasts and creeping things [evolution]. Wherefore God also gave them up to uncleanness through the lusts of their own hearts, to dishonour their own bodies between themselves. Who changed the truth of God into a lie, and worshipped and served the creature more than the Creator, who is blessed for ever. Amen." (Rom 1:18-25)

"[God] has made everything beautiful in its time. He has also set eternity in the hearts of men, yet they cannot fathom what God has done from beginning to end." (Ecc 3:11 NIV)

"Or speak to the Earth, and it shall teach thee; and the fishes of the sea shall declare unto thee. Who knoweth not in all these that the hand of the LORD hath wrought this?" (Job 12:8-9)

"For though we walk in the flesh, we do not war after the flesh. For the weapons of our warfare are not carnal, but mighty through God to the pulling down of strongholds. Casting down imaginations, and every high thing that exalteth itself against the knowledge of God, and bringing into captivity every thought to the obedience of Christ." (2 Cor 10:3-5)

"O Timothy, keep that which is committed to thy trust, avoiding profane and vain babblings, and oppositions of science falsely so called: Which some professing have erred concerning the faith. Grace be with thee. Amen." (1 Tim 6:20-21)

"Beware lest any man spoil you through philosophy [lit. 'science'] and vain deceit, after the tradition of men, after the rudiments of the world, and not after Christ." (Col 2:8)

159

"Blessed is that man that maketh the LORD his trust, and respecteth not the proud, nor such as turn aside to lies." (Psa 40:4)

"For all those things hath Mine hand made, and all those things have been, saith the LORD: but to this man will I look, even to him that is poor and of a contrite spirit, and trembleth at My word." (Isa 66:2)

"But there were false prophets also among the people, even as there shall be false teachers among you, who privily shall bring in damnable heresies, even denying the LORD that bought them, and bring upon themselves swift destruction. And many shall follow their pernicious ways, by reason of whom the way of truth shall be evil spoken of.

And through covetousness shall they with feigned words make merchandise of you: whose judgment now of a long time lingereth not, and their damnation slumbereth not." (2 Pet 2:1-3)

These are the sort of things a *personal* God might say. In fact, the Message System predicts rather more than just the creation/evolution debate. Unlike the other religious books of the world, the Bible stands alone in presenting a God Transcendent. Unearthly. Up to his elbows in man's life on Earth. Inhabiting the vastness of space and the wings of a butterfly. Knowable yet infinite. One simultaneously outside his Creation and within it. And with more Godlike language to boot.

Prophecy

A Being who made time, the universe and everything in it should be able to manipulate his creation as proof of his identity – what reason would a Creator have of remaining unknown if he desired fellowship with his creations? And if known, has he ever been wrong?

One third of the Bible is prophecy in the form of pre-written history of the twelve tribes of Israel, God's holy bloodline. Most of this prophecy has been discharged, giving us a unique view of how well God has done. The remaining prophecies cover key events of worldwide significance in the 'last days' before Christ's return. In total, the Bible contains over 8,000 predictive verses with 1,817 specific prophecies on over 700 matters, dwarfing the attempts of Michel de Nostradame, Edgar Cayce and Gordon Michael Scallion to peek behind the veil and get it right ten out of ten. None of the other great religious books on Earth contain prophecy for self-verification either, states Missler:

"The Bible is the only book on Planet Earth that will stake its credibility on its track record in prophecy. You will not find that true of the Koran of Islam, or the Vedas of the Hindus, or the Bhagavad Gita of India, or the Book of Mormon or [even] Nostradamus's *Centuries…* [which has] many known failures. Occultic mediums, channelers and New Age spirit guides may make claims of this sort of thing but they will not stand up under investigation, certainly not with a 20/20 unbroken track record."[211]

Many religions claim 'to know God', says Josh McDowell, but only one has a God who actually shows up one time. Such a performance is worthy of further study, if only to unhorse an imposter. In the Bible, three hundred of these specific prophecies, *written hundreds of years in advance,* tell in detail of the Designer coming to Earth as a man. Here are fifty-four of them, together with their fulfilments:

1. Messiah is born of a virgin: Predicted Isa 7:14. Fulfilled Matt 1:18-25
2. Messiah will be of the line of Jesse: Predicted Isa 11:1. Fulfilled Matt 1:6
3. Messiah will be of the House of David: Predicted Jer 23:5. Fulfilled Mark 9:10
4. Messiah will be born in Bethlehem: Predicted Mic 5:2. Fulfilled Matt 2:1

[211] **Missler, Chuck** *Macrocodes: 'Past',* www.khouse.org

5. Magi, or Wise Men, will bring gifts: Predicted Psa 72:10. Fulfilled Matt 2:1,11

6. Children will be massacred as wicked men try to kill Messiah: Predicted Jer 31:15. Fulfilled Matt 2:16-17

7. The Holy Spirit will come upon Messiah: Predicted Isa 11:2. Fulfilled Matt 3:16-17

8. Messiah will teach using parables: Predicted Psa 78:2. Fulfilled Matt 13:34

9. Messiah will visit the Jerusalem Temple: Predicted Mic 3:1. Fulfilled Matt 21:12

10. Messiah will enter Jerusalem riding on a donkey: Predicted Zech 9:9. Fulfilled 9:9

11. Messiah will be a problem for the Jews (a **stone of stumbling**): Predicted 118:22. Fulfilled 1 Pet 2:7

12. Messiah will come to save the Gentiles: Predicted Isa 60:3. Fulfilled Acts 13:47-48

13. Messiah will be pierced in His hands and feet: Predicted Psa 22:16; Psa 109:24. Fulfilled Matt 27:5; Luke 23:33

14. The pierced Messiah will be a firstborn: Predicted 12:10. Fulfilled Matt 2:1; 27:35

15. Messiah will die and be resurrected: Predicted Psa 16:10. Fulfilled Luke 24:46

16. Messiah will ascend into heaven: Predicted: Psa 41:9. Fulfilled Acts 1:9 before witnesses

17. Messiah will commence His ministry in the region of Galilee: Predicted Isa 9:1. Fulfilled Matt 4:12-17

18. Messiah will be betrayed to accusers for 30 pieces of silver: Predicted Zech 11:12. Fulfilled Matt 26:15

19. The 30 pieces of silver will be thrown into the Temple: Predicted Zech 11:13. Fulfilled Matt 27:5

20. Messiah will be accused by liars: Predicted Psa 35:11. Fulfilled Matt 26:59-61

21. Messiah will be silent before His accusers: Predicted Isa 53:7. Fulfilled Matt 26:63; 27:14

22. Messiah will be beaten, disfigured and bruised: Predicted Isa 53:5. Fulfilled Matt 27:26

23. Messiah will be beaten and spat upon: Predicted Isa 50:6. Fulfilled Matt 26:67

24. Messiah shall die among criminals: Predicted Isa 53:12. Fulfilled Matt 27:38
25. They shall hate Messiah without a reason: Predicted Psa 69:4. Fulfilled John 15:25; 19:15
26. Messiah will be scorned and mocked: Predicted Psa 22:7-8. Fulfilled Matt 27:31
27. People will shake their heads at Messiah's death: Predicted Psa 109:25. Fulfilled Matt 27:39
28. Messiah shall be born of 'the seed' of a woman: Predicted Gen 3:15. Fulfilled Matt 1:20; Gal 4:4
29. Messiah shall be the Son of God: Predicted Psa 2:7; (cf. 1 Chron 17:11-14; 2 Sam 7:12-16). Fulfilled Matt 3:17
30. Messiah shall be of the seed of Abraham. Predicted Gen 22:18. Fulfilled Matt 1:1; Gal 3:16
31. Messiah shall be of the seed of Isaac. Predicted Gen 21:12. Fulfilled Luke 3:23, 34; Matt 1:2
32. Messiah will be rejected by His people, the Jews: Predicted Isa 53:3. Fulfilled John 7:5, 48
33. Messiah is the pre-existent one: Predicted Mic 5:2 (cf. Isa 9:6; 41:4; 44:6; Psa 102:25). Fulfilled Col 1:17; John 1:1, 2; 8:58
34. Messiah will be called 'LORD': Predicted Psa 110:1. Fulfilled Luke 2:11; Matt 22:43-45
35. Messiah shall be called 'Immanuel' ('God with us'): Predicted Isa 7:14. Fulfilled Matt 1:23
36. Messiah shall be a prophet: Predicted Deut 18:18. Fulfilled Matt 21:11; John 4:19
37. Messiah shall be a priest: Predicted Psa 110:4. Fulfilled Heb 3:1; 5:5, 6
38. Messiah shall be the Judge of mankind: Predicted Isa 33:22. Fulfilled John 5:30
39. One shall come preparing the way for Messiah: Predicted in Isa 40:3. Fulfilled Matt 3:12.
40. Messiah's ministry will be replete with miracles, including healing the sick: Predicted Isa 35:5-6. Fulfilled Matt 9:35; 11:4-6; Mark 7:33-35, etc.
41. The blood money for Messiah's betrayal will be given to a potter in the house of the LORD: Predicted Zech 11:13. Fulfilled Matt 27:7

42. Messiah will make intercession with God for His accusers: Predicted Isa 53:12. Fulfilled Luke 23:34
43. Messiah will be stared upon as He dies: Predicted Psa 22:17. Fulfilled 23:35
44. Messiah will be betrayed by a friend: Predicted Psa 41:9. Fulfilled Matt 10:4
45. Messiahs garments are divided up and lots cast for them: Predicted Psa 22:18. Fulfilled John 19:23-24
46. Messiah will suffer thirst as He suffers: Predicted Psa 69:21 (cf. Psa 22:15). Fulfilled John 19:28
47. Messiah will be offered gall and vinegar: Predicted Psa 69:21. Fulfilled Matt 27:34
48. Messiah will cry **"My God, My God, why have You forsaken Me?"** Predicted Psa 22:1. Fulfilled Matt 27:46
49. Messiah will vocally commit Himself into the hands of God upon dying: Predicted Psa 31:5. Fulfilled Luke 23:46
50. Messiah's bones shall not be broken: Predicted Psa 34:20. Fulfilled John 19:33
51. Messiah will die of a ruptured heart: Predicted Psa 22:14. Fulfilled John 19:34[212]
52. Messiah's side shall be pierced: Predicted Zech 12:10. Fulfilled John 19:34
53. Darkness shall come over the land upon the death of Messiah: Predicted Amos 8:9. Fulfilled Matt 27:45
54. Messiah shall be buried in a rich man's tomb: Predicted Isa 53:9. Fulfilled Matt 27:57-60

All three hundred were fulfilled by the life of Jesus of Nazareth in very specific ways. Statisticians have calculated that the cumulative odds of just sixteen of these prophecies coming true by chance for one life vastly exceed those calculated for the law of gravity to fail. Could Jesus have deliberately fulfilled all these prophecies? Could Christ have had human control over the place of his birth? Over the timing of it? How about arranging for his

---

[212] Blood and watery serum is medically indicative of a heart that has literally burst.

mother to be a virgin? Could he have engineered his own crucifixion and burial in a rich man's tomb? Would it not take a lunatic of quantum proportions to think of organising something like that? Did Jesus set up his own betrayal at the hands of Judas and somehow arrange for 30 pieces of silver to be the blood money? How could Jesus have arranged for Judas to become remorseful and throw the money into the Temple? How could he coerce the priests into using the money to buy a potter's field after his death? Did Jesus orchestrate his own mocking, the spitting and wagging of heads and beatings just to fit the jacket of Messiah the Jews were expecting?

Science speaks

Professor Peter Stoner's models for biblical prophecy have become a standard to many.[213] The prophecies in the above list were given statistical probabilities and the odds calculated for any combination coming true as accurately as they did by chance for one life. Stoner's work has attracted much critical attention. H Harold Hartzler of the American Scientific Affiliation, Goshen College, writes in the forward to Professor Stoner's work:

"The manuscript for *Science Speaks* has been carefully reviewed by a committee of the American Scientific Affiliation members and by the Executive Council of the same group and has been found, in general, to be dependable and accurate in regard to the scientific material presented. The mathematical analysis included is based upon principles of probability which are thoroughly sound, and Professor Stoner has applied these principles in a proper and convincing way."

Eight prophecies were selected by Stoner and the odds calculated (prophecies 4, 10, 13, 18, 19, 21, 39, 44):

---

[213] **Stoner, Peter W** *Science Speaks,* Moody Press, Chicago: 1963

"We find that the chance that any man might have lived down to the present time and fulfilled all eight prophecies is 1 chance in 100,000,000,000,000,000."

Stoner cites as an example that this number of silver dollars would cover the entire state of Texas to a depth of two feet. If one silver dollar is marked and returned to the pile, the odds a complete stranger could walk up and select that particular coin, having roamed throughout Texas, are the same for those eight prophecies coming true for one life by chance the way they did for Jesus of Nazareth. Did the prophets who wrote these predictions dream them up? (Isaiah's prophecies were eight centuries old). If so, they had a 1 in 10^{17} chance of being right, and they were.

48 prophecies

In calculating the odds of 48 of these prophecies completing by chance for one life, Stoner writes,

"This is a really large number and it represents an extremely small chance. Let us try to visualize it. The silver dollar, which we have been using, is entirely too large. We must select a smaller object. The electron is about as small an object as we know of. It is so small that it will take 2.5 times 10^{15} of them laid side by side to make a line, single file, one inch long. If we were going to count the electrons in this line one inch long, and counted 250 each minute, and if we counted day and night, it would take us 19,000,000 years to count just the one-inch line of electrons. If we had a cubic inch of these electrons and we tried to count them, it would take us, counting steadily 250 each minute, 19,000,000 times 19,000,000 times 19,000,000 years or 6.9 times 10^{21} years."[214]

This amount is still short of the 1 in 10^{157} required to satisfy the random probability of just 48 of these prophecies, and there are over 300 proclaiming Messiah. 10 with 157 zeroes following is a number so large, no concept model can be applied to give it a yardstick. 10^{157} also exceeds Dembski's Universal Probability

---

[214] Ibid, pp.109-110

Bound threshold of 1 in 10^{150}, in effect rendering God a mathematical certainty.

The Designer throws down the gauntlet for impostors to match his unbeaten track record of prognostication: **"Present your case,"** **says the LORD. "Set forth your arguments," says Jacob's King.** **"Bring in your idols to tell us what is going to happen. Tell us** **what the former things were, so that we may consider them and** **know their final outcome. Or declare to us the things to come, tell** **us what the future holds, so we may know that you are gods. Yes,** **do good or do evil, that we may be dismayed and see it together.** **Indeed you are nothing, and your work is nothing. He who** **chooses you is an abomination."** (Isa 41:22-24)

"I am God, and there is none like Me, declaring the end from **the beginning, and from ancient times the things that are not yet** **done, saying, "My counsel shall stand and I will do all My** **pleasure.'"** (Isa 46:9-10)

"I have declared the former things from the beginning. They **went forth from My mouth and I caused them to hear it.** **Suddenly I did them and they came to pass. Even from the** **beginning I have declared it to you. Before it came to pass I** **proclaimed it to you, lest you should say, 'My idol has done** **them, and my carved image and my moulded image have** **commanded them'."** (Isa 48:3,5)

Josh McDowell writes:

"The purpose of prophecy is to let us know that God exists and that He has a plan for this world. By the foretelling of persons, places and events hundreds of years before their occurrence, the Bible demonstrates a knowledge of the future that is too specific to be labelled a good guess. By giving examples of fulfilled prophecy, the Scriptures give a strong testimony to their own inspiration."[215]

---

[215] **McDowell, Josh & Don Stewart** *Answers to Tough Questions,* Here's Life Publishers, Inc., 1980, pp.22-23

The return of the Jews to Israel

There is war in heaven. The Bible recounts that the adversary, Satan, appears on Earth as an evil world leader in the last days, triggering a period of great terror and tribulation. Many believed Adolf Hitler was the Antichrist. Certainly his world conquest ambitions, 'Final Solution' for the Jews and declaration of a 1,000-year Reich marked him out as a likely candidate.[216] The Second World War was certainly a great tribulation and we'll examine it later, but scripture reveals that God's chosen people, the Jews, would have to be back in Israel in the last days for the coming of the Antichrist (*lit.* Greek: 'pseudo-Christ') and Messiah. So World War 2 has a problem. The Jews were driven out of Israel after the Roman emperors Titus and Hadrian laid waste to Jerusalem in 70AD and 135AD. For almost two thousand years, the Jews have wandered landless among the nations, shunned and reviled. Seventy years ago, following international recognition of their persecution under the Nazis during World War 2, the Jews were abruptly given Palestine. With little warning. And, as some scholars maintain, *divinely* (Isa 66:8).

The return of the Jews to Israel is significant for a number of reasons. Firstly, their ancient language has been resurrected – a unique event. Secondly, in spite of being hunted, ostracised, beaten and murdered in the intervening centuries (Lev 26:14-39), the Jews incredibly retain their cultural identity. Why on earth would a Jewish person want to be visibly Jewish in the Middle Ages, when to be so was to invite all manner of recriminations? The survival of the Jewish identity is unprecedented and miraculous, yet Ezekiel 39 makes it clear the Jews will be occupying the Holy Land in the last days before Christ returns, and before that, the coming of the Antichrist and Messiah.

---

[216] Mimicking the thousand-year Millennial Kingdom of Jesus Christ.

Scholars of every faith and of none continue to examine the Bible as an intricate cipher. Dr Chuck Missler has collected the evidence and patiently run the numbers. In Ezekiel 4:1-8, a period of 430 years of divine judgment had been allocated to the Jews – divided into the House of Israel and House of Judah – for their apostasy against God. Missler calculates Ezekiel's prophecies and writings were recorded between 593BC and 573BC, around the time the Babylonian general Nebuchadnezzar sacked Jerusalem and deported the southern Kingdom of Judah into exile.

Ezekiel's prophecy is dealing with the period of punishment both Houses will have to endure before their land will be given back to them in perpetuity by God. Missler writes that the Babylonian captivity of the House of Judah accounts for 70 of those 430 years, reducing the balance to 360 years. These remaining 360 years of punishment do not seem to fit into subsequent Jewish history but Leviticus 26:18, 21, 24 and 28 call for the multiplying of the punishment seven times because of the Israelites' continued hard-heartedness against the Lord. It was a fact that most of the Jews were unwilling to return from Babylon to Jerusalem under Zerubbabel and later Ezra when the Persian king Cyrus released them with his famous decree.

Dr Missler lays out God's mathematics. It's what we would expect from a mathematical prodigy. We learn from Genesis 7:24, 8:3,4 that the Bible uses a 360-day year[217] (42 months = 3.5 years and 1260 days being equivalent in Revelation), thus:

360 years x 7 = 2,520 years of further punishment or...

2,520 years x 360 days = 907,200 days of further grief.

Or

---

[217] The original 360-day year is thought to have shifted to 365.25 days after certain cosmological events occurred around 700-800BC. These also upset the precise alignments of temples around the world. This evidence is examined in more detail in *Origins II – Holy War*.

Adjusted for the Julian calendar (our modern calendar which has 365.25 days each year), this works out to 2,483 years, 9 months and 21 days.

The servitude of the nation

The release from the Babylonian Servitude of the Nation occurs for the Jews on July 23rd, 537 BC, writes Missler. So the remaining period of God's punishment for the Jews computes as follows:

End of the Babylonian Servitude	-537y	7m	23d
(no 'year 0' between 1BC and 1AD):	1y		
Remaining Term of Punishment	2483y	9m	21d
	1948y	**5m**	**14d**

14th May 1948.

It is on this date that David Ben Gurion declares the re-establishment of Israel as the new Jewish homeland.

The desolations of Jerusalem

Missler also cites another 'coincidence'. The Servitude of the Nation should not be confused with the Desolations of Jerusalem, which was punishment for not yielding to the Servitude: (Jer 27:6, 8, 11; 38:17-21; cf. Jer 29:10; Dan 9:2). Both the Servitude of the Nations and the Desolations of Jerusalem were predicted to last 70 years, but these were also 360-day years:

70 years (360) = 25,200 days = 69 years (365) less 2 days.

16th August 518BC was the completion of the Desolations of Jerusalem (69 Julian years less 2 days from the sacking of the Jerusalem by Nebuchadnezzar in 587BC). However, the Desolations were to run for the same term as the Servitude before Jerusalem was to be opened up to the Jews once more. Dr Missler's calculation is as follows:

End of the Desolations	-518y	8m	16d
(no 'year 0' between 1BC and 1AD):	1y		
Remaining Term of Punishment	2483y	9m	21d
	1967y	**6m**	**7d**

7th **June 1967** is the day, as a result of the 'Six Days War', when Israel regains control of the Old City of Jerusalem for the first time since Titus levelled it in 70AD (*cf.* Luke 21:24).[218]

Biblical timelines

An interesting study has been undertaken by scholars from the days of Rabbi Elias, two hundred years before Christ, through the early church fathers, to more modern theologians. This work centres around the discovery of eight prophetic time cycles laid out in the Bible which all appear to culminate early in the 21st century. These cycles are: **The LORD's Grand Sabbath Week, the Revival and Inauguration Cycle, the Cleansing of the Sanctuary, the Times of the Gentiles, the Times of Israel, the Great 490 Year Cycle for Israel, the Jerusalem Temple Cycle and the Great Jubilee Period.** Author Grant Jeffrey writes:

"Despite the apparently random nature of historical dates and events, a curious pattern of astonishing complexity emerges when we examine the biblical prophecies regarding the nation of Israel and their precise fulfilments. More than forty of the most significant events in Israel's history have occurred precisely to the day on the anniversaries of the feast days of the biblical calendar…. The odds against this phenomenon occurring by chance are staggering."[219]

---

[218] Research from **Koinonia House**, PO Box D, Coeur D'Alene, ID USA, 83816 www.khouse.org

[219] **Jeffrey, G** *Armageddon – Appointment With Destiny,* Waterbook Press, 1997, p.11

Jeffrey cites as examples:

THE FIRST DAY OF NISAN
Theme: Cleansing and new beginnings

- The Dedication of the Jewish tabernacle during the Exodus (Exo 40:17)
- The cleansing of the Temple by Hezekiah (2 Chron 29:2-3)
- Ezra and the fifty thousand exiles begin their return from Babylon (Ezra 7:9)
- The decree given by Nehemiah to rebuild the walls of Jerusalem (Neh 2:1-18)
- The possible date for the cleansing of the Millennial Temple (Eze 45:18)

THE FOURTEENTH DAY OF NISAN
Theme: The Covenant relationship with God

- God makes a covenant with Abraham – the Promised Land (Exo 12:41)
- The Passover Supper is eaten in preparation for the Exodus (Exo 12:41)
- The first Passover in Canaan – the Covenant renewed (Josh 5:11-12)
- The Book of the Law found and reaffirmed under Josiah (2 Chron 34:31)
- The dedication of the Second Temple (Ezra 6:16-19)
- The Last Supper – A new covenant is offered by Christ (Luke 22:19-20)

THE NINTH DAY OF AV
Theme: A fast of mourning

- The twelve spies return with their pessimistic report of the Promised Land. The Israelites lose faith and the originals from the Egyptian captivity are condemned to die in the wilderness (Mishna – Ta'anit 29a)
- The destruction of Solomon's Temple by the Babylonians in 587BC (Ma'am Lo'ez – Rabbi Y Culi/Jerusalem Talmud – T'anit 29a)
- The destruction of the Second Temple by the Romans in 70AD (*Wars of the Jews* – Flavius Josephus)
- The Roman army ploughs Jerusalem with salt in 71AD (Micah 3:12/Jerusalem Talmud – Ta'anit 26a)
- The destruction of Simon bar Kochba's army of resistance in 135AD (Isa 7:8/Dio Cassius)
- Edward I of England expels all Jews in 1290AD
- Spain expels all Jews on 2nd August 1492
- World War 1 is declared on 9th Av 1914. Russia mobilises its armies and launches persecutions against the Jews in eastern Russia.

Blessings and cursings

As part of his original covenant with Abraham, God states: **"I will bless them that bless thee and curse them that curseth thee."** (Gen 12:3). When you study Jewish history from the viewpoint of what happens to those who bless or curse God's chosen, an interesting pattern emerges. For example, the expulsion of the Jews in both of the above cases presages hard times for the persecutors. In the case of Spain, the Jewish expulsion in 1492 marks the start of her decline as an empire power. In England's case after 1290, the Hundred Years War follows between the houses of Lancaster and York. Plague and war will constantly afflict England throughout the Middle Ages until the Lord Protector, Oliver Cromwell, grants the Jews Right of Settlement in 1657. From this point forward, England begins her ascent as an empire power on land and sea – a rule that will last for the next three centuries.

On 2nd November 1917, Lord Arthur Balfour issues his famous declaration, which endorses the inauguration of Palestine as a national homeland for the Jewish people. The move is largely brought about by Chaim Weizman's contribution to the British war effort, and Weizman later becomes Israel's first president. At the same time, a British army officer, Colonel T Lawrence ('Lawrence of Arabia') is promising the Arab people that England will give them tracts of Palestine in return for their assistance in defeating Germany and Turkey in World War 1.

During this time, the Arabs never demand the area of modern-day Israel, as the land is barren and uninviting to their people. Britain continues to reverse its promises to the Jews from 1920 to 1948. Britain also ends emigration to Palestine during this period, which means the Jews have nowhere to flee to when the Nazis commence their persecutions from the early 1930's onward.

Finally, on 14th May 1948 following the end of World War 2, the Jews receive only 17.5% of the land promised by the Balfour Declaration and League of Nations British Mandate. Britain is to be punished. From 1917 to 1975, she loses her entire empire across one quarter of the globe and declines to the status of a second-level power. Today, the British do not even rule Britain. Successive governments have treatied away her national sovereignty to the European Union and almost 100% of her laws are now determined in Brussels. As the foremost proponent of evolutionary atheism today, 21st century Britain is unrecognisable from the nation she once was, with sky-high crime rates, a justice system which favours the criminal, and the highest rate of teenage pregnancy and abortion in the Western world.

Grant Jeffrey is one among many who writes extensively on the prophetic phenomenon. Another is British researcher Frank L Paine, who spent 50 years studying biblical chronologies and the timing of world events. His book, *Miracle of Time,* details the boggling maths built into the Bible stories some of us still tell our children at bedtime. Frank Paine's conclusions? Man is at the eleventh hour of God's dealings with Planet Earth. The Designer apparently concurs. After a full life, Mr Paine was called home in 1983 in the eleventh hour of the eleventh day of the eleventh month.

IN THE BEGINNING...

We live in a miraculous world, set in a miraculous solar system, between two spiral arms of a miraculous galaxy, which is an infinitesimal part of a truly stupendous universe. Thus far, mankind's frame of knowledge palls before such complexity and order – we need to reach for something more to explain it, says Gonzalez. But before we throw up our hands and mutter, *"So God's the only alternative?"* what do the early sources say? Why are we frightened of them? Academic James Williams is certainly scared. *Daily Mail,* 4th July 2009, reports:

"Children as young as five should be taught about evolution to prevent pupils mistaking Barney the Dinosaur and Fred Flintstone for scientific fact, an academic has claimed. The failure to teach primary school children scientific truth is playing into the hands of advocates of creationism - the belief that God created the world in six days, according to James Williams, lecturer in education at Sussex University….

He cited creationist literature which contained images of dinosaurs in the Garden of Eden or descriptions of dinosaurs dying out during the great flood.

'This wilful distortion of real science in favour of pseudoscience is nothing less than intellectual abuse,' he said. 'While creationists have a right to publish and voice their views, no matter how far from real science they may be, the science education community must respond by introducing evolution <u>and the reality of how life developed and diversified</u> much earlier in the curriculum <u>to combat the establishment of creationist misconceptions</u>.'"

James Williams does not want your kids watching Fred, Wilma, Barney and Bam-Bam because they protray dinosaurs living with man rather than dying out over 65 million years ago in an asteroid strike. Also on the banned list will be *One Million Years BC* and *10,000 years BC* for the same reason. Notice how *Jurassic Park, Primeval* and *Walking With Dinosaurs* all try to have their cake and eat it by maintaining an evolutionary stance while re-

introducing dinosaurs with humans. James Williams is terrified his
religion is losing credibility, and well he should be.

The Designer revealed

One of the great enigmas can be seen in the first few verses of
the Bible: **In the beginning, God made the heavens and the Earth.
The Earth was without form and void and darkness was on the
face of the deep. And the Spirit of God was hovering over the
face of the waters. Then God said, "Let there be light", and there
was light.**

- From these verses we infer:
- There was an Earth before God started creating in
  Genesis 1:3
- It was a dark, forbidding place without form (land) and
  covered entirely with water
- God is outside the Creation progress but literally
  becomes part of what He creates according to John 1:1-
  5, which exhibits startling quantum language. Here also
  we learn that Jesus is 'the Word' and was **'in the
  beginning with God'**:

"In the beginning was the Word, and the Word was with
God, and the Word was God. He was in the beginning with God.
All things were made <u>through Him</u>, and <u>without Him nothing
was made that was made. In Him was life</u>, and the life was the
light of men. And the light shineth in the darkness, and the
darkness comprehended it not." (John 1:1-5)

Colossians 1:15-17 is even more specific: **He [Jesus] is the
image of the invisible God, the firstborn over all creation. For by
him all things were created that are in heaven and that are on
Earth, visible and invisible, whether thrones or dominions or
principalities or powers. All things were created through him
and for him. And he is before all things, and in him all things
consist.**

In other words, Jesus is God, he made everything and literally inhabits his creation. Kent Hovind believes Earth was created finished and mature, Adam was an adult and ate fruit off the trees that night and, like the fruit, the starlight was already created. Honestly, with all the baloney served up by evolutionists on how *they* think it all started, God's tale is as good as any. No human witnessed the beginning but we can draw fascinating conclusions from what the evidence tells us.

Water canopy

A few verses on in the Genesis creative process, we read: **"Then God said, "Let there be a firmament in the midst of the waters, and let it divide the waters from the waters." Thus God made the firmament, and divided the waters which were under the firmament from the waters which were above the firmament, and it was so."**

This section has been argued over for centuries and still divides scholars. There were waters *above* the atmosphere? In the original Hebrew, 'firmament' is translated from **râqîya'**, which implies thin layers hammered into strips. Later in the New Testament (NT) the apostle Peter highlights man's attitudes in the last days before the return of Christ, giving us more information on the subject:

"Knowing this first, that scoffers will come in the last days, walking according to their own lusts, and saying, "Where is the promise of His coming? For since the fathers fell asleep, all things continue as they were from the beginning of creation." For this <u>they will be willingly ignorant</u>: that by the word of God the heavens were of old, <u>and the Earth standing out of the water and in the water</u>, <u>by which</u> the world that then existed perished, being flooded with water." (II Peter 3:3-7)

The above states that:

- Scoffers in the last days will be walking according to their own lusts (doing what they want)
- These scoffers believe in uniformitarianism
- They will be 'willingly ignorant' that God created the heavens and the Earth. In other words, the evidence will be deliberately ignored
- They will be 'willingly ignorant' that the Earth stood out of the water and in the water…
- <u>By which</u> **the world that then existed perished, being flooded with water.**
- In other words, they will be ignorant of the Flood.

Not a bad summation of current scientific attitudes. Genesis 1:7 and Psalms 148:4 imply that a canopy of water existed above the atmosphere (the first heaven) prior to the Flood. There is evidence to suggest that at some point the planet had a type of atmospheric shield causing a radically different eco-structure, one not dissimilar to a modern-day tropical terrarium at a tourist attraction. The Bible states that there was no rain as we know it prior to the Flood, **but a mist went up from the Earth and watered the whole face of the ground** (Gen 2:6).

Pre-Flood Eden

Dr Henry Morris believes a planetary canopy pronounced 'very good' by God would have filtered out harmful ultra-violet and gamma rays of the sun and allowed a sympathetic greenhouse-type eco-system to produce ideal conditions for growth and longevity. Unusual metal and halogen combinations can be compounded in such conditions, as borne out by archaeological finds we'll examine in a minute. Because of the increased pressure, the atmosphere would have been thicker prior to the Flood, making it easier to breathe the air and for larger birds to fly. The existence of continental shelves under the oceans today argues for the seas being shallower prior to the Inundation. More carbon dioxide and less oxygen would have been held in the thicker atmosphere, slowing human and animal metabolisms. These factors, combined with a pure gene pool and an absence of harmful solar energies filtered out by the canopy, would have dramatically increased the lifespans of humans and animals. The Bible is unabashed. Some humans lived over 900 years before the Flood.

Evolutionists still cannot work out how dinosaurs did not starve because of their metabolic rates, nor can they explain how a 52-foot wingspan pterodactyl could ever have flown in today's atmospheric pressure. The answer is, it couldn't. Dr Carl Baugh contends that in the proposed thicker air of the Eden era, these great flying beasts would have had little trouble lifting off the ground. How does an 80-foot apatosaurus breathe with nostrils the size of a horse's? It couldn't today. But before the Flood, under the canopy theory, dinosaur metabolic rates would have been slower with the lower oxygen content. After the Flood, the increased oxygen would have eventually proved disastrous for the descendants of the air-breathing dinosaur babies Noah took with him on the Ark.[220] Once fully grown, these great reptiles would have experienced trouble eating quickly enough to feed their heightened metabolisms, and so would have been in a state of perpetual hunger. As time passed, it is reasonable to suppose that the physical size of successive generations would have greatly diminished.

There were giants in those days....

The pre-Flood exotic conditions would have had a remarkable impact on the environment, abundant evidence of which is still be with us today. The additional pressure would produce a hyperbaric effect, causing all organic matter to grow prolifically (including plants, humans, insects and animals). How tall humans

---

[220] **Baugh, Carl** *Dinosaur,* Promise Publishing, CA, USA, 1987

like Adam were, we can only surmise from uncovered skeletons. Genesis 6:4 states: **There were giants in those days, and also afterward...**

A tropical forest has been discovered deep below the tundra in Alaska.[221] One tree alone was 300 feet in height and had actually been drilled down into before being brought to the surface.[222] A metal hammer comprising iron and chlorine has been found compounded without the presence of silicon, a feat impossible to achieve in today's 14.7 lbs sq./in pressure.[223]

Human skeletons over 12 feet tall have been dug up around the world and recorded. Seven skeletons were discovered in Minnesota measuring 7 to 8 feet tall. The find was written up in the *St Paul Pioneer Press*, 29th June 1888.

A mound near Toledo, Ohio, held 20 skeletons, seated and facing east with jaws and teeth 'twice as large as those of present day people'. Beside each was a large bowl with 'curiously wrought hieroglyphic figures'. This find was reported in the *Chicago Record*, 24th October 1895.

The skeleton of a huge man was uncovered at the Beckley farm, Lake Koronis, Minnesota, while at Moose Island and Pine City, bones of other giant humans came to light, recorded in the *St. Paul Globe*, 12th August 1896.

In February and June of 1931, large skeletons were found in the Humboldt Lake bed near Lovelock, Nevada. The first of these two skeletons measured 8 1/2 feet tall and was wrapped in a gum-covered fabric similar to the Egyptian manner. The second skeleton

---

[221] www.cbc.ca/health/story/2002/03/21/arcticwood020321.html

[222] Hovind, Kent, op. cit.

[223] "The London Artefact, discovered in June, 1934 by Frank and Emma Hahn near London, Texas. This artefact is a metal hammer in Cretaceous rock. The hammer is composed of 96.6% iron, 0.74% sulphur, and 2.6% chlorine. This chlorine composition in compound with metallic iron renders this artefact irreproducible by modern scientific methods." – www.creationevidence.org

was almost 10 feet long. The find was reviewed in *The Miner*, 19th June 1931.

On 4th August 1947, *The San Diego Union* reported the discovery of the remains of several men, 8 to 9 feet in height. Howard E Hill stated:

"These giants are clothed in garments consisting of a medium length jacket and trouser extending slightly below the knees. The texture of the material is said to resemble grey dyed sheepskin, but obviously it was taken from an animal unknown today."[224]

Massive tools, sledgehammers and other artefacts found have been puzzled over. Fossilised cockroaches as long as mobile phones. Dragonflies with 3-foot wingspans.[225] Even in an evolution textbook we read:

"The insects were many and varied but nearly all belonged to primitive, extinct orders. Among the most common and the most familiar kinds were primitive cockroaches, most of which were larger than their living descendants. One species attained a length of about 4 inches. Close relatives of the modern dragonflies were also common and exceptionally large. One species found in the Coal Measures of Belgium had a wingspan of about 29 inches. The insects generally were large. Out of some 400 known species more than a score exceeded 6 inches and three exceeded a foot in length. No other period has produced insects so large."[226]

Most of these 'giants' have been found in coal layers attributed to the 'Carboniferous' period which, in creation-speak, comprises the layers deposited by the Flood. Overly prolific vegetation exists in places where it shouldn't.[227] And then, of course, we have the

---

[224] A collection of newspaper articles, reports and photographs can be viewed at http://s8int.com/giants3.html

[225] **Levin, HL** *The Earth Through Time,* Saunders College Publishing, New York. 1992, p.406; also www.bumblebee.com

[226] **Dunbar, CO and KM Waage** *Historical Geology,* John Wiley and Sons, 1969, p.283

[227] www.drdino.com

dinosaurs themselves. What can such finds tell us about the bygone conditions of our planet?

The protector

Some surmise the canopy may have been made of super-cold ice or crystalline hydrogen. The barrier would not need to be thick to double the atmospheric pressure to approximately 29 lbs/sq. in. to produce such results. Thought by some creation scientists to have been 10-12 miles above the Earth's surface, this protective layer may have caused the sky to appear pink rather than the blue we witness today. Others dispute this, citing Genesis 1:14-18 which states, **He made the stars also. And God placed them in the expanse of the heavens to give light on the Earth**, which would be a neat trick through a crystalline hydrogen canopy ten miles above the Earth. Some scientists argue that the Earth would have superheated with such a canopy. Others, that the concept of a canopy, like an atmosphere, is perfectly feasible, depending on its dimensions and what it is made from. Whatever its composition, the Bible seems quite specific that something was 'up there' pre-Flood, and that the old Earth and the new Earth were very different environments due to whatever was up there coming down... **'by which the world that then existed perished, being flooded with water.'**

Evidence of the canopy's existence in scripture (apart from Gen 1:7 and Psalms 148:4) can be inferred by what happens immediately after the Flood. If the canopy collapsed onto the Earth, contributing to the chaos of the Flood and the dramatic halving of the planet's atmospheric pressure, the evidence should determine whether a huge amount of fresh water was added to the world's oceans where the canopy is said to reside today. *Reader's Digest*, which adopts an evolutionary stance, writes:

"One of the most fascinating scientific discoveries in recent times regarding a universal flood came from some scientists who were not searching for any evidence of the Flood. It came from oceanographers in the Gulf of Mexico who were doing some rather routine research on coral and sediments of the ocean floor.

Their two oceanographic vessels had pulled from the bottom of the Gulf of Mexico several long, slender core samples of the sediment, which includes the fossil shells of one-celled plankton called foraminifera. While still alive, these organisms lock into their shells a chemical record of the temperature and salinity of the water. When they reproduce, the shells fall away and drop to the bottom. A cross-section of that ocean bed carries a record of climates that the oceanographers say go back more than 100 million years.

The cores were analyzed in two different investigations—by Cesar Emiliani of the University of Miami, and by James Kennett of the University of Rhode Island and Nicholas Shack of Cambridge University. Both analyses pointed to a dramatic drop in the salinity of the water, providing compelling evidence of a vast flood of fresh water into the Gulf of Mexico thousands of years ago.

Cesar Emiliani explains the results: "A huge amount of ice-melt water rushed into the Gulf of Mexico and produced a sea-level rise that spread around the world with the speed of a tidal wave." He adds, "We know this because the oxygen isotope ratios of the foraminifera shells show a marked temporary decrease in the salinity of the waters of the Gulf of Mexico. It clearly shows that there was a major period of flooding from 12,000 to 10,000 years ago, with a peak about 11,600 years ago. There is no question that there was a flood and there is also no question that it was a universal flood."[228]

Certainly, evidence of higher water levels and continental shelves is everywhere. Consider that for one sea to be higher, all the world's open seas and oceans must be higher. Perhaps now the phenomenon of lost cities, doomed civilisations and highways running into the sea makes more sense. Were these built by the inhabitants of the pre-Flood era and destroyed by the Flood? Two other factors corroborate a canopy-pressure scenario. Firstly, the

---

[228] www.ucgstp.org/lit/gn/gn047/worldwideflood.htm; "Noah, the Flood, the Facts", *Reader's Digest*, US edition, September 1977, p.133

lifespans of biblical figures reduce drastically after the Flood. Two, as we'll see in the next chapter, Noah gets drunk!

The Biblical picture of the pre-Flood world, therefore, is one of a single land mass containing lush countryside and animals 'producing after their own kind', not changing into other animals. Adam and Eve are man's original ancestors and were created 'in the beginning'. This presents problems for Christians attempting to meld evolution with creation. Jesus did not believe in the Day-Age theory or theistic evolution. He knew Adam and Eve were in on things from the start: **"Have you not read that He who made them at the beginning, made them male and female...?"** (Matt 19:4). Mark 10:6 says the same thing: **"But from the beginning of the creation, God made them male and female...."**

Moreover, Adam and Eve's progeny appear *in a state of civilization* as Genesis progresses. There are no cavemen, at least not in the sense we know them today. The inference is that this advanced knowledge is due to man's direct interaction with God and the angelic realm before the Flood. Neither was there a Bronze or Iron Age in the sense we know them today. Tubalcain had brass and iron from the get-go:

And Adah bare Jabal: he was the father of such as dwell in tents, and of such as have cattle. And his brother's name was Jubal: he was the father of all such as handle the harp and organ. And Zillah, she also bare Tubalcain, <u>an instructor of every artificer in brass and iron</u>: and the sister of Tubalcain was Naamah. (Gen 4:20-22)

Reduction in lifespans

The Bible finds it necessary to record meticulous genealogies and the lifespans of the patriarchs. Why do that unless the reader is meant to have this information? The decay in lifespans after the Flood is reasonably explained by the increase in solar radiation and cell decay now the canopy is gone. Also, the hyperbaric benefits of double atmospheric pressure would have come to an end if the pressure halved to today's 14.7 lbs/sq. in. Within a few generations, the lifespans of the post-Flood patriarchs drop from 900 to around 400, then 200, and eventually to 120 years - the same we witness today with the Hunzas and other longevity cultures.

Lifespans of the Pre-Flood patriarchs

Adam	930 years
Seth	912 years
Enosh	905 years
Cainan	910 years
Mahalaleel	895 years
Jared	962 years
Enoch	365 years (translated)
Methusaleh	969 years
Lamech	777 years
Noah	950 years

Post-Flood patriarchs

Noah	950 years
Shem	600 years
Arphaxad	438 years
Salah	433 years
Eber	464 years
Peleg	239 years
Serug	230 years
Nahor	148 years
Terah	205 years
Abraham	175 years
Isaac	180 years
Jacob	147 years
Joseph	110 years

The other surprising thing about these early genealogies is what you find when you plot them in real time.[229] Adam lived long enough to know Lamech, Noah's father. Noah survived long enough to know Abraham, considered to have lived around 2000BC. And Noah's son, Shem, who survived the Flood, lived long enough to know Abraham, Isaac and Jacob, dying around 1846BC. Thus the first 2,157 years of the Earth's biblically recorded history is covered by three men, Adam, Methusaleh and Shem. The oral tradition about the Flood and its effects would therefore have been strong, and this is borne out by Flood stories existing today from cultures all over the world.

In the pre-Flood world we are told Noah made wine. We know this because he knew how to make it afterwards (Gen 9:21). Interestingly, grape juice does not ferment under double atmospheric pressure but does, as we know, in today's 14.7 lbs/sq. in. Did Noah make wine after the Flood and become intoxicated, unaware of the prevailing atmospheric conditions?

---

[229] These genealogies can be found in Genesis 5 and 11, as well as 1 Chronicles 1 and Luke 3.

THE FLOOD

There are literally scores of legends existing throughout the world which tell of a cataclysmic flood that destroyed civilisation. Though these stories are ancient and from all parts of the world, they do appear to describe the same event. Dr John Morris writes:

"Over the years, I have collected more than 200 of these stories, originally reported by various missionaries, anthropologists and ethnologists. While the differences are not always trivial, the common essence of the stories is instructive as compiled below:

- Is there a favored family? 88%
- Were they forewarned? 66%
- Is flood due to wickedness of man? 66%
- Is catastrophe only a flood? 95%
- Was flood global? 95%
- Is survival due to a boat? 70%
- Were animals also saved? 67%
- Did animals play any part? 73%
- Did survivors land on a mountain? 57%
- Was the geography local? 82%
- Were birds sent out? 35%
- Was the rainbow mentioned? 7%
- Did survivors offer a sacrifice? 13%
- Were specifically eight persons saved? 9%

Putting them all back together, the story would read something like this: Once there was a worldwide flood, sent by God to judge the wickedness of man. But there was one righteous family which was forewarned of the coming flood. They built a boat on which they survived the flood along with the animals. As the flood ended, their boat landed on a high mountain from which they descended and repopulated the whole Earth."[230]

---

[230] www.icr.org/article/570/

This is the tale taught at Sunday school today. Another source writes:

"Stories of the Nochian Flood have been found in almost every civilization in the world. Dr. Aaron Smith of the University of Greensboro collected a complete history of the literature on Noah's Ark. He found 80,000 works in 72 languages about the Flood. About 70,000 of them mention the wreckage of the Ark." [231]

In the Chaldean given by Berosus, Xisuthrus is saved from the Flood by building a boat. In Hindu legend, it was Satyavrata in the ark. The Shoo-King, one of China's ancient sacred books, describes the 'Great Water' reaching the tops of the mountains. The Parsees say that when the Earth became wicked, God destroyed it with a deluge. The Zend-Avesta, the oldest sacred book of the Persians, describes the Flood. In Greek mythology, it is Deucalion with his wife, Pyrrha, who step forth from the ark onto a new and desolate Earth. In Celt-lore, Drayan and Droyvach survive the Flood to colonise Britain. The Scandanavian Edda speaks of Coxcox, his wife and six others surviving a worldwide Flood. These and many other tales from countries all over the world substantially agree with the Bible's story of Noah and his family surviving the destruction of the old world and re-establishing the new.

One theory is that God did not erase mankind with multiple, well-aimed thunderbolts but used a Flood to leave copious evidence for the future to learn of divine judgment on sin.[232] All well and good, but the claim of a flood covering the entire surface of the Earth is no small potatoes. One would reasonably expect literally mountains of evidence to be left behind to support such an event. But is it even conceivable that the Earth at some point was covered with water 'as high as the mountains'? Some believe it was a local flood (the Black Sea theory), since it could not possibly have

---

[231] www.allaboutcreation.org/global-flood-faq.htm
[232] Hovind, Kent, *Creation seminar series*, op. cit.

rained hard enough over forty days and forty nights to produce enough water to cover **'the mountains of the Earth'.** Where did all the water come from, and where did it go?

Others believe it may not have been 'rain' as such that did it. Adherents of the canopy theory believe fresh water streaming down from a ruptured shield would provide ample occasion for catastrophe. Others dispute this, citing alternative models. Whatever the theories, Henry Morris believes the evidence for a global inundation is irrefutable:

> "The Biblical Flood in the days of Noah has become a great divide between two watersheds of belief. On the one hand there are those who say it is either a purely mythological event or else possibly a local or regional flood. This group includes practically all evolutionists, but it also includes the 'old-earth creationists'.
>
> These all accept the so-called geological ages as the approved record of Earth history, recognizing that a global hydraulic cataclysm would have destroyed any evidence for such geological ages. The geological ages concept and a worldwide devastating Flood logically cannot co-exist.
>
> On the other hand, 'young-earth creationists' accept the Biblical record of the Flood as a literal record of a tremendous cataclysm involving not only a worldwide Flood, but also great tectonic upheavals and volcanic outpourings that completely changed the crust of the Earth and its topography in the days of Noah. Those of us who hold this view are commonly ridiculed as unscientific and worse, so it would be more comfortable and financially rewarding if we would just go along with the evolutionist establishment, downgrade the Flood, and accept the geological ages."[233]

Alfred Rehwinkel writes: "The Flood marks the end of a world of transcendent beauty, created by God as a perfect abode for man, and the beginning of a new world, a mere shadowy replica of its original glory. In all recorded history there is no other event except the Flood which has had such a revolutionary effect upon the topography and condition of this Earth, and which has so profoundly affected human history and

---

[233] **Morris, Henry M** "Why Christians Should Believe in a Global Flood," *Back to Genesis*, El Cajon, CA: Institute for Creation Research, 1998

every phase of life as it now exists in its manifold forms in the world. No geologist, biologist, or student of history can afford to ignore this great catastrophe." [234]

Let's look at the story

"And God said to Noah, "The end of all flesh has come before Me, for the Earth is filled with violence <u>through them</u> [Them? Who?];[235] and behold, I will destroy <u>them</u> from the Earth. Make yourself an ark of gopherwood; make rooms in the ark, and cover it inside and outside with pitch. And this is how you shall make it: the length of the ark shall be three hundred cubits, its width fifty cubits, and its height thirty cubits." (Gen 6:13-15)

Why tell Noah to build an ark if the Flood will be local? Why not instruct Noah and his family to move to a different location? God does not. The plans for the Ark's monumental construction are passed to Noah, who is told he has a grace period in which to build it, during which he must attempt to persuade the population to clean up their act and repent (1 Peter 3:18-20). Some say this period was 7 years, others 120 years (Jasher 5:11). In the end, Noah's evangelism fails but his engineering project does not. The Ark standing before him is 450 feet long, 75 feet wide and 45 feet high with a capacity exceeding 500 railroad stock cars. The barge-like shape of the vessel will make it difficult to capsize.[236]

And what about those animals? Answers in Genesis writes:

"In the book, *Noah's Ark: A Feasibility Study:* ...creationist researcher John Woodmorappe suggests that, at most, 16,000 animals were all that were needed to preserve the created kinds that God brought into the Ark. The Ark did not need to carry every kind of animal—nor did God command it. It carried only air-breathing, land-dwelling animals, creeping

---

[234] **Rehwinkel, Alfred M** *The Flood,* St. Louis, MO, Concordia, 1951

[235] The 'Them' is a provocative subject dealt with in *Origins II – Holy War.* For now, why did God take the unprecedented decision to destroy mankind? God must have known what would happen in advance, yet he still gave man free will.

[236] **Heyford, Jack** *Spirit Filled Bible* (NKJV), Thomas Nelson, 1991, p.15

things, and winged animals such as birds. Aquatic life (fish, whales, etc.) and many amphibious creatures could have survived in sufficient numbers outside the Ark. This cuts down significantly the total number of animals that needed to be on-board.

Another factor which greatly reduces the space requirements is the fact that the tremendous variety in species we see today did not exist in the days of Noah. Only the parent 'kinds' of these species were required to be on-board in order to repopulate the Earth. For example, only two dogs were needed to give rise to all the dog species that exist today." [237]

One can imagine the stick Noah and his family got during the construction phase. These were not nice people. "What's that, Noah? A boat?" "A flood's coming in?!!" "Ha! Ha! Ha! Ha! Ha! Ha! Ha! Ha! Ha!" "Here, take my wife! Glad to be rid of her!"

Ground zero

"Then the LORD said to Noah, "Come into the ark, you and all your household, because I have seen that you are righteous before Me in this generation. You shall take with you seven each of every clean animal, a male and his female; two each of animals that are unclean, a male and his female; also seven each of birds of the air, male and female, to keep the species alive on the face of all the Earth. For after seven more days I will cause it to rain on the earth forty days and forty nights, and I will destroy from the face of the Earth all living things that I have made." And Noah did according to all that God commanded him. <u>Noah was six hundred years old</u> when the floodwaters were on the Earth." (Gen 7:1-6)

Noah's longevity is consistent. Notice also that God says, "**<u>Come</u> into the ark**". The Designer's going with them! Did a meteor strike the canopy, resulting in the evolutionist's destruction of the dinosaurs? Creation science is unequivocal. The geological evidence indicates that the formation of mountains, deep oceans

---

[237] www.answersingenesis.org/articles/nab/really-a-flood-and-ark

and almost all current geological phenomena is best explained by flood processes arising from this cataclysmic judgment on mankind (Psa 104:5-9). The Earth's crust is only 3 miles thick in certain places under the sea. That's the same relative thickness as the skin of an apple to the fruit. Certainly, trillions of tons of water hitting the Earth over a forty-day period would have appalling effects on both geology and climate. At the same time, 'the <u>fountains</u> of the deep' were broken up, blasting super-heated magma, water and roiling steam up from the Earth's innards and out into the oceans and sky.

Massive damage to the Earth's crust would have resulted, releasing the power of continental super-quakes, huge tsunamis and constant volcanic activity from the Earth's furious energies. Today the planet is still settling, as evidenced by moving tectonic plates and continued earthquakes, volcanic eruptions and tsunamis.

On Everest, petrified clams have been discovered in the closed position above 20,000 feet. Elsewhere, giant oysters have been discovered 11.5 feet wide. The *Express Times* reports:

"Palaeontologist Arturo Vildezola rests on a giant fossilized oyster Tuesday in Acostambo, Peru, where more than 500 fossilized giant oysters were found 2 miles above sea level. The discovery of the oysters, which are 11.5 feet wide and 661 pounds, reinforces the scientific theory that 200 million years ago the Andes Mountains were covered by the ocean."[238]

Or perhaps it reinforces the theory that these oysters grew large in the pre-Flood conditions, were caught up in the Flood and buried alive in soft sediment (the closed position), and then the mountains arose.

Kent Hovind cites the discovery of a baleen whale skeleton 80 feet long found buried at an upward angle in diatomaceous earth at Lompoc, California, near the San Andreas Fault. How long

---

[238] *Express Times*, (Eastern PA), 2nd March 2001, p.A2

would a whale have to balance on its tail for the layers to deposit around it under evolutionary processes? What other explanation properly accounts for this find?

"Whales, dolphins, trillions of fish and even pterodactyls have been found preserved in diatomaceous [fossil] earth."[239]

Hovind believes the lack of human fossils can best be explained by the fact that humans would have been the last to die in the Flood, would not have been buried, and thus rotted apart. Nevertheless, about 4,000 sets of fossilized human remains have been found. Around the world, fossilized graveyards are common for dinosaurs and smaller animals. Most of the carcasses rotted. Dr Don Patton writes:

"Skeletons of ten perfectly modern humans have been excavated from fifty eight feet down in the Dakota Sandstone, over an area spanning about 50 by 100 feet. This formation is a member of the Lower Cretaceous, supposedly 140 million years old. It is known for its dinosaurs and is the same formation found at Dinosaur National Monument. At least four of the ten individuals are female. One is an infant. Some of the bones are articulated.[240] Some are not, appearing to have been washed into place. No obvious tools or artifacts were found associated with the bones. The bulldozer driver who uncovered the first bones in 1971 expresses certainty that there were no tunnels or cracks in the extremely hard overlying layers of rock. The bones are partially replaced with malachite (a green mineral) and turquoise, thus appropriately named 'Malachite Man'.

The evidence appears obvious that these 10 men, women and children were buried rapidly by some catastrophe, like a flood. Articulated skeletons indicate rapid burial. Some propose to explain these bones by arguing that they were mining when the mine collapsed. However there is no indication of tunnels, and woman and small children would not likely be included in a mining operation. Additionally, no tools have been found and there are no crushed bones which would be expected if the

---

[239] Hovind, Kent, *Creation seminar series,* op. cit.
[240] Connected together as in life.

mine caved in. Another explanation is that this is a mass grave and they were buried. This cannot be true because the living would have to dig a grave 50-100 feet deep through extremely hard sandstone layers. The modern mining operation was halted in the 1970's because the sandstone was so hard it was destroying the bulldozers. These humans appear to have been buried by the same catastrophe that buried dinosaurs in this continent-spanning formation. Humans and dinosaurs must have lived at the same time."[241]

Rush hour

During the Flood, swirling trees would have formed huge log-jams and become buried and compressed into coal. As the water relocated to the opening trenches and the waters assuaged, the washout would have been dramatic. Psalm 104 reads of the waters: **You covered it** [the Earth] **with the deep as with a garment; the waters stood above the mountains. At Thy rebuke they <u>fled</u>, at the voice of Thy thunder, they <u>hasted</u> away. They go up by the mountains; they go down by the valleys unto the place which thou hast founded for them. <u>You have set a boundary</u> that they may not pass over, that they may not return to cover the Earth.** (vs. 6-9).

Mountains form the boundary and mountain ranges follow coastlines. Dr Walt Brown believes this is because they were formed at the same time. If you examine the continental shelves, it appears there was less water than today. Russia and Alaska would have been connected. Australia to Indonesia. Ireland and Britain connected to Europe, and so on. In the centuries following the Flood, as the ice melted and raised the ocean levels, the geography of the continents would change. Some lands, such Australia, Britain and Ireland become islands with their indigenous animals. Ongoing erosion continues. Niagara Falls breaks rocks every year and moves back, carving its canyon. How long has it been doing that? Thanet was still an island off Kent, England at the time of the

Battle of Hastings (1066). The silting continued after, and the last ships navigated the Wantsum Channel in the 1600's before Thanet became part of mainland Britain. The sea is a global system. If Thanet had been around for millions of years, why did the Wantsum not close up long ago because of the deposition of silts?

Some hills exhibit what look like water flows and fans coming down the slopes, of the kind produced when water shapes its path. Almost all such rock is classified as 'sedimentary' - in other words, *flood sediment.* Angled strata bend in some of these rock formations. Hard rock does not bend this way without cracking. Curving strata run for miles at the Grand Canyon, compressed as drying mud into sedimentary rock. Sandstone and limestone features are an obvious product of the Flood, says geologist John Morris, and indeed contain in their womb billions of fossils in silent witness to the violence of this worldwide disaster.[242]

The end

One can only imagine what it must have been like to witness such incredible forces first-hand. Panic must have set in among the Earth's inhabitants as everyone – man, woman, child and beast – attempted to flee the rising waters until there was no high ground left to run to.

And the waters increased and bare up the ark, and it was lifted up above the Earth. And the waters prevailed and were increased greatly upon the Earth and the ark went upon the face of the waters. And the waters prevailed exceedingly upon the Earth, and all the high hills that were under the whole heaven were covered. And all flesh died that moved upon the Earth, both of fowl, and of cattle, and of beast, and of every creeping thing that creepeth upon the Earth, and every man. All in whose nostrils was the breath of life, of all that was in the dry land,

---

[242] Morris, John, *The Young Earth,* op. cit.

died. And every living substance was destroyed which was upon the face of the ground, both man, and cattle, and the creeping things, and the fowl of the heaven; and they were destroyed from the Earth. And Noah only remained alive and they that were with him in the ark. And the waters prevailed upon the Earth an hundred and fifty days. (Gen 7:17…24)

It could have taken months for the last creatures to die. The eight on the boat could only have an inkling of the huge changes underway below them. As the Earth's crust folded and sank, great ocean trenches opened, into which the waters rushed. Massive forces upthrust new geological features into mountains, which even today bear the horizontal striations of hydrologic sorting and washout. Animals would have been buried in sludge according to density. Evolutionists maintain that birds evolved last because their remains are found on top, yet birds are the last creatures to die in a Flood and their bones are hollow so they float. Dr John Morris writes:

"Evidence for catastrophism abounds…. Many leading geologists now even identify themselves as 'neo-catastrophists', and have begun to invoke large-scale, dynamic processes for the production of geologic layers and Earth features. Consider for a moment the perspective of Dr Derek Ager, former President of the British Geologists' Association. While attempting to distance himself from creationist geologists who believe in Noah's Flood, he has spearheaded a revival in geology back towards flood processes. "The hurricane, the flood or tsunami may do more in an hour or a day than the ordinary processes of nature have achieved in a thousand years…. In other words, the history of any one part of the Earth, like the life of a soldier, consists of long periods of boredom and short periods of terror.""[243]

This is hugely significant. Some geologists have come to view the geologic layers – for instance in the Grand and Bryce Canyons – as hydrologically (water) sorted strata, yet continue to hold the

---

[243] Ibid.

view that the Earth is billions of years old. The standard evolutionary stance is uniformitarian – that such layers were formed slowly and progressively with the speed of processes observed today (wind, rain, storm erosion, etc.). Morris disputes this:

"One way to show that only a short time elasped between the deposition of one bed and the deposition of an overlying bed is to show that the various surface features present on the top surface of the lower bed would not last long if exposed. Therefore, these features had to be covered rather quickly before they had a chance to erode or be destroyed.

One very common feature, seen in many rock layers in many locations, is the presence of 'ripple marks', formed as water moves over a surface. These can frequently be seen on a beach after the tide has receded, and can also be seen on the ocean bottom where a particular current direction dominates. In many other situations we see what has been called 'raindrop impressions', although these 'raindrop marks' may actually be blisters formed as air bubbles escaped from rapidly deposited sediments under water. Animal tracks are also common. In any case, these features, which had to be formed in soft sediment, are very fragile and if present on any surface, unconsidated material or hard rock, will not last very long. Keep in mind that almost every sedimentary rock layer was deposited under water. Every geologist agrees with this."[244]

Polystrate fossils

Another indication that these layers were deposited at the same time can be seen in the 'kettles' observed in the roof of 'Carboniferous era' coal mines, which run through multiple layers (polystrates). These circular, fossilised features can break away and fall into the mine, causing great danger. They are, some scientists say, fossilised tree trunks which bobbed upright during the Inundation, sank, and the sedimentary layers filled in around them. This same phenomenon was observed during the eruption of Mount St Helens in the USA in May 1980.

---

[244] Ibid, pp.94-95

Blowing its top

The landmark event in Washington State rocked America's western seaboard and produced stratisferic effects that were observed across the country. When Mount St Helens blew, over one million trees were blasted off the mountain, seared of their leaves and branches, and driven into Spirit Lake to form 2,000 acres of floating wood. Here they became waterlogged and many sank upright, burying their bases into the river bottom. How credible is it to explain polystrate fossils as trees which survived *unrotted* for millions of years while the layers formed around them through endless processes? Wood exposed to water rots in a matter of decades. These polystrate trunks tie in the layers through which they run, the soft sediment even bending around them before drying. They were formed at the same time and by the same processes – no scientist who has studied the eruption denies this. In *Seven Wonders of Mount St Helens,* Lloyd Anderson writes of the eruption's after-effects:

"The landslide of May 18th buried the river and highway to Spirit Lake to an average depth of 100 feet. It also buried most other drainages in the 23 square miles of the Upper Toutle Valley and plugged the valley's mouth. For twenty-two months, water had no established path to the lower waterway.

Then on March 19th, 1982, an eruption melted a large snow pack that had accumulated in the crater over the winter. The waters mixed with loose material on the slopes of the mountain, creating an enormous mudflow. In nine hours while no eye watched, the mudflow carved an integrated system of drainages over much of the valley and re-opened the way to the Pacific Ocean. The drainages included at least three canyons 100 feet deep. One was nicknamed "The Little Grand Canyon of the Toutle" because it was a 1/40th scale model of the Grand Canyon."[245]

---

[245] **Anderson, Lloyd** *Seven Wonders of Mount St Helens,* Mt St Helens Creation Info Center, 360-274-5737

Even *Geology* is constrained to come clean:

"Deposits of recent mud flows on Mount St. Helens demonstrate conclusively that stumps can be transported and deposited upright. These observations support the conclusions that some vertical trees in the Yellowstone 'fossil forests' <u>were transported in a geologic situation directly comparable to that of Mount St. Helens.</u>"[246]

Coal

… does not take millions of years to form, just lots of pressure.[247] Wood has become coal in as little as sixty years under certain circumstances. Peat is wood found under minimal pressure near the surface. Anthracite is coal found deeper and more heavily pressured. Coal is always found in sedimentary rock. Sedimentary rock is, as its name states, sedimentary (flood) mud which hardened to stone. One explanation is that the coal we mine today was formed by pre-Flood forests compressed by billions of tons of Flood sediment exerting enormous pressure. Under such conditions, coalification is known to occur rapidly.

The fossil problem

Dr David Raup, Curator of Geology at the Field Museum of Natural History in Chicago, states:

"Darwin's theory of natural selection has always been closely linked to evidence from fossils, and probably most people assume that fossils provide a very important part of the general argument that is made in favour of Darwinian interpretations of the history of life. <u>Unfortunately, this is not strictly true.</u>" [248]

---

[246] **Fritz, William J** "Stumps Transported and Deposited Upright by Mount St. Helens Mud Flows," *Geology,* vol.8, December 1980, p.588

[247] **Hill, George R** "Aspects of Coal Research", *Chemical Technology,* 1972, p.296; also: *Organic Chemistry,* 6:463-471, 1984

[248] **Raup, David M** *Field Museum of Natural History Bulletin,* 'Conflicts Between Darwin and Paleonotology' vol.50(1), January 1979, p.22

Darwin voiced his reservations about the record's ability to liberate his theory from speculation:

"Why then is not every geological formation and every stratum full of such intermediate links? Geology assuredly does not reveal any such finely graduated organic chain; and this, perhaps, is the most obvious and serious objection which can be urged against the theory. <u>The explanation lies, as I believe, in the extreme imperfection of the geological record</u>."[249]

Charlie put his hope in tomorrow, that sometime in the future geology would redeem him. If Darwin were alive today, he'd still be looking for his missing link. The fossil record resoundingly endorses the Flood. Creation science tends to date almost all fossils from around 2345BC, since fossils can only be formed if the animal is buried in sediment. If their carcasses are not buried, they are consumed by other creatures in a matter of days. Why do we have billions of fossils? Is it so unreasonable to conclude that these animals were killed and buried by flood waters before they were eaten?

Evolution cannot explain the evidence through uniformitarian processes. In fact, high deceit is used to date many fossils today. When a scientist tells you a fossil is millions of years old, how is he getting this figure? Carbon dating is widely known to be accurate only to a few thousand years. Other dating methods such as potassium-argon or rubidium-strontium are as arbitrary, since these isotopes decay at different rates and give greatly differing data. Dating from isotopes makes an assumption that the chosen isotope will decay at a constant rate, which is false if the Earth's magnetic field is weakening, which it is.

The laboratory will ask you where you found your fossil and attempt to identify which level of strata buried it. They will then

---

[249] **Darwin, Charles** *On the Origin of Species by Natural Selection, or the Preservation of Favoured Races in the Struggle for Life,* JM Dent & Sons Ltd, London, 1971, pp.292-293

apply the dating method giving the closest dating desired. Isotope dating is not as helpful as most believe. The shell of a living lobster has been dated to 3,000 years using the wrong isotope standard.[250]

We are led to believe that fossilisation needs millions of years – another lie. Dr Don Patton writes:

"A rubber-soled boot with a petrified cowboy leg was found in a dry creek bed near the West Texas town of Iraan, about 1980 by Mr. Jerry Stone, an employee of Corvette oil company. The boot was hand made by the M L Leddy boot company of San Angelo, Texas which began manufacturing boots in 1936. Gayland Leddy, a nephew of the founder, grew up in the boot business and now manages Boot Town in Garland, Texas. He recognized the 'number 10 stitch pattern' used by his uncle's company and concluded that the boot was made in the early 1950's.

Only the contents of the boot are fossilized, not the boot itself, demonstrating that some materials fossilize more readily than others. The bones of the partial leg and foot within the boot were revealed by an elaborate set of CT scans performed at Harris Methodist Hospital in Bedford, Texas on July 24, 1997. The radiologic technician was Evelyn Americus, AART. A complete set of these scans remains with the boot at the Creation Evidence Museum in Glen Rose, Texas.

The fact that some materials can fossilize rapidly under certain circumstances is well known by experts in the field and is not really a scientific issue. However, the general public has been misled in order to facilitate the impression of great ages. The dramatic example of the 'Limestone Cowboy' immediately communicates the truth of the matter. Fossilization proves nothing about long periods of time." [251]

Salts and silts

Rivers bring dissolved salts off the land and down into the oceans. The accumulation of these salts can be measured using different methods to assess the input and output processes.[252] The

---

[250] www.drdino.com

[251] **Patton, D** www.bible.ca/tracks.htm

[252] Input processes include silicate weathering, chloride solution, sea-spray, ocean floor sediments, pulverised sediments in glacial ice, atmospheric and

age of a sea can be determined by the amount of salt in it and the volume of silts arriving by river. The older the sea, the more salt and silt in it. Salt and silt dating completely corroborate the Biblical Flood and its time-frame. The Mississippi and Nile Deltas both show an outside age of between 10,000-13,000 years, the former having worn a gorge 100 feet deep and 8 miles long at the St Anthony Falls in about 7,000 years. These rivers are not millions of years old. They were probably formed only 4,400-5,000 years ago after the Flood washed out the sediment in the first few days of abatement. Geologist John Morris comments:

"We all know that the ocean is salty to the taste, and it stands to reason that it is getting more and more salty each year as rivers dump dissolved salts from the continents into the ocean. Evolutionists have traditionally assumed that life evolved in a salty sea some 3 to 4 billion years ago. If the ocean is so old, and must have been salty long ago, wouldn't it be too salty by now?" [253]

Using the minimum and maximum values for the salts and silts, the Earth could only be a maximum of 62 million years old, not billions. Of course, an assumption is again made for the quantity of salt in the oceans to begin with, and the 'fountains of the deep' are not even considered. The rate of continental erosion, or rather lack of it, also bothers Morris:

"The volume of the continents above sea level has been measured at 383 million billion tons. At present erosion rates, all the continents would be reduced to sea level in 14 million years! But they are thought to be many times that old already. Were they many times greater in bulk when they uplifted? No, because rocks thought to be on the surface at the time of uplift are still on the surface, and have hardly eroded at all!

[Elsewhere], there has been significant erosion – just look at Grand Canyon. But much of the Colorado River drainage basin is virtually

---

volcanic dust, coastal erosion, glacial ice, ground-water seepage and sea-floor hydrothermal vents. (Morris John, op. cit. p.85)
[253] Ibid.

untouched – a flat, featureless, uplifted plateau, bearing no evidence of 70 million years of erosion." [254]

If we suspend disbelief for a minute, we could tailor the erosion rates to be a fraction of what they are today (all the continents gone in 14 million years), but such a supposition is without scientific foundation. What we observe does great violence to an ancient Earth. Sedimentary rock strata deposited worldwide in a global inundation is support enough for the catastrophism we see in countless hill and mountain features across the world. Flows and ripples in their contours are unmistakable. On the hard path up to the Timpanagos Caves in Utah, one can marvel at fossilized fish set into the rock face thousands of feet above sea-level.

Erosion

Evolutionary science holds that the Grand Canyon was formed by the Colorado River eroding a canyon complex over millions of years. Any visitor will baulk at this explanation the moment they clap eyes on that hole. The Canyon is miles wide and simply vast, and way down there from your observation point on the lip, the Colorado River snakes its way through the rocky defiles in a tiny glitter of water. The canyon walls are hydrologically sorted. Another interpretation, based on the evidence, might be that receding Flood waters washed out the Grand Canyon in a matter of days, carving the canyon's features as they fled, leaving the Colorado River behind for the future, flowing out to the Gulf of Mexico. There is no way the Colorado River carved Grand Canyon. What about the side canyons? What carved those?

---

[254] Ibid. Also, **Judson S** "Erosion of the land – or what's happening to our continents?" *American Scientist,* vol 56, 1968, pp.356-374

Oldest tree

The oldest tree ever found is the Methuselah Tree in California. It's 4,300 years old. If the Earth is billions of years old, why can we not find an older tree? Where are trees dated at 10,000 or 20,000 years? They have never been found. In the White Mountains of California, 17 bristlecone pines and some giant sequoias have been dated by dendrochronology at around 4,000 years. For a Flood date of around 2345BC, this is entirely consistent with the Genesis Inundation. The seeds for the Methuselah Tree and giant sequoias were probably among the first to take root after the Flood.

Niagara Falls

Observers of this beautiful landmark on the border of America and Canada recognise that Niagara Falls breaks rocks from the sides of the canyon and moves back about five feet every year. These days, the Canadian government has constructed concrete buttresses preventing the falls from eroding Canadian soil, so this rate has been interrupted. The Falls represent a significant difference in height between Lakes Ontario and Erie. Niagara Falls today is only 12 miles from where it began, which places its age at the outside at 10,000 years, not billions. A standard evolutionary textbook states:

"A gorge about 7½ miles long runs just below Niagara Falls. A simple calculation shows that it has been 9,900 years…"[255]

Which begs the question: What got Niagara Falls going in the first place? The official cause is something called the Wisconsin Glaciation. Glaciations are, by their nature, not as catastrophic as the evidence left to us in Niagara Gorge, which contains 'ancient fossils' and barefaced evidence of hydrologic sorting. Kent Hovind surmises that Niagara is only 4,400-5,000 years old, plus one large

---

[255] **Holt R & W** *Earth Science,* Holt McDougal, 1984, p.384

Flood. If the Earth is millions of years old, why has Niagara Falls not eroded all the way up to Lake Erie?[256] Something happened. The evidence left shouts of catastrophism, not uniformitarianism.

Oil - the big squeeze

Oil does not take millions of years to form. Scientists are able to compress a ton of garbage into a barrel of oil in 20 minutes in the laboratory. All it takes for oil to form is tremendous pressure. It is reasonable to consider that almost all the oil was created by the sedimentary pressure of the Flood upon matter which sank to the bottom before being buried in hundreds of feet of fast-moving sludge and rock. This might explain the huge dinosaur 'graveyards' found across the world. Bodies of similar density are buried together through hydrologic sorting.

Oil and natural gas remain under extreme pressure beneath the Earth today, which also argues against millions of years. Geologists state that this tremendous pressure can only exist for around 10,000 years before cracking the rock and seeping out, especially after seismic activity.

The source of the races

Curiously, the location of the Edenic paradise is not usually questioned, even by evolutionists. Most agree the evidence points to humankind's origins in the 'cradle of civilisation' between the Tigris and Euphrates rivers in Mesopotamia. If this is the case, it begs an important question: If mankind was supposed to have ascended (evolved) from a common piece of amoebic protoplasm, how come it chose this precise location? How come this is where the Bible places Eden? Why did our enterprising germ not raise itself to distinction in the Bronx? Or on Alcatraz? Why in Mesopotamia?

---

[256] www.drdino.com

William Williams calculates that if you grant generous dimensions to Eden, there are 4,000 other such similar land-areas on the planet where man could have originated. Isn't it too convenient that there is only a 1 in 4,000 chance that pond slime could have evolved into a race of monkey-men precisely where the Bible said mankind was created by God already in a state of civilisation – in Mesopotamia? Williams believes the geography of the early origins of man points clearly to his creation, not his evolution. How come brute-like, anthropomorphic monstrosities weren't evolving up the Khyber, along the Costa Del Sol or in Hollywood, California? If amoebas were developing everywhere, why do all civilisations point to Eden as their source, a fact generally accepted even in anthropology? [257]

Human population

At the time of writing, we have 6.77 billion people on the planet. The Berlin census report of 1922 put the world's population at 1.8 billion. The estimates of world population at 1AD vary between 170 and 400 million.[258] If one plots known census figures to form a parabola, the world's population appears to begin 4,400-5,000 years ago, when the Bible states eight people survived a worldwide Flood. Repopulation of the planet begins from an area around the Turkish Caucasus, where there still exists a small settlement known from antiquity as Kazan, or 'Village of Eight'.

William Williams takes the Berlin census figure of 1,804,187,000 for the population of the Earth in 1922 and calculates that man's numbers would have to have doubled 30.75 times from two original ancestors. Based on Bible chronology, one can quite reasonably arrive at today's population from eight people

---

[257] Williams, William, *The Evolution of Man Scientifically Disproved*, op. cit. pp.23-24
[258] http://www.census.gov/ipc/www/worldhis.html

surviving the Flood 4,400-5,000 years ago. With these figures, it requires 168.3 years each time for the population to double.

Williams quotes the Jewish yearbook's population of Jews to be 15,393,815 in 1922. He calculates the Jewish population must have doubled its numbers 23.8758 times from the days of its patriarch Jacob (3,850 years since Jacob's marriage to Leah), or once every 161.251 years. This is a stunning, independent correlation with the Berlin census for the planet's population rate. Furthermore, a calculation of Muslims alive in 1922 (25,000,000) from the birth of Abraham's illegitimate son, Ishmael, (3,988 years) produces an aggregate population doubling every 162.275 years. Williams exults:

> "We would not expect the figures to be exactly the same, nor be greatly surprised if one period were twice the other. But their correspondence singularly corroborates the age of the human race and of the Jewish people, as gleaned from the word of God by the most proficient chronologists." [259]

When these population statistics are applied to the theory of evolution, serious problems arise, says Williams. Even if the evolutionist is granted a population expansion only 1/10th that proven to date, the population today, derived from two common ancestors 2 million years ago, would be 18,932,139,737,991 vigintillion, vigintillion, vigintillion, vigintillion, vigintillion, vigintillion, or 2^{1240}. If man has been evolving for millions of years, where is everyone?

> "If the human race is 2 million years old and must double its numbers 32 times to make the present population," writes Williams, "then each doubling would take 65,040 years. At this rate, going from the marriage of the Jewish patriarch Jacob an estimated 4,000 years ago, we would only have four Jews alive today! Even if we assume the founding pair of humans to be only 100,000 years ago [a time-frame impossible for

---

[259] Williams, William, *Evolution Scientifically Disproved*, op. cit.

evolution], it would take 3,252 years to double the population and, at this rate, there would only be five Jews!"[260]

Dr Henry Morris also calculated how much time it would take to generate today's population from two original ancestors. He came up with 4,400 years which, he states:

"…is the Ussher date for the Flood, when the present population got its start, according to the Bible. All known population data fit these factors very well, indicating the Biblical record of population origins is very reasonable and conservative."[261]

Where are the transitional forms?

Professor Stephen J Gould, Geology & Palaeontology, Harvard University, writes:

"The absence of fossil evidence for intermediary stages between major transitions in organic design, indeed our inability, even in our imagination, to construct functional intermediates in many cases, has been a persistent and nagging problem for gradualistic accounts of evolution…. We fancy ourselves as the only true students of life's history, yet to preserve our favored account of evolution by natural selection, we view our data as so bad that we never see the very process we profess to study."[262]

So where are all these transitional forms, especially between the monkey and the human? There should be mountains of them, yet all we've been shown are a few scraps of tooth and bone fabricated by artists to resemble 'an early ancestor'. These 'missing links' have all been exposed as frauds. If rats turned into bats, where are the millions and millions of rat-bats that must be out there? Pray, show me a rat-bat. Show me one with the wings only half-developed when it was a pathetic excuse for a rat-bat, which had neither legs to run nor wings to fly as it flopped along through

---

[260] Ibid. p.17-18
[261] **Morris, Henry** *Many Infallible Proofs,* Master Books, 1974, p.296
[262] **Gould, Stephen J** *Natural History,* vol.86(5), May 1977, p.14

life in its useless, transitional state. And if it was so useless in its transitional state, how did it survive natural selection?

One answer is, there are no transitional forms because evolution never took place. Witness the sorry state of the evolutionist's creed:

23 million years of missing transitional forms precede the proterosuchians.

23 million years of missing transitional forms precede the erythrosuchians.

33 million years of missing transitional forms precede the rauisuchians.

37 million years of missing transitional forms precede the aetosaurs.

37 million years of missing transitional forms precede the phytosaurs.

23 million years of missing transitional forms precede the ornithosuchids.

37 million years of missing transitional forms precede the lagosuchids.

43 million years of missing transitional forms precede the crocodilians, then they appear in the fossil record from 225 million years ago to the present.

41 million years of missing transitional forms precede the pterosaurs.

36 million years of missing transitional forms precede the herrerasaurs.

136 million years of missing transitional forms precede the deinonychosaurs.

186 million years of missing transitional forms precede the oviraptorosaurs.

111 million years of missing transitional forms precede ornithomimosaurs.

44 million years of missing transitional forms precede the carnosaurs and coelurosaurs.

178 million years of missing transitional forms precede the segnosaurs.

46 million years of missing transitional forms precede the prosauropods.

58 million years of missing transitional forms precede the sauropods.

49 million years of missing transitional forms precede the fabrosaurids.

58 million years of missing transitional forms precede the scelidosaurs.

96 million years of missing transitional forms precede the stegosaurs.

91 million years of missing transitional forms precede the ankylosaurs.

99 million years of missing transitional forms precede the ornithopods.

56 million years of missing transitional forms precede heterodontosaurids.

141 million years of missing transitional forms precede the ceratopsians.

141 million years of missing transitional forms precede pachycephalosaurs.

121 million years of missing transitional forms precede birds, then they appear in the fossil record 150 million years ago continuing to the present.[263]

George G Simpson, Professor of Vertebrate Palaeontology at Harvard University, writes:

"...it remains true, as every palaeontologist knows, that most new species, genera, and families, and that nearly all new categories above the level of families, <u>appear in the record suddenly</u> and are not led up to by known, gradual, completely continuous transitional sequences." [264]

It seems the apostle Paul scored a direct hit eighteen hundred years before Darwin when he wrote: **"...Professing to be wise, they became fools, and changed the glory of the incorruptible God into an image made like corruptible man – and birds and four-footed animals and creeping things."** (Rom 1:22-23)

---

[263] Research by Penn Highlands, P.O. Box 622, Uniontown, PA 15401. www.evolutionisfalse.org

[264] **Simpson, George G** *The Major Features of Evolution*, Columbia University Press, New York, 1953, p.360

Frozen mammoths

We've heard the stories. Thousands of woolly mammoths have been found frozen to death in the standing position, food undigested in their stomachs, buttercups on their lips. Were there that many? Answers in Genesis states:

"When writing about the number of mammoth bones, tusks, and carcasses, researchers commonly emphasize the large number of bones that have been found. For instance, Valentina Ukraintseva[265] states that the mammoths from Siberia were abundant, based on their numerous remains. Dale Guthrie, University of Alaska in Fairbanks, estimates that hundreds of thousands of mammal bones have been concentrated along streams in inland Alaska. Of course, a single animal has many bones, but Guthrie's estimate does not include the bones not yet washed out of valley deposits or those that remain buried in the uplands.[266] Irena Dubrovo remarks that there are a great number of woolly mammoth remains in Siberia.[267] Explorers have always reported the remains as abundant.[268]

The top expert on the woolly mammoths of Siberia is Nikolai Vereshchagin, who has spent nearly half a century researching the mammoth fauna. Since 1940, he has identified approximately a million bone fragments from many types of animals found within the permafrost of Eurasia.[269] He states that the abundance of

---

[265] **Ukraintseva, VV** *Vegetation Cover and Environment of the "Mammoth Epoch" in Siberia*, Mammoth Site of Hot Springs, South Dakota, Inc., Hot Springs, SD, p.224, 1993

[266] **Guthrie, RD** *Frozen Fauna of the Mammoth Steppe – The Story of Blue Babe*, University of Chicago Press, Chicago, IL, 1990, p.67

[267] **Dubrovo, I** The Pleistocene Elephants of Siberia; in: *Megafauna and Man – Discovery of America's Heartland*, The Mammoth Site of Hot Springs, South Dakota, Inc., Hot Springs, SD, scientific papers, vol.1, p.3, 1990

[268] **Péwé, TL and DM Hopkins** "Mammal Remains of Pre-Wisconsin Age in Alaska", *The Bering Land bridge*, D.M. Hopkins (Ed.), Stanford University Press, Stanford, CA, p.266, 1967

[269] **Vereshchagin, NK** "An Experiment in the Interpretation (Visual Assessment) of Mammalian Bones from Sediments of the Quaternary Period", *Late Quaternary Environments and Deep History: A Tribute to Paul S Martin*, D.W.

remains in Siberia is remarkable.[270] There are many hundreds of thousands of large mammals buried[271] with many millions of bones.[272] Many of these carcasses are found in the sitting or standing position as if they had bogged down and frozen.[273] Michael Oard writes:

"Strangely, scientists investigating three woolly mammoths and two woolly rhinos, including the Beresovka mammoth, found that they all died by suffocation. For a live animal to die of suffocation, it had to be buried rapidly or drowned. Several of the carcasses have broken bones. Both of the upper front leg bones and some of the ribs of the Selerikan horse were broken. It was also missing its head. The Beresovka mammoth had a broken pelvis, ribs, and right foreleg. It takes quite a force to break the bones of a mammoth. The broken bones have inspired the story that the Beresovka mammoth was grazing on grass and buttercups when it accidentally fell into a crevasse in the permafrost. Then it was rapidly covered and suffocated. Buttercups, as well as leaves and grasses, were found in the mouth of the Beresovka mammoth between its teeth and tongue.

Not only is it difficult to explain the upright burial, but even more challenging is the question of how this many mammoths and other animals ended up inside the permafrost layer. Both carcasses and bones had to be buried quickly, below the summer melt layer of the permafrost before they rotted."[274]

Steadman and J.I. Mead (Eds.), The Mammoth Site of Hot Springs, South Dakota, Inc., Hot Springs, SD, p.61, 1995

[270] **Vereshchagin, NK and GF Baryshnikov** "Paleoecology of the Mammoth Fauna in the Eurasian Arctic", *Paleoecology of Beringia*, D.M. Hopkins, J.V. Matthews Jr., C.E. Schweger, and S.B. Young (Eds.), New York: Academic Press, p.267, 1982

[271] **Vereshchagin, NK** "The Mammoth Cemeteries of North-East Siberia", *Polar Record* 17(106), p.3, 1974

[272] www.answersingenesis.org/home/area/fit/chapter1.asp#n8#n8

[273] **Tolmachoff, IP** "The Carcasses of the Mammoth and Rhinoceros Found in the Frozen Ground of Siberia", *Transactions of the American Philosophical Society* 23, p.26, 1929

[274] **Oard, Michael** *Frozen in Time*, www.answersingenesis.org

What can account for thousands of mammoths freezing so quickly, some standing up, that they don't even have time to rot? We'll look at a scenario which fits the facts in a forthcoming chapter.

THE TERRIBLE LIZARDS

"Either God exists or He doesn't. Both alternatives are frightening."

– Anon

Noah was required by God to save two unclean animals of every kind and seven clean animals of every kind (for later sacrifices – Gen 8:20). Noah did not need to take dozens of different types of dogs – there were probably not that many. Neither was he instructed to take insects which breathe through their skin, nor the sea-dwelling animals, which would have more than enough water with what was to follow.

Which raises the question of dinosaurs. Did they dwell with man? Today's general knowledge of dinosaurs only came into existence when the first works of organised archaeology began uncovering remains from the start of the 19th century. The start of organised evolutionary thought also began around this time with Lyell and Hutton. Dinosaurs were immediately co-opted as 'ancient creatures who lived millions of years ago'. The public was discouraged from examining the facts free of evolutionary bias. The indoctrination starts early today. Children love dinosaurs. Most of their entry-level reading books on the subject begin with the usual "Millions of years ago…"

The huge reptiles were supposed to have died out 65 million years ago 'after an asteroid strike' and could never have dwelt with man. Therefore, if anyone comes up with a living dinosaur today, evolution has a big problem. In fact, we still have dinosaurs today, though we do not refer to them as such. Look at a rhinoceros, elephant or monitor lizard. It's not hard to imagine much larger versions living prior to the Flood. It is a peculiar trait of lizards that they never stop growing, so lizards could get very large if they lived a few hundred years in the right conditions. But what about the genuine dinos such as brachiosaurus, t-rex and apatosaurus?

215

Judging by how they behaved in *Jurassic Park,* why would Noah ever have wanted to save such creatures?

The Bible states that everything was vegetarian prior to the Flood (Gen 1:29-30) and Creation was in harmony. **Then God saw everything that He had made, and indeed it was very good (Gen 1:31).** God probably would not have called his efforts 'very good' if Veloceraptors and T-rexes were kicking off on the zebras. Noah would have taken babies with him rather than the full-grown kind which, though not yet carnivorous until after the Flood, still would have wrecked the ark with their size and weight.

Dinosaurs are even mentioned in the Bible, though there are not referred to as such, since the term was only coined by Sir Richard Owen in 1841. Thirty-four verses of the Bible are given over to describing two beasts in some detail (Job 40:15-24; 41:1-34). Read the descriptions of 'behemoth' and 'leviathan' carefully. Clearly these animals are not 'hippos', 'elephants' or other animals researchers have claimed – they can only be dinosaurs. Job in his day was obviously quite familiar with them (Job 38-41). Ask yourself how the writer of the book of Job could have known how to describe a dinosaur this accurately if they all died out 65 million years before he was born.

Many sea-dwelling dinosaurs would have survived the Flood, such as whales, sharks and plesiosaurs. Those air-breathing dinosaurs not saved by Noah would have drowned. Their bodies were buried in sedimentary mud where they collectively solidified and fossilised into the huge graveyards one can view today in Vernal (Utah), the Badlands (South Dakota) and elsewhere. From the lack of damage to their remains, it is evident that these animals were not hunted or killed by other animals, their carcasses rotted apart. Bones of dinosaurs in certain areas are so numerous they have to be removed by bulldozers.

The Victoria Cave in Yorkshire, England, was found to contain the bones of grizzly bear, bison, reindeer, mammoth, hyena, hare, hippopotamus and fox.[275] This cave is 1,450 feet above sea level. The Elbolton Cave is 800 feet up and contained bears, reindeer and mammoths. The Raygill Quarries at 750 feet, excavated in 1880, contained the remains of bear, lion, hippo and slender-nosed rhinoceros. Three things to note here:

> None of these remains show signs that the animals perished in combat

> What are lions and hippos doing in Yorkshire? Could it be that this area, along with the rest of the planet, had a radically different eco-structure prior to the Flood?

> What are these types of animals doing together in a cave? What circumstances could have driven them to seek shelter together before being buried in sediment?

In the years following the Flood, we learn that man begins eating meat (Gen 9:3). Rather than being a social fad, meat-eating may have been necessary to supply the body with extra protein and calories required for the heightened metabolisms needed in the lower pressure conditions after the catastrophe. Consider also that dinosaurs would have been a staple source of food for the post-Flood civilisation and would have been hunted, especially if they were harassing humans due to perpetual hunger.

In the centuries following the Flood, we would expect dinosaur offspring to become progressively more stunted and sickly as they try to adapt to the new conditions. Gradually they would die out or be hunted to extinction. The only dinosaurs with a chance of survival would be those sea-dwelling creatures able to exist and thrive in the increased pressures of the deep. We are, of course, familiar with whales, sharks, squid and octopi today, but what of more exotic creatures?

---

[275] www.capra.group.shef.ac.uk/4/bonecavechamberlain.html

Earning your word-fame

Literally hundreds of legends across the world tell of warriors earning reputations fighting and slaying monsters and fire-breathing 'dragons'. The Norse Voluspa describes the terrible Nithhoggr or 'corpse-tearer'. In Anglo-Saxon literature, Beowulf slays the dragons Grendel, Grendel's mother and a third unnamed creature, which eventually does for Beowulf. St George kills a dragon. Around 336BC, King Morydd of Wales is witnessed being gulped down by a huge reptile. If dinosaurs died out millions of years ago, why does a recovered mosaic show King Nebuchadnezzar with a captured dinosaur in Babylon around 550BC? How could he even have known what a dinosaur was? Eddie Snipes writes:

"A Mesopotamian cylinder depicts dinosaur-like creatures similar to an apatasaurus. Over 1100 Inca ceremonial burial stones were found in tombs in Peru during the 1930's. Many of these have realistic and accurate depictions of dinosaurs. In 1571, the Spanish conquistadors were the first to report burial stones with strange creatures carved on them. In 1945, Waldemar Julsrud discovered carvings that depicted dinosaurs at El Toro Mount near Acambaro, Mexico. Over the next few decades, over 30,000 of these carvings were unearthed. The carvings date between 800BC and 200AD. These findings have been challenged and tested by researchers on multiple occasions and have remained as authentic artefacts. One is believed to be an iguanodon which was unknown until over 30 years after these carvings were discovered."[276]

The existence of dinosaurs is corroborated in the Apocryphal 16th chapter of the prophet Daniel, who was exiled to Babylon during the House of Judah captivity era. Terrestrial and flying 'dragons' were evidently something of a rarity to be celebrated in the 6th century BC, but not yet completely gone. In the story, Nebuchadnezzar, king of Babylon:

---

[276] Dinosaur mosaics can be viewed at www.exchangedlife.com /Creation/dinosaurs.shtml

"…kept a dragon in the temple of the god Bel and when the prophet Daniel denounced the worshipping of false gods, the king introduced Daniel to the dragon, saying it "liveth and eateth and drinketh; you cannot say that he is no living god; therefore worship him." Daniel fed the dragon lumps of tar, fat, and hair which killed the animal, proving it was mortal and not a god."[277]

Dragons are mentioned 34 times in the Bible. Kent Hovind wants to know why the Chinese calendar features eleven real animals and one 'mythical' dragon. The Ishtar Gate at Babylon is covered with lions and dragons.[278] After spending 17 years in China (around 1271AD), Marco Polo reported that the Chinese Emperor was raising dragons to pull chariots in his parades.[279] Were these ancients deluded? More recently, Marie Trevalyan records that another exotic species was causing problems:

"…the woods around Penllin Castle, Glamorgan [Wales], had the reputation of being frequented by winged serpents, and these were the terror of old and young alike. An aged inhabitant of Penllyne, who died a few years ago, said that in his boyhood the winged serpents were described as very beautiful. They were coiled when in repose, and "looked as if they were covered with jewels of all sorts. Some of them had crests sparkling with all the colours of the rainbow." When disturbed they glided swiftly, "sparkling all over", to their hiding places. When angry, they "flew over people's heads with outspread wings, bright, and sometimes with eyes too like the feathers in a peacock's tail." He said it was "no old story invented to frighten children" but a fact. His father and uncle had killed some of them, for they were as bad as foxes for poultry. The old man attributed the extinction of the winged serpents to the fact that they were "terrors in the farmyards and coverts"."[280]

[277] www.cryptozoology.com/articles/ishtar.php
[278] Staatliche Museum in Berlin
[279] **Cooper, Bill** *After the Flood*, New Wine Press, Colchester, 1995
[280] **Trevelyan, M** *Folk-Lore and Folk Stories of Wales*, 1909, (*cit.* **Simpson, J** *British Dragons*, BT Batsford Ltd., London, 1980)

The national flag of Wales features a dragon. Bill Cooper says England had similar problems. A 1405 chronicle states:

"Close to the town of Bures, near Sudbury, there has lately appeared, to the great hurt of the countryside, a dragon, vast in body, with a crested head, teeth like a saw, and a tail extending to an enormous length. Having slaughtered the shepherd of a flock, it devoured many sheep…. In order to destroy him [therefore], all the country people around were summoned. But when the dragon saw that he was again to be assailed with arrows, he fled into a marsh or mere and there hid himself among the long reeds, and was no more seen."[281]

Such stories are scoffed at but someone is worried. *The Times,* 27th July 1977 reports:

"Japanese fishermen caught a dead monster, weighing two tons and 30 feet in length, off the coast of New Zealand in April, it was reported today. Believed to be a survivor of a prehistoric species, the monster was caught at a depth of 1000 feet off the South Island coast near Christchurch. Palaeontologists from the Natural Science Museum near Tokyo have concluded that the beast belonged to the plesiosaurus family - huge, small-headed reptiles with a long neck and four fins... After a member of the crew had photographed and measured it, the trawler's captain ordered the corpse to be thrown back into the sea for fear of contamination to his fish."[282]

Cooper remarks of this incident:

"It is thought-provoking to consider that the Japanese have no problem with officially owning up to the present-day existence of dragons, sea-monsters or dinosaurs. Indeed, they even issued a postage-stamp with a picture of a plesiosaurus to commemorate the above find. Only we in the West seem to have a problem with the present-day existence of these creatures, for only nine days after the appearance of *The Times* article, it was sombrely announced on the 30th July 1977 by the

---

[281] Cooper, Bill, *After the Flood,* op. cit. The author writes: "This chronicle was begun by John de Trokelow and finished by Henry de Blaneford. It was translated and reproduced in the Rolls Series. 1866. IV. ed. H.G. Riley." (cit. **Simpson, J** *British Dragons,* B.T. Batsford Ltd. 1980. p.60)
[282] *The Times,* 21st July 1977

BBC that the monster only looked like a plesiosaurus. It in fact was a shark that had decomposed in such a way as to convey the impression that it had a long neck, a small head and four large paddles.

How they, or their informants at the Natural History Museum in Kensington, could tell this since the creature was no longer available for examination, we can only guess at, especially considering that the marine biologist on board the vessel, the Zuiyo-maru, had sketched the creature's skeletal structure and it is nothing like that of a shark. Marine biologists are highly trained scientists whose ability to detect disease and mutations in fish and marine mammals is crucial to the health of the consumer, let alone the profits of the fishing vessel concerned, so their knowledge of marine life is necessarily very great. Yet the BBC would have us believe that Michihiko Yano, the government-trained and highly qualified marine biologist who examined, photographed and measured the monster, wouldn't know a dead shark when he saw one!"[283]

Concerning a land-borne sighting, Cooper quotes an official document from Scotland, dated 1793:

"In the end of November and beginning of December last, many of the country people observed dragons appearing in the north and flying rapidly towards the east; from which they concluded, and their conjectures were right, that... boisterous weather would follow."[284]

Plesiosaurs today?

Cryptozoologists study animals that don't fit the mould. Certain sea-dwelling dinosaurs may still be alive today, some say, if not their land and air-dwelling counterparts also. Photographs are available of beasts dwelling in Lake Champlain and Loch Ness.[285] Nearly all the good eye-witness accounts of these sea and lake creatures report that they look like plesiosaurs. Many other lakes across the world are reporting sightings of these beasts. Based

---

[283] Cooper, Bill, *After the Flood,* op. cit. ch.10

[284] "Flying Dragons at Aberdeen", *A Statistical Account of Scotland,* 1793, vol. VI. p.467

[285] **Hovind, Kent A** *Creation Science,* 29 Cummings Road, Pensacola, FL 32503 USA (www.drdino.com)

on the available evidence, there seems little doubt what these creatures are, in spite of denials.

In 1905, off the coast of Brazil, a plesiosaur swam past a boat-load of boggled scientists.[286] Such plesiosaur-type animals were reported in over 20,000 separate cases in the 20th century alone in Loch Ness, lochs in Ireland, Scandinavia, Siberia and elsewhere. A beast called 'Ogopogo' is all the rage in Canada, there's 'Champ' in Lake Champlain (Vermont), 'Nessie' in Scotland, 'Mokele Mbembe' in Zaire, 'Bessie' in Lake Erie, 'Caddy' in Cadboro Bay, British Columbia, to name a few.

Plesiosaurs today would not be as large as their ancestors were, and might logically dwell at great depths to avail themselves of the pressure needed to survive. Doubtless they run shy of noisy diesel engines, whose vibrations travel extensively under water, giving the animal plenty of time to flee. They seem to like mammal meat. A Loch Ness plesiosaur has been viewed on three separate occasions lumbering across the lakeside road with a sheep in its mouth before disappearing into the water. AnswersinGenesis.org writes:

"While movie mogul Steven Spielberg prepared for the premiere of his US$50 million blockbuster dinosaur film *Jurassic Park* in early 1993, equally spectacular dinosaur-type news was flowing in from around the world. From China there were claims that more than 1,000 people had seen a dinosaur-like monster in two sightings around Sayram Lake in Xinjiang.[287] From Scotland came the latest Loch Ness monster sighting: Mrs Edna MacInnes reported on June 24 that she had seen a 15-metre-long creature with a neck like a giraffe in Loch Ness.[288]

From Canada, Professor P LeBlond of the University of British Columbia told a meeting of zoologists about the many sightings of

---

[286] Ibid.

[287] **Lai Kuan and Jian Qun** "Dinosaurs: Alive and Well and Living in Northwest China?", *China Today*, Vol. XLII No. 2nd February 1993, p.59

[288] *The Weekend Australian*, 26–27 June 1993, p.15; Radio National (Australia) 8 am news report, 25th June 1993

'Caddy'—short for Cadborosaurus—around the British Columbia coast and as far south as Oregon. The remains of a three-metre juvenile 'Caddy' have actually been found in the stomach of a whale.[289]

It's been a big year for monsters. Russian scientists were startled to find remains of dwarf mammoths on Wrangel Island, off the Siberian coast, which they said were living only 3,700 years ago.[290] And British explorer Colonel John Blashford-Snell returned from an isolated Nepalese valley in March with photos of living creatures which looked something like mammoths or extinct stegodons."[291]

England's vast Andredesweald forest in the south-east seems to have been the haunt of such beasts from Saxon times. Thick and impenetrable, with only three roads running through it from the north Weald to the coast, the Andred's impassable barrier proved a hearty defence from invasion and certainly daunted William, Duke of Normandy, after he disembarked his army at Pevensey. The Normans and Saxons knew all about dragons.

Consider that troublesome wildlife is progressively hunted and killed as man moves into new areas. Bears and wolves roamed wild in the Andred but have since been cleared because no-one wants to live close to such creatures. Bear-baiting was a common festivity in medieval times but today the bears and wolves are long gone. In the years following the Flood, Noah's descendants would have hunted far bigger game. We would reasonably expect such beasts to be mentioned in scripture and they are. Many species would have died out but not all. Knowledge of these mighty creatures would have remained with man and fostered the legends which survive to this day.

www.polenth.com writes:

---

[289] 'Is Caddy a mammal?' *Science Frontiers*, May–June 1993, p. 2; **Park, Penny** "Beast from the Deep Puzzles Zoologists", *New Scientist*, 23rd January 1993, p.16

[290] "Reassessing the marvellous mammoths", *The Age* (Melbourne), 29 March 1993

[291] "The elephant that time forgot", *The Mail on Sunday*, 23 May 1993

"A knucker can refer to any dragon that lives in a knucker hole. This is a local word in some areas of Sussex for a pond where the source is hidden (such as an underground stream). They often have streams running out of them, making it seem like the water is coming from nowhere. Knucker is thought to come from the Anglo-Saxon word 'Nicor', meaning water monster.

The most famous knucker is the Lyminster Knucker. Knucker caused many problems in the Lyminster area, carrying off animals and people and generally being a nuisance. Eventually Knucker was killed, although there are several different versions of the story describing this event.

In one version, the King of Sussex offered his daughter in marriage to anyone who would kill the dragon. It was said that a wandering knight battled Knucker, killed him, married the princess and then settled in Lyminster. The second version of Knucker's end said that Jim Pulk, a local farmer's boy, outwitted the dragon. He cooked the dragon a poisoned Sussex pie, which the dragon ate, then died. Knucker got his revenge in the end though, because after Jim when off to celebrate he fell down dead. Probably he hadn't washed his hands after baking the poisoned pie.

The third version also has a local man outwitting Knucker in a similar way. This man is called Jim Puttock and comes from Wick. Rather than poisoning the pudding, he simply gave it to the dragon (these puddings are known for being rather heavy to eat). When the dragon was feeling bad, Jim cut off his head. In this version it is the Mayor of Arundel offering a reward. Unlike Jim Pulk, Jim Puttock does not die at the end.

To get an idea of what Knucker may have been like, here is an extract of dialogue between Knucker and Jim Puttock (as told by a local, and printed in the Sussex County Magazine in 1929):

And he sees thisyer tug a-coming, and sings out, affable-like, 'How do, Man?'

'How do, Dragon,' says Jim.

'What you got there?' says Dragon, sniffing.

'Pudden,' says Jim.

'Pudden?' says Dragon. 'What be that?'

'Just you try,' says Jim.

Other examples

- Stephen Caesar writes: "The scientific world was rocked in 2005 when palaeontologist Mary Schweitzer announced that she had discovered soft tissue in the fossilized skeleton of a tyrannosaurus rex, dated by conventional methods to 68 million years ago. One of the creature's legs was broken, so Schweitzer took it to her laboratory at North Carolina State University in Raleigh and dissolved the bone fragments in acid. When she examined the result, she noticed soft tissue consisting of blood vessels and structures that looked to be whole, intact cells, something impossible under the reigning theory of fossilization."[292]
- In Norse legend, the hero Siegfried slays the dragon Fafnir, which guards the treasure
- Dragons, serpents and gargoyles adorn castles all over Europe
- There are brass carvings of dinosaurs on the tomb of a bishop in Carlisle's 15th century cathedral

ChristianAnswers.net reports that the town of Nerluc in France was renamed in honour of the killing of a dragon there. By the descriptions given, it appears to have been a triceratops or similar. A medieval science book, the *Historia Animalium*, claims that 'dragons' were not extinct in the 1500's but the animals were said to be extremely rare and relatively small by then.[293]

---

[292] **Fields, H** "Dinosaur Shocker!" *Smithsonian* 37, no. 2, p.50, 2006. Per www.rae.org

[293] **Konrad Gesner** *Historiae Animalium* (Tigvri: C. Froschovervm, 1551-1587) Verrill, p.224

SO WHAT DID HAPPEN?

Earth is a strange place, not least for the creatures found upon it and deep in its oceans. Theories abound among creation scientists on what the Flood was, how it happened, and how the extraordinary evidence can be interpreted. This writer has spent the last twenty years examining Flood evidence and believes it is possible to get close to the truth. We have colossal and very bizarre evidence, some of which we've looked at. We have those mammoths and 'dragons' (dinosaurs) buried in compromising positions by the thousand. A whale on its tail at Lompoc. Billions of clams found in the closed position indicating they were buried alive, even on mountains. Flood legends all over the world. A population of just 6.7 billion today, pointing to 4,000 – 5,000 years of growth. The Ice Age. The ice caps. A wandering magnetic pole. The Earth tilted over at $23.5°$, beset with Chandler's Wobble, suggesting that something may have hit it. Damage all over the moon, and yet no-one has ever seen a major impact on the moon. Damage on Mars and Mercury. The rings of Saturn still separating in the Poynting-Robertson effect, indicating they are not billions of years old. Dozens of anthropic indicators pointing to a young Earth. Huge forests and coal deposits found under hundreds of feet of ice in Alaska and Antarctica. And on and on and on.

"Scientists have reported discovering the first set of dinosaur fossils ever to be found in the interior of Antarctica. The fossils are said to be the remains of a plant-eating dinosaur, 25-30 feet long, that lived about 200 million years ago in what geologists call the Jurassic age. The bones were spotted at a small section of exposed rock alongside the mountain, which lies about 400 miles from the South Pole."[294]

---

[294] **Raymond, Chris** "Scientists report finding fossils of dinosaurs in Antarctica's interior", *Chronicle of Higher Education,* 20th March 1991, p.A11

The Hovind theory

Kent Hovind thinks a comet was responsible. *National Geographic* reports:

"An estimated ten million rocky asteroids and ice-and-dirt comets pirouette in outer space, and once in a while their paths fatefully intersect our planet's. One such encounter took place a hundred miles from present-day Washington, D.C., where a 53-mile-wide crater lies buried beneath Chesapeake Bay—the scar left when a two-mile-wide rock smashed into the seafloor 35 million years ago. More notorious is the titan, six miles in diameter, that barrelled into the Gulf of Mexico around 65 million years ago, releasing thousands of times more energy than all the nuclear weapons on the planet combined. "The whole Earth burned that day," says Ed Lu, a physicist and former astronaut. Three-quarters of all life-forms, including the dinosaurs, went extinct."[295]

Hovind discounts the 'millions' and 'billions' of years and says the Earth did not burn, it drowned. A comet will increase its speed through the Inverse Square Law as it approaches Earth. From calculations of its 1,400-year half life, Earth's magnetic field is estimated to have been fifteen to twenty times stronger in 2345BC. The Flood comet must have been a big one, reaching Roche's Limit as it came in, the point at which the comet's own gravity is overtaken by Earth's. The comet disintegrates into ice boulders and shards. Four of the planets today have ice and rock rings around them. Others, like the moon, show vigorous impacts but no projectile debris. Again, no-one's ever seen anything hit the moon and yet it is covered in craters. Mars hosts over 43,000 craters over 5km in diameter.[296] 93% of Mars' craters *are on one side,* implying that these were formed at one time.

What can account for the frozen mammoths, some of them frozen so quickly they were preserved in the standing position? We

---

[295] *National Geographic*, August 2008
[296] **Wright, Shawn** *"Infrared Analyses of Small Impact Craters on Earth and Mars"*, University of Pittsburgh, April 4, 2003

know that they died of suffocation, some with food still in their mouths and stomachs. The ice crystals found in their blood lead scientists to conclude that they were frozen in about five hours. Kent Hovind points out that this would require something of a super-cold phenomenon involving temperatures far lower than any recorded on Earth (the record to date is -127°F at Vostok, USSR).

At minus 300°, comet ice is magnetic and drawn to the Earth's poles. Hovind suggests that the super-cold remnants of the comet struck the Earth across the northern latitudes around 2345BC, burying the vegetation and mammoths and cracking the crust. Today, coal can be found under the South Pole along with abundant evidence of huge forests and leaves, yet there are no living trees on the surface.[297] Hovind believes the comet pulverised the canopy as it came in, raining down impacts which broke the Earth's crust and released another great force of nature secreted in the planet's bowels – **'the great fountains of the deep'**.

Oceans under the oceans

The Bible says there was water within the crust of the Earth (Psa 24:1-2; Psa 33:7; Psa 136:6) and that these **'fountains of the deep'** burst open at the time of the Flood and shot to the surface (Gen 7:11-12; Job 38:8-11). Kent Hovind believes the continental fault lines were formed at this time, and to this day cause the Earth problems with their tectonic activity. Ham and Lovett write:

"In other words, earthquakes, volcanoes, and geysers of molten lava and scalding water were squeezed out of the Earth's crust in a violent, explosive upheaval. These fountains were not stopped until 150 days into the Flood—so the Earth was literally churning underneath the waters for

---

[297] **Prentice Hall** *Science* 1989, p.297. Frozen palm leaves have been found buried on Antarctica. (**Lewis, Richard** *S A Continent for Science: The Antarctic Adventure,* Viking Press, New York, 1965, p.130-4)

about five months. The duration of the Flood was extensive and Noah and his family were aboard the Ark for over a year."[298]

Was the Flood the result of a 'deep impact'? The Bible says the 'windows of heaven' were opened up as well as the 'fountains of the deep'. Many scientists discount Noah's Flood simply because it cannot rain enough under current processes to produce enough water in forty days and nights to cover the mountains. But what if it wasn't rain as such that did it? And what if today's mountain ranges did not exist until they were formed by Flood processes? Did the canopy shower its water down on the Earth as it collapsed, halving the atmospheric pressure over a matter of days, at the same time the 'fountains of the deep' produced their catastrophic volumes of water to fill the Earth? Regarding comets, Dr Immanuel Velikovsky is curious as to why there is so little meteoric dust on surface snow today, yet it makes up a substantial portion of oceanic sediment.[299] S A Cranfill writes:

"Velikovsky notes that there are an estimated half a million elliptical craters, all parallel in orientation from northwest to southeast with elevated rims on the southeast, that are found from New Jersey to Florida, and believes they could have been formed by a closedly passing comet breaking into meteors. There are 28 fields of sharp, burned, broken stones and craters in Arabia, and a number of craters in Australia. Of course, there is the incredible meteor crater in Arizona which is 4,000 feet across and 600 feet deep with a rim 200 feet high."[300]

Logically, any craters existing today would have to be the result of further impacts occurring *after* the Flood or they would not have survived the catastrophe. In *Origins II - Holy War*, we'll examine evidence that this could indeed have been the case – that

[298] **Ham K & T Lovett** www.alwaysbeready.com, 11th October 2007
[299] **Velikovsky, Immanuel** *Earth in Upheaval*, Garden City, New York: Doubleday & Co., 1955
[300] **Cranfill, S A** *They Came From Babel*, The Write House, 1994, p.51

various cataclysms may have dogged man up until a stabilisation event occurred in the 8th century BC.

The hydroplate theory

Dr Walt Brown has a Ph.D in mechanical engineering from the Massachusetts Institute of Technology (MIT). His hydroplate theory goes some way towards explaining the processes that may have followed the original impacts.

"We can see on our planet certain very strange features that can now be systematically explained as a result of a cataclysmic global flood, whose waters erupted from subterranean chambers with an energy release exceeding the explosion of ten billion hydrogen bombs. This explanation shows us just how rapidly major mountains formed. It explains the coal and oil deposits, rapid continental drift, why the ocean floor has great trenches and hundreds of canyons and volcanoes. It explains the formation of the layered strata and most of the fossil record, the so-called ice ages, and major land canyons, especially the Grand Canyon."[301]

Brown's hydroplate theory states that the Earth has interconnected subterranean chambers ten miles down which used to contain vast oceans of water, but today produce the deep-sea vents with which geologists are familiar. When the crust above these geothermal chambers failed around 2345BC, cracks began spreading out around the world at around three miles per second, following the paths of least resistance. These immense tears in the Earth's skin would have encircled the planet in under two hours. The tremendous pressure of ten miles of rock pressing down on the subterranean chambers caused the water within them violently to erupt out through the fault-lines and high into the atmosphere.

The spray from these global fountains would have produced torrential rains. The Bible states that all the fountains of the deep burst open in one day. These effects, Brown believes, can now be

---

[301] Hovind, Kent, *Creation seminar series,* "The Hovind Theory", op. cit.

tied together scientifically in cause-and-effect order to reveal what happened next.

The eruption of this steam from the deep produced violent winds. Some of the water blasted high into the atmosphere froze and fell as rain, snow and ice storms. The Earth heated up. The subterranean eruptions eroded the plate fissures on either side, widening them. As the Earth filled with water, humans, animals and vegetation were buried under trillions of tons of water mixed with sediment in a matter of weeks. Laboratory studies demonstrate how immense pressure applied to organic matter creates coal and oil deposits rapidly.

As the trenches widened, the compressed basalt beneath was compelled upward, forcing the hydroplates either side to retreat to form what is now the mid-Atlantic oceanic ridge. The plates, with lubricating water still beneath them, slid downhill as the ridge arose. When they met resistance, they buckled, crushed and thickened, and the portions of plate forced down formed the ocean trenches, while those forced up formed the ridges and mountains. This folding effect can be seen in mountain ranges in British Columbia today where the mountains are compressed *lengthwise*. Mountain ranges, says Dr Brown, are generally found running parallel to coastlines and the oceanic ridges from which they slid.[302]

The downward buckling formed oceanic trenches and chasms into which the Flood waters rushed. In time as the Earth's crust stabilised, land appeared coated in mud as the water level dropped. Every continental basin became a vast inland lake, receiving the water draining from the higher elevations before spilling over the lowest point of its own rim. As the water ran over the lip, the breach widened and deepened until the water roared out and carved a canyon through soft sediment which emptied into

---

[302] www.creationscience.com

the run-off. Where harder rock remained, a waterfall resulted, as in the case of Niagara Falls where Lake Erie empties into Lake Ontario.

Carving canyons

Most scientists agree there was once a huge lake, half the size of the state of Utah, located north and east of the Grand Canyon. Dr Brown names this Grand Lake. The dumping of its water would have approximated the emptying of all five Great Lakes at one time in a very rapid process. Dr Brown believes Grand Lake egressed at its lowest lip twenty miles south of Page, Arizona. As the breach widened, the washout carved out the Grand Canyon and its features in around two weeks. After that, the mud dried and hardened.

If you log onto Google Earth, find Page, Arizona, and trace the washout south through the Canyon, you can see this process unfolding. Now lower the view-angle to 45°. As the three-dimensional canyons come into focus, the water looks like it came off the surrounding plateau, washing out the smaller canyons as it cascaded down to the Colorado's principle egress.

Mars has a canyon much larger than Grand Canyon. Scientists writing in *Scientific American* believe such canyons were formed in a few weeks, and that this region of Mars was covered by a huge lake which overflowed its rim into a nearby impact crater, carving out the canyon as the waters rushed through soft sediment.[303] Kent Hovind is not amused.

"Why can they see a canyon on Mars, where we can't find any water for sure, and say 'this thing formed quickly', and you can look at Grand Canyon on Planet Earth and can't conclude that water formed that canyon very quickly…?"[304]

---

[303] Scientific American, 1998. Also on MSNBC News, 20th June 2002

[304] Hovind, Kent, *Creation seminar series*, "The Hovind Theory", op. cit.

Frozen stiff

The Ice Age followed the Flood as the Earth cooled. In the northern states of the US, score marks can be seen gouged out by glaciers which formed lateral and terminal moraines as they advanced, piled-up rocks pushed to the side or before the glacier's onslaught. When the ice melted, it left behind 'kettle' lakes such as those found in the US state of Minnesota, known as 'the land of 10,000 lakes'.

Other evidence is also intriguing. Hovind recounts the time he took a boat trip out to examine the Portage Glacier in Alaska. A fellow traveller was an oilman who told how, just a few months earlier, he had been drilling down through one thousand feet of permafrost at Barrow, Alaska (north coast) and brought up wood in the core sample. They discovered they were drilling vertically down through a tree which was an estimated 300 feet tall. There are no trees on the surface in Barrow, Alaska, but there is one 300 feet tall buried in the standing position under 1,000 feet of permanently frozen ice. How did it get there? And all the forest down there with it?

Hovind quotes the work of famous Australian astronomer George Dodwell, who studied the solstice shadows recorded by the ancients. Temples around the world, originally built to align with the solstice, are no longer true. This is observed at Stonehenge, the Temple of Amun-Ra and Eudoxus. Dodwell concluded that something must have struck the Earth 4,350 years ago and caused the planet to wobble, then progressively stabilise. The Earth's tilt, measured by ancient astronomers, bears this out. Today, the tilt is 23.5°, which gives us the seasons. Interestingly, the first mention of seasons in the Bible is given in Gen 8:22, after the Flood.

"Over the next few hundred years," concludes Hovind, "the ice caps would slowly melt back, retreating to their current size. The added water from the ice melt would raise the ocean level, creating a continental shelf. It would also absorb carbon dioxide out of the atmosphere, which allows more radiation to shorten people's lifespans. And in the days of Peleg, it finally took effect.[305] The Earth today still shows the effects of this devastating flood."[306]

[305] Genesis 10:25

[306] Hovind, Kent, *Creation seminar series,* "The Hovind Theory", op. cit.

- Part 2 -

The disaster of
social and political
evolution

NOT JUST DUMB BUT DANGEROUS

"The world – including mankind – as it truly is, is without any purpose, and is nonsense!" – **Friedrich Nietzsche**

It has been said that 'religion' has been at the heart of most of mankind's woes, and this is cited as the reason why many today choose not to 'believe'. Certainly those acting in the name of Christianity, Islam, Judaism and a hundred other beliefs have carried out the slaughter of millions, and our current study would be iniquitous without the examination Judaism, Islam and Christianity warrant in *Origins II – Holy War*.

But what about evolution? Extreme effort is made on behalf of evolutionists to cloak their religion as science. The public's perception of this slippery belief is usually derived from their education in a biology lab, reinforced by David Attenborough examining some obscure beetle and making unscientific pronouncements, while the socio-political ramifications of Darwin's theory go unremarked. In the following chapters, we'll discover that evolutionary philosophy has been responsible for more murders and atrocities in the past 150 years than those committed by all other religions *combined* throughout history. To understand why this state of affairs continues today, it is necessary to return to the scientific crucible of 19th century Europe, not only to reveal how Charles Darwin himself came to view his life's work, but to discover what happened when less scrupulous men co-opted his theory and unleashed neo-Darwinism on the 'Age of Enlightenment' that followed.

Do not allow your worst animals to breed

The 1800's were a pivotal time for man. Fuelled by the momentum generated by the technological discoveries of Newton, Descartes and the industrial pioneers, the industrial revolution was in full swing. The Victorian era became synonymous with the heady and buoyant enthusiasm of man gaining the ascendancy over his unforgiving environment, and these ideas spread into Europe and America and their respective principalities to change Western culture forever.

A time for new ideas. New technologies were being developed yearly. Rail travel, steamships, global trade and travel, the new mail services, banking, electricity, exploration and indeed mass-produced newspapers to report all such wondrous things opened up a new world for even the most humble citizen to consider and be amazed. One technological discovery rapidly begot another. Few, however, were prepared to consider the long-term implications of such rapid advances in science, finance, engineering, textiles, travel, medicine, warmongering, social order and justice. Indeed, the expanding differences these discoveries made, not only to the material world in which man lived, but in how he spiritually came to view himself, would change forever his perceptions of the world around him.

Thomas Robert Malthus (1766-1834)

British economist Thomas Malthus gave voice to a major problem he believed was dogging society. That while food production was increasing in a linear fashion, the population was growing exponentially. Malthus saw a future in which indiscriminate population growth would outstrip mankind's ability to feed itself. Malthus blamed the problem on the expanding working classes and proposed an end to their rampant 'sexual mania'. His published work, *An Essay on the Principle of Population as it Affects the Future Improvement of Society*, became required reading for the British aristocracy, who were noting with alarm the growth of the working classes and already anticipating future control problems. Malthus' sentiments, to those who adopted them, seemed scientific, well articulated and proposed an outline of self-preservation for the upper classes.

The Malthusian model advocated that the wages of the working classes be frozen so as not to allow the latter the financial resources to afford more children. Welfare would be abandoned in case it produced laziness in the population and increased the size of families to claim more benefits. Malthus saw social catastrophes such as famine, starvation, pestilence and war as natural, even desirable guardians of the status quo – a belief that still influences much of Third World population politics today.[307] Malthus proposed enforcing all necessary measures to curb "the reckless fertility of the poor". He also believed that, if necessary, a nation should "subject itself to the periodically recurring shrinking of the population surplus through famine, pestilence or war." [308]

In their book, *Psychiatrists – The Men Behind Hitler,* authors Röder, Kubillus and Burwell describe the real legacy of Malthus' persuasions:

"Malthus was received in certain circles 'like a divine revelation', writes historian Will Durant. But Malthus was less visionary than he was father of a new kind of witch-hunt – the pursuit of the expendable inferiors. It was Malthus' influence that caused William Pitt, then the British Prime Minister, not only to withdraw the legislation which he had introduced to improve the welfare of the poor, but also to call for cuts in the wages of working people.

In 1834, Malthus achieved one of his biggest successes. The British Parliament passed legislation that provided for the establishment of poor houses in which men and women would be strictly separated – to check "the unstoppable population surplus". Malthus' idea of introducing moral

---

[307] **Ransom, Steven & Phillip Day** *The Truth About HIV,* Credence Publications, 2006

[308] **Durrant, Will** *Die Napoleonische Ära*, Frankfurt, Berlin, 1982, p.91

239

barriers to limit population growth had been legislatively implemented in tangible form." [309]

Charles Darwin (1809-1882)

In his autobiography, Darwin wrote:

"In October 1838... I happened to read for amusement Malthus on Population.... it at once struck me that under these circumstances favourable variations would tend to be preserved and unfavourable ones to be destroyed.... Here then I had at last got a theory by which to work."[310]

It must have been intoxicating for Charlie, a privileged citizen of the most powerful empire on Earth, to admire the spectacular successes of the industrial sciences and their impact on society. Through the development of impressive new military technology, such as battleships, the new breach-loaded artillery and rifle, followed by the machine gun, science was teaching that man now held dominion, not only over 'lesser animals', but over the world's own destiny. New empires were arising in America, Germany, Russia, Austria and Japan, buoyant on the passionate new superhuman ethic which was now celebrated in opera, symphony, theatre and the arts.

The new science of archaeology was uncovering unthinkably large bones, inviting new theories on man's beginnings – beliefs which would bring their supporters into direct challenge with the traditional beliefs of the Church. Against the backdrop of 19th century human achievement and its concomitant belief that man was now capable of anything, religion came to be viewed with a covert, almost apologetic scepticism by proponents of the new scientific method. God was a crutch. Man could be strong on his own.

---

[309] **Röder, Thomas, Kubillus, Volker & Anthony Burwell** *Psychiatry – The Men Behind Hitler*, Freedom Publishing, Los Angeles: 1995, p.12
[310] Durrant, Will, *Die Napoleonische Ära*, op. cit. p.93

As time passed, the irresistible tide of materialistic advancement emboldened those who defied traditional beliefs and ethics, as the boundless possibilities of new theories offered an unchaining of traditional paradigms and were daily reported in the newspapers. Challenges to the Church were soon being openly heard. The public sniffed a forbidden liberation in the air. The religious accounts of man's origins and his place under the yoke of a morally accountable God were soon being written up in the popular press as mythical, fanciful and plain unscientific.

In the 1830's, Englishman Charles Lyell invented the Geologic Column, which chronologically tabulated the different eras he believed existed since the formation of the world. New and unfamiliar terms such as the Cretaceous, Jurassic, Cenozoic and Palaeozoic Eras became the road-signs describing the ancient ascendancy of man over his environment and other creatures. Vitalised by the prehistoric dinosaur and advances in astronomy, physics and chemistry, science closed ranks around the new knowledge. Theory became fact as the leading thinkers unleashed their imaginations on the enormous questions concerning man's distant past, uncertain present and ultimate destiny.

The impact of Lyell on the public mind was epoch-shaping, but it was Darwin, the keen supporter of Malthus' population ideas and Lyell's Geologic Column, who would solidify schools of evolutionary thought by the mid 19th century. His 1859 publication of *On The Origin of Species by Means of Natural Selection, or the Preservation of Favoured Races in the Struggle for Life,* became the new Bible for the world – an alternative explanation of man's origins which, as part of its legacy, brought the Trojan Horse of an unfamiliar liberty.

The Great Change

Evolution explained the development of life on Earth without the involvement of a Creator God. A natant, primordial germ had

241

developed which, over the millions of years following, mutated and bred through the survival of the fittest transitions into the different branches of living organisms we see today. Soon neo-Darwinists were proposing that insects, fish, amphibians, reptiles, birds, mammals and humans – indeed all living things had originated from the same ultimate, microscopic, simple-celled ancestor and begun their evolutionary ascent through genetic mutation.

Contrary to Church notions of a biblically derived young Earth, the world of Lyell and Darwin had to be immensely ancient, for otherwise there would not be enough time for evolution's haphazardry to work its plan. Countless scientifically-named epochs had to range off into the dim corridors of the past in order for monkeys to turn into men, reptiles to grow feathers and turn into birds, cows to become dolphins, rats to morph into bats, and fish to grow legs, crawl up onto dry land, shed their scales and begin breathing air. Each form had to evolve into a more complex version of its predecessor through *beneficial* mistakes, in direct contravention of the Second Law of Thermodynamics, the universal law of entropy, which teaches that matter is breaking down from the complex to the simple, and energy in the universe is becoming more unavailable as time passes. In the world of the evolutionist, nothing on Earth was designed by God. Indeed, to many who followed Darwin, there was no God, no universal right or morality – just blind, random chance. Survival of the fittest meant that man had finally become man, yet nothing more than an evolved animal which had triumphed over impossible odds to conquer its unforgiving environment.

Darwin's body-snatchers

Anthropologists became so obsessed with finding 'the missing link' between apes and humans that successive expeditions set off to scour the Earth for an upright 'in-between'. Some scientists had noticed from naturalists' sketches that Australian Aborigines possessed the requisite protruding brows and other supposed features of a human transitional form. So off the scientists sailed with their shovels and picks to dig up a few corpses and bring them back for analysis.

The problem was, Darwin's soldiers soon ran out of Aborigine graves to rob, so they started shooting the indigenous natives for specimens. Not one full-blooded, Tasmanian Aborigine escaped the genocide and so none exist today. At present, there are an estimated 33,000 sets of human remains in the crypts of the American Smithsonian and British Natural History Museum, stockpiled in an attempt to prove evolution. Dr Carl Wieland writes:

"Good prices were being offered for such specimens. There is no doubt from written evidence that many of the 'fresh' specimens were obtained by simply going out and killing the Aboriginal people. The way in which the requests for specimens were announced was often a poorly disguised invitation to do just that. A death-bed memoir from Korah Wills, who became mayor of Bowen, Queensland in 1866,[311] graphically describes how he killed and dismembered a local tribesman in 1865 to provide a scientific specimen.[312]

Edward Ramsay, curator of the Australian Museum in Sydney for 20 years from 1874, was particularly heavily involved. He published a museum booklet which appeared to include Aborigines under the designation of 'Australian animals'. It also gave instructions not only on how to rob graves, but also on how to plug up bullet wounds in freshly killed 'specimens'. Many freelance collectors worked under his guidance. Four weeks after he had requested skulls of Bungee (Russell River) blacks, a keen young science student sent him two, announcing that they,

---

[311] According to the records of the Bowen Shire Council.

[312] **Monaghan, D** "The Body-Snatchers", *The Bulletin,* 12th November 1991, pp.30-38. The article states that journalist Monaghan spent 18 months researching this subject in London, culminating in a television documentary called *Darwin's Body-Snatchers,* which was aired in Britain on 8th October 1990

the last of their tribe, had just been shot.[313] In the 1880s, Ramsay complained that laws recently passed in Queensland to stop Aborigines being slaughtered were affecting his supply."[314]

Darwin's strange mix of his own evolutionary sentiments, combined with Malthus' solutions to preserve the British aristocracy, come together in a darkly prophetic letter to William Graham, Professor of Jurisprudence in Belfast. Darwin writes:

"Looking at the world at no very distant date, what an endless number of the lower races will have been eliminated by the higher civilised races throughout the world." [315]

Friedrich Wilhelm Nietzsche (1844-1900)

Contemporary to Darwin was another of the new thinkers – the German philosopher Friedrich Nietzsche. Nietzsche's iconoclastic declarations, couched in the most momentous rhetoric, were later condemned as some of the most outrageous and inhuman concepts ever to blight humanity. But the 1800's were famous for citizens having their minds boggled, and Nietzsche was only too happy to oblige them. Karl Schlechta, a comprehensive researcher of Nietzsche, sums up the philosopher's core teachings as follows:

- Values and virtues, charity and kindness are an irrelevance and mean nothing:

"Here is an insight, which has been formulated by me for the first time; that there are no moral truths at all.... Morality is only an interpretation of certain phenomena, or, more precisely, a misinterpretation." [316]

- The existence of man and his physical realm are without design or purpose and cannot be comprehended:

---

[313] Ibid.
[314] www.onehumanrace.com/docs/darwins_bodysnatchers.asp
[315] **Darwin, Charles** *Die Abstammung des Menschen und die geschlechtliche Zuchtwahl, Part 1,* Stuttgart, 1871, p.146 (translated)
[316] **Nietzsche, Friedrich** *Book III,* p.425

244

"The world – including mankind – as it truly is, is without any purpose, and is nonsense!"[317]

- A woman is an inferior being.
- The only life worthy to be lived is that of the 'superhuman', who is characterised by a desire for war, power, and possesses the physical strength to use force as a means of achieving control.[318]
- War is beautiful - a natural force that should be embraced:

"They [the superhumans] are always looking for an enemy. In some of them is a hatred at first sight. They love peace as a means towards new wars, and they love a short peace more than a long one."

- Certain races are superior to other races.

Religion despised

Nietzsche's hatred of Christianity marks him as one of the proponents of the new 'free morality'. Nietzsche conveys the idea to his readers that the concepts of mercy, kindness, charity and love, as expounded by Jesus, are in fact the complete antithesis of the true way, since Jesus, in Nietzsche's view, seeks to help the weak at the expense of the strong:

"Christianity, rooted in Jewish tradition and nothing more than a plant from its soil, is a counter-movement against any morals of the breeding, the race, the privileges – it is the anti-Aryan religion par excellence: Christianity, the transformation of all Aryan values... the evangelism of the poor, the inferior, the complete rise of all the down-trampled, the wretched and poor against the Race...." [319]

Nietzsche loathes the idea that the meek stand even the slightest chance of inheriting the Earth. His ideas about the Master Race, The Cleansing of the Race and the Industrious Race, revolve around the mythical Aryan ideal. That the Aryans will triumph

---

[317] **Nietzsche, Friedrich** *Book V*, p.91
[318] **Nietzsche, Friedrich** *Book II*, p.589
[319] **Nietzsche, Friedrich** *Book III*, p.428

over the Earth in a glorious struggle is a foregone conclusion to the philosopher. The Aryan will conquer the Deteriorated Races.[320] Here we see, prior to 1900, the fully formed idea of a genetically superior race – the Aryans – wielding war and power as a glorious, mighty thing to behold. At the same time, Nietzsche conditions his readers to ignore the suffering and eventual demise of the 'deteriorated' races.

Francis Galton and the birth of eugenics

English psychologist Francis Galton, Darwin's half-cousin, coined the concept of 'social Darwinism', merging Darwin's evolutionary sentiments on animals with the desire to manipulate human evolution. He named his 'science' *eugenics*. Here Man is an animal and therefore, to obtain the optimum quality of this animal in society, selective breeding of superior humans, with the simultaneous 'reducing' of inferior or diseased stock, will guarantee the eradication of the negative aspects of natural selection. Evolution needs a helping hand, after all.

According to Galton, negroes are closer to ape than humans and are still in their evolutionary ascent:

"The average intellectual standard of the Negro is some two grades below our own."[321]

Galton also voices his views on another sector of humanity:

"The Jews are specialised for a parasitical existence upon other nations."[322]

Galton's ideas are to influence even the influencers. Darwin himself is convinced of the need for eugenics when he writes:

---

[320] **Nietzsche, Friedrich** *Book IV*, p.430
[321] Quoted in **Lapon, Lenny** *Mass Murderers in White Coats*, Springfield, Massachusetts, Psychiatric Genocide Research Institute, 1986, pp.75-76
[322] Quoted in Lapon, Lenny, *Mass Murderers in White Coats*, op. cit. pp.75-76

"With the savage, the weak in body or mind are soon eliminated; and those that survive commonly exhibit a vigorous state of health. We civilised men, on the other hand, do our utmost to check the process of elimination; we build asylums for the imbecile, the maimed, and the sick; we institute Poor Laws; and our medical men exert their utmost skill to save the life of every one to the last moment.... Thus the weak members of society propagate their own kind. No one who has attended the breeding of domestic animals will doubt that this must be highly injurious to the race of man. It is surprising how soon a want of care, or care wrongly directed, leads to the degeneration of a domestic race; but excepting in the case of man himself, hardly anyone is so ignorant as to allow his worst animals to breed." [323]

Eugenics soon gains a foothold in the minds of the forward-thinkers of Darwin's day, but a more powerful scientific clique would co-opt eugenic social engineering for its own ends, spawning the racist and nihilistic philosophies which, for the next seventy years, would plunge Earth into the abyss of two global wars.

---

[323] **Schreiber, B** *Geheime Reichssache: Die Manner Hinter Hitler: Eine Deutsche Warnung an Die Welt,* Section 5 Books, 1983), pp.11-12

DOYENS OF THE MIND: THE NEW BRAIN SCIENTISTS

'God is dead. God remains dead. And we have killed him'.
– Friedrich Nietzsche

Evolution, eugenics and the new sciences of the 1800's birth a new science of the mind – psychiatry. Although the word means 'doctor [*iatros*] of the soul', psychiatry would ironically deny the concept of a human soul almost from the profession's inception.

Psychiatry as a recognised profession began humbly enough in the early 1800's, concerning itself with the custodial care of the madman. Since ancient times, the insane and the mentally impaired had always been a enigma for society, requiring constant care and control. However, this new service to society, which began with the localising of the mentally impaired in almshouses and sanitaria, albeit as brutal as the infamous British Bedlam 'hospital' of the thirteenth century with its whips and chains, soon expanded in the 19th century under the influence of a self-styled American expert on 'the diseases of the mind', Dr Benjamin Rush.

Benjamin Rush

American Founding Father Rush is even today regarded as the founder of the modern mental health movement, so much so that his likeness adorns the seal of the American Psychiatric Association (APA). Yet Rush's methods and theories were, to say the least, extraordinary. Rush believed crime to be a curable disease. Understanding murder and rape to be symptoms of this disorder, Rush advocated having criminals transferred from police custody to that of psychiatrists.[324]

---

[324] **Rush, Benjamin** *Medical Inquiries and Observations upon the Diseases of the Mind,* published 1812.

The doctor's therapies for the insane included revolving them in a specially designed chair for extended periods, torturing them with frigid water baths, bleeding the patient profusely to relieve the 'excessive action' in their brain, and terrifying them with threats of further 'treatments'. "The deception," Rush stated, "would be a justifiable one if it served to cure him of his disease." Rush believed that only through the physician exercising total control over his patient in every respect – physically, psychologically and spiritually – could madness be cured.[325]

Influenced by the evolutionist and supremacist sentiments of Weishaupt, Voltaire, Rousseau and Lyell – that the lower animals were in dire need of guidance by a knowledgeable élite – Benjamin Rush's view of the black race was summed up in his theory of 'negritude' – namely that black skin was a disease affliction and that the healthy Negro should be white. Psychiatrist Thomas Szasz quotes Rush, in the latter's *Medical Inquiries*, stating,

"However well they appear to be satisfied with their colour, there are many proofs of their preferring that of the white people."[326]

American William Cobbett was so vehemently opposed to Rush's beliefs that he published *The Rush-Light*, a periodical produced specifically to expose Rush and his methods. Even after Rush sued and virtually bankrupted Cobbett for defamation, the dogged investigator moved to another state and continued his attacks.[327] Dr Carl Binger, a modern-day Rush biographer, writes:

"The doubts that Cobbett cast on Rush's claims for his methods were, as a matter of fact, justifiable. Indeed, in the long run, they probably helped discredit a system of medicine that time has not sustained.

---

[325] **Szasz, Thomas** *The Manufacture of Madness*, Harper and Row, New York: 1970, pp.146-147

[326] Szasz, Thomas, *The Manufacture of Madness*, op. cit. p.45

[327] **Binger, Carl** *Revolutionary Doctor: Benjamin Rush 1746-1813*, W W Norton & Co., New York: 1966, pp.246-247

Cobbett claimed to have established mathematically that Rush had killed more patients than he had cured." [328]

Rush's experiments were regarded by many as barbarous and lethal; many of his patients in the Philadelphia area perished with the trauma of their 'cures'.[329] Yet even today, Rush is still venerated as the consummate mental health authority of his day.

Was Rush simply buying into the élitist sentiments of his 'free-thinking' contemporaries? Bavarian revolutionary Adam Weishaupt's concept of iron obedience wielded by a ruling cryptocracy, if necessary applied through brute force, was designed to produce in the target population a feeling of resignation, apathy and lack of resistance. The idea was that the 'cattle' would be so cowed by the superior power as to believe that all resistance was useless, and thereby render themselves more easily controlled. This concept became successfully installed as one of the main tenets of psychiatry and the treatment of 'mental' patients by Rush. As early as 1810, Johann Christian Reil, Professor of Medicine at the University of Berlin, who first coined the term 'psychiatry', was already articulating this sinister concept when he wrote:

"Through strong painful impressions we capture the patient's attention, accustom him to unconditional obedience, and indelibly imprint on his heart the feeling of necessity. The will of his superior must be such a firm, immutable law for him that he will no more resist it than he would rebel against the elements." [330]

---

[328] Ibid.

[329] Szasz, Thomas, *The Manufacture of Madness*, op. cit. p.157

[330] Quoted in **Kraepelin, Emil** *One Hundred Years of Psychiatry*, Philosophical Library, Inc., New York: 1961, pp.92-94, translated from the German essay written in 1917.

Wilhelm Wundt

Towards the end of the 19th century, psychiatry became restless, impatient to break out of the asylum and flex its new ethos. A psychiatric worldview was in full development by the time the profession began moving from supervising the custodial insane to the concept of the prevention and eradication of insanity in general society. Not content to deal with life's incarcerated human wretches, the pioneers in mental health moved with determination into the public eye with several far-reaching agendas.

Wilhelm Wundt, of Leipzig University in Germany, made his historic declaration in 1879 that man had no soul. Wundt, an ardent evolutionist, reported that man, this higher form of animal, was nothing more than a stimulus-response creature whose behaviour could be controlled using science. Wundt's implicit challenge to the

Church's continued right to administer mental and spiritual healing to the populations was the catalyst which brought a new alternative to religious counselling into the public mind –a new 'science of the mind' that could benefit all society – the science of 'psychiatry'. Psychologist G Stanley Hall, an ordained minister, was an avid student of Wundt's and keen supporter of eugenics. Studying at the University of Berlin in 1868, his courses included anatomy, theology, anthropology and psychiatry. Hall's biographer, David Hothersall, writes:

"Given Hall's theoretical position, we should not be surprised that he was interested in eugenics. He was in fact

251

an enthusiastic proponent of eugenic controls and left money in his estate to establish a chair of genetic psychology at Clark University [USA]. Hall was a firm believer in 'higher' and 'lower' human races. He believed the Negro race to be at an early stage of human development, and dependent upon the 'higher', more advanced white race for its development and supervision." [331]

Bruce Wiseman agrees that the confluence of materialism, evolutionary theory, revolutionary sentiments against the Church, and exploding influence of science into society in the late 1800's was the ideal womb that birthed the modern mental health movement:

"Materialism is merely an idea that says that nothing exists but matter - the physical. There is no God, no soul, no validity to religion and its accompanying moral stance. One can readily see the consequences of such a belief riding in on the coat-tails of a rapidly advancing science and even being passed off as scientific fact – as indeed it has been.

Through intellectual sleight-of-hand, scientific materialism boldly claims that since spiritual matters or the mind or the will can't be measured with physical instruments, they therefore don't exist and have no place in scientific theory." [332]

Wundt's influence on the public to view psychiatry as a 'medical science' dovetailed completely with Darwin's evolutionary and eugenics influences. Wiseman states that the spectacle of 'great men of science' such as Wundt and Hall – imposing looking, dignified, well-versed in speech – declaring that man was no more than the result of his haphazard evolution, and as such, not responsible for his behaviour, turned 19th century Europe on its head. Science, materialism and evolutionary viewpoints became the hot topics of the day and the public, spurred on by the vivid pictures painted for them by the

---

[331] **Hothersall, David** *History of Psychology*, Temple University Press, Philadelphia, 1984, p.268

[332] Wiseman, Bruce, *Psychiatry - the Ultimate Betrayal*, op. cit.

newspapers of a society about to take a quantum leap into the future, found themselves enthralled, captivated and impatient for more.

Wundt's philosophies also attacked the concept of 'free will'. If man was now able to assign his behaviour to causes beyond his control, then the Christian religion, which teaches that a person has 'free will' to exercise moral choices and is responsible for his actions, was surely, according to the new science, nothing more than cringing tradition – an embarrassing superstition; at best, a narcotising influence on the masses; at worst, an inflexible barrier to the freeing of man's restless, imprisoned genius.

William James

William James, a student of Wundt's, is sometimes regarded as 'the Father of American Psychology'. James' solicitous belittling of religion as 'a therapeutic' which could make people 'feel better', is more properly understood in the context of his age. James biographer Clarence J Karier clarifies:

"By the time James published 'The Varieties of Religious Experience' in 1902, Friedrich Nietzsche, in 'Gay Science' (1882), had already declared: 'God is dead. God remains dead. And we have killed him'. With both Nietzsche and James, we pass from a culture with God at its centre to a culture with man at its centre. This fundamental shift in Western thought initiated a corresponding shift in the ideological

253

structure of the social system.... Western society underwent a transformation of the basis for personal and collective values.... Salvation was now a matter of survival, sin became a physical sickness, and such religious rituals as confession, designed to alleviate guilt and atone for sin, were replaced by individual and group psychotherapeutic interventions, designed to alleviate the guilt of anxiety neurosis.

These then were the signs of an emerging therapeutic society, a society born in the closing decade of the nineteenth century and nourished in the secular world of the twentieth century.... William James, as one of the first secular theologians of this new therapeutic society, conceptualised the fundamental ideas that came to underpin that society."[333]

Ivan Pavlov

Before long, new stars were rising in the 'science of the mind' pantheon. Early in the twentieth century, Russian physiologist and psychologist Ivan Pavlov, together with his colleague, Vladimir Bekhterev, a student of Wundt's, were inducing conditioned responses in dogs, causing them to salivate with the ringing of a bell, having trained the animals to link the bell's tone to food and pleasure. Pavlov's testimony is cited almost invariably in every beginner's psychology textbook; Pavlov, moving the psychology/psychiatric student in the desired direction, namely, to conclude from his work that man, like the dogs, is nothing more than a

---

[333] **Karier, Clarence J** *Scientists of the Mind*, Chicago: University of Illinois Press, 1986, p.28

stimulus-response animal. In later decades, Pavlov's theories on mind-conditioning would lead to the brainwashing and mind control programs carried out in the Soviet Union, China, Great Britain, the United States and Canada.[334]

Emil Kraepelin

German psychiatrist Emil Kraepelin gave the world the word 'paranoia'. Another dubbed 'the Father of Psychiatry', Kraepelin's evolutionary beliefs also led him down the path of humans-as-animals and the right to 'play God' over those diagnosed 'mentally ill'. At the time of psychiatry's genesis as the new method of diagnosing the mentally disturbed, caring for the latter was a thankless task few wanted, with patients incarcerated under the most appalling conditions. In his *One Hundred Years of Psychiatry*, Kraepelin quotes an anonymous reporter who, in 1795, was constrained to write:

"A humanitarian is bound to shudder when he discovers the plight of the unfortunate victims of this dreadful affliction; many of them grovel in their own filth on unclean straw that is seldom changed, often stark naked and in chains, in dark, damp dungeons where no breath of fresh air can enter. Under such terrifying conditions, it would be easier for the most rational person to become insane than for a madman to regain his sanity."[335]

The question confronting Kraepelin, Wundt and others was simple: could insanity be explained and cured? Psychiatry was labelling 'insanity' a physical disease of the mind with no proof, resorting to a brutalising force to overwhelm the patient mentally and physically. Thomas Szasz writes:

---

[334] ww.cchr.org; see also **Veracity, Dani** "Human medical experimentation in the United States: The shocking true history of modern medicine and psychiatry (1833-1965)", www.naturalnews.com

[335] Quoted in Kraepelin, Emil, *One Hundred Years of Psychiatry*, op. cit. p.11

"These have included whipping, flogging, the application of ants, scabies and stinging nettles, surgical removal or cauterising (burning) of the clitoris and removing a woman's ovaries. Masturbation, originally considered a mental illness, was treated by circumcision and cauterising the spine and genitals." [336]

Later would follow psychosurgery (lobotomy) – the surgical removal of tissues from the brain – along with electro-convulsive therapy (ECT) to the head and psychotropic drugs to alter behaviour. Behind the scenes the terror continued. Dr Elliot S Valenstein reports that within a five-year period in the 1930's, insulin coma, metrazol shock, electroshock and lobotomies were widely prescribed by psychiatrists worldwide. All caused physical damage to the patients. None ever cured.[337] German authors Drs. Hans Georg Guse and N Schmake recount that Emil Kraepelin had,

"…adopted the central thesis of Social Darwinism, whereby a person's social rank is the expression of a natural allotment of qualities and abilities.… Kraepelin then began to consider the mentally handicapped as 'a heavy burden for our nation'. Along with many other academics, he saw the solution to social disorder in a strong leader: 'An unrestricted ruler with the power to intervene in our way of life would bring about the reduction in insanity within a few decades!' Kraepelin supported the idea of sterilisation for certain psychopaths, maintaining that the passing on of inferior hereditary traits would thus be avoided."[338]

Kraepelin's support for Malthusian social intervention was by no means an isolated sentiment. In 1897, Dr M W Barr, president of the American Association for the Study of Feeblemindedness,

---

[336] Szasz, Thomas, *The Manufacture of Madness*, op. cit. pp.278, 310-311; also **Howells, John G** *World History of Psychiatry*, Brunner/Mazel, Inc. New York: 1975, p.264

[337] **Valenstein, Elliot S** *Blaming the Brain*, Free Press, New York: 1998, p.205

[338] **Guse, Hans Georg & N Schmake** "Psychiatry and the Origins of Nazism", *International Journal of Health Services*, vol.10, No.2, 1980

strongly advocated sterilisation as a eugenics measure.[339] Bruce Wiseman reports:

"In the early twentieth century, psychiatrist Edwin Katzen-Ellenbogen, who was ultimately convicted of war crimes as a doctor at Buchenwald concentration camp, 'drafted for the governor the law of sterilisation of epileptics, criminals and the incurably insane for the State of New Jersey.' Other states – 22 in all – followed suit with similar laws."[340]

It is testament to the mistaken direction psychiatry took from the outset to cure 'mental illness' that the answer to the question of whether so-called mental disorders could be treated and cured at all proved troubling for one of psychiatry's chief architects. A pondering Emil Kraepelin wrote in 1917:

"The impenetrable darkness that hides the innermost workings of the brain and their relation to psychic manifestations, and finally the inadequacy of our instruments for dealing with extremely complicated issues, must cause even the most confident investigator to doubt whether it is possible to make any appreciable progress towards psychiatric knowledge and understanding." [341]

The 'scientific underpinning' of eugenics

Kraepelin's observations were to be one of many indictments against psychiatry and its brutal methodologies which followed. By 1914 and the onset of World War 1, the head of the American Medico-Psychological Association, today known as the American Psychiatric Association (APA), was confirming that mental illness was hereditary, and as such should be controlled through the eugenics system:

"That a radical cure of the evils incident to the dependent mentally defective classes would be effected if every feeble-minded person, every

[339] Lapon, Lenny, *Mass Murderers in White Coats*, op. cit. p.76
[340] Wiseman, Bruce, *Psychiatry – The Ultimate Betrayal,* op. cit. p.62
[341] Kraepelin, Emil, *One Hundred Years of Psychiatry*, op. cit. p.9

imbecile, every habitual criminal, every manifestly weak-minded person, and every confirmed inebriate were sterilised, is a self-evident proposition. By this means we could practically, if not absolutely, arrest, in a decade or two, the reproduction of mentally defective persons, as surely as we could stamp out smallpox absolutely if every person in the world could be vaccinated." [342]

Here we see a number of pivotal developments already entrenched in the minds of evolutionists, psychiatrists and psychologists by 1914. The above words are spoken at a presidential address to the forerunner organisation of the American Psychiatric Association, the body governing all areas of mental illness at the time. Firstly, we learn that the 'benefits' of sterilisation to prevent reproduction by 'mental defectives' are already 'self-evident'. Secondly, we deduce that presumably only the American Medico-Psychological Association has the expertise to define who is a 'mental defective' and who isn't, thus giving eugenics 'a scientific respectability'. Thirdly, alcoholism is now a mental illness and habitual crime a derangement rather than the result of greed, social factors or just the plain, 'sane' desire to commit a crime.

Sigmund Freud

Another shaper of the age, Sigmund Freud, proposed that man was a product of his past experiences. With Freud we once again see man as the sum total of the evolutionary effect of his environment and not in control of his actions. Under Freud, past psychological abuse becomes the explanation for current criminal behaviour or stress, however extreme. Therefore, although

---

[342] **Castel Robert, Castel Francoise & Anne Lovell** *The Psychiatric Society*, (Translated by Arthur Goldhammer), Columbia University Press, New York: 1982, pp.46-47. Source for quote is **Carlos F MacDonald** "Presidential Address", *American Journal of Insanity*, July 1914, 71:9

culpable of the crime, the criminal is not responsible if evidence can be found in his past to 'justify' why he committed the crime.

Freud, himself owning a serious and well-known libido-stimulating cocaine addiction (which no doubt influenced his views on sex), preached sexual promiscuity, even with children, to free man of his 'inhibitions' and all that stress:

"Free sexual intercourse between young males and respectable girls" [was urgently required, or society was] "doomed to fall victim to incurable neuroses which reduce the enjoyment of life to a minimum, destroy the marriage relation, and bring hereditary ruin on the whole coming generation." [343]

In a personal interview, Al Parides, Professor of Psychiatry at UCLA in Los Angeles, declared that psychiatric values had been:

"…very influenced, especially by the Freudian influence in regard to sex and morality generally…. If you look at the personal lives of all Freud's followers – his initial disciples – these people certainly have an unbelievable amount of particular problems in the sexual area…. The amount of deviancy as far as their sexual behaviour and so forth is enormous. If you are saying that psychiatry promotes a certain form of morality that is a deviant morality in regard to many areas including sexual behaviour - yes, I would agree." [344]

Freud had a particular passion for denouncing religion. Religion was the Enemy. The implacable Spoiler of Carnal Pleasures. The Jailer of the Emotions and Stern Guardian over the Primeval, Stone-Age Urges of Humankind. Freud predicted the eventual death of religion – especially Christianity:

"The scientific spirit generates a certain posture towards matters of this world; before matters of religion it stops for a while, hesitates, at last there too crosses the threshold. In this process there is no stopping; the more the treasures of our knowledge become accessible to people, the

---

[343] **Mindless, Harvey** *Makers of Psychology: The Personal Factor*, Insight Books, New York, 1988, p.32

[344] Interview between Bruce Wiseman and Al Parides, 17th December 1993

more the defection from religious belief will spread, at first only from its obsolete, offensive vestments, but then from its fundamental pre-suppositions as well." [345]

Psychiatrist Thomas Szasz's research highlights an interesting fact. "Although an entire volume of the Standard Edition of Freud's collected works is devoted to an index, there is no entry for 'responsibility' in it. True to the faith of the master, his acolytes must have felt that responsibility was so unscientific a concept that it was not worth indexing." [346]

Freud today has been widely discredited in professional circles but still remains in the public's mind a giant in the field of mental health. Psychology professor Frank Sulloway, author of *Freud: Biologist of the Mind*, believes "Freud was wrong in almost every respect." [347]

Aleister Crowley

The encroaching influence of psychiatry's architects at the turn of the 20th century was to have a disastrous impact upon religion. The banishment of God by this time had also spawned a strong interest in the occult, encouraging tarot readings, séances and Luciferian doctrines, along with their eccentric proponents. No investigation into the huge change in social and religious attitudes of this period can be understood without appreciating the extent to which necromancy and occultism had penetrated European culture by 1900.

In 1904, one of Britain's most devious free-thinkers, Aleister Crowley, sits down to write a book. Crowley is originally a member of the Christian Plymouth Brethren sect, but evidently

---

[345] **Freud, Sigmund** *The Future of an Illusion*, SE XXI, p.38

[346] **Szasz, Thomas** *Insanity: The Idea and its Consequences*, John Wiley & Sons, New York: 1987, p.245

[347] **Horgan, John** *The Undiscovered Mind*, The Free Press, New York: 1999, p.74; **McFarling, Usha Lee** "Analyze This: Why Freud, Discredited, Still on Minds", *The Commercial Appeal*, 21st May 2000

from his youth is a difficult child exhibiting alarming behaviour. His own mother brands him 'spawn of Satan'.

Crowley becomes influenced by the writings of Madame Helena Petrovna Blavatsky, a Satanist and founder of the Theosophical Society.[348] Crowley admits that he does not know precisely what caused his defection from Christianity:

"I accepted the theology of the Plymouth Brethren. In fact, I could not conceive of the existence of a people who would doubt it. I simply went over to Satan's side and to this hour cannot tell why.... I was not content to believe in a personal devil and serve him in the ordinary sense of the word. I wanted to get hold of him and become his chief of staff."[349]

Crowley claims *The Book of the Law*, first published in 1908, was dictated to him by a spirit he later identifies as Satan.[350] Crowley, it seems, has been instructed to prepare the world for the coming One World Order of the Antichrist, a future world ruler who would be Satan's incarnation sold to the world as the real Christ. Crowley's constant usage of the term 'New Aeon' leads to the popularity of the phrase, 'New Age'. In his widely read *The Book of the Law*, Crowley's aims are expounded upon with deadly seriousness. According to his writings, the coming New Age will be ushered in on a wave of

[348] **Blavatsky, Helen P** *The Secret Doctrine*, Theosophical University Press, 1989

[349] **Symonds, John & Kenneth Grant** *The Confessions of Aleister Crowley*, Viking Penguin, 1989

[350] **Crowley, Aleister** *The Book of the Law*, Samuel Weiser Inc., 1989

hallucinogenic drugs, strange music and free sex – an improbable prophecy to be given back in the first century of the post-Victorian era. Later, the 1960's arrive and people rapidly begin changing their minds.

Crowley's watchword is *"Do what thou wilt shall be the whole of the law"* (do whatever you want) – the complete unhinging of society from the moral concepts of personal accountability and right/wrong, couched in the quasi-Biblical language of the occult. The world is ill-prepared for the psychedelic explosion of moral rebellion that follows in the 1960's. Psychiatric mind-altering drugs, such as heroin, cocaine, thorazine, methadone and LSD, flood popular culture, relentlessly promoted by those such as psychologist and pop-drug mystic Timothy Leary, who invites the world to study Crowley and 'turn on, tune in and drop out.' Parents begin losing their children to a more alluring force, one against which they realise they have no power.

Crowley is run out of France for his evil ways. At one point he is labelled 'the most wicked man on Earth', having owned up to child sacrifice. Nevertheless, Crowley is privately admired by many for his ability to go to the max and posthumously becomes the 'patron saint' of rock stars. Thus canonised, his philosophies would be taken up and sung from a thousand stages in a hundred nations to billions of attentive and impressionable minds around the world in the decades that followed.

GETTING GOD OFF THE BACKS OF THE PEOPLE

"[Secrets.] I will not confide them to you. I can only tell you that all this is very much more serious than you think." – **Le Comte de Virieu**

That the moral and religious revolutions of the 19th and 20th centuries can be laid at the door of Darwin, Galton, Wundt, Nietzsche, Freud, Pavlov and James, is clear in the minds of Dr Parides and Bruce Wiseman. The latter author, former chairman of the Department of History at the John F Kennedy University and US national president of the Citizen's Commission on Human Rights (CCHR), a mental health watchdog, states in his *Psychiatry – The Ultimate Betrayal*:

"Yet while its progress has indeed remained minimal, psychiatry's materialist and anti-religious slant has survived and even prospered. In a 1976 survey of members of the American Psychological Association, 95% reportedly admitted to being atheists and agnostics.[351] So did a majority of psychiatrists in an American Psychiatric Association Task Force report.[352] Dr Al Parides, a former California state chairman for the American Psychiatric Association, confirmed this, saying psychiatrists are 'more likely to be atheists'."[353]

But as the power and influence of the medical and media establishments grew, so did their commensurate and unrepresentative influences on society. Wiseman puts this into perspective:

"Webster's defines an atheist as one who 'rejects all religious belief and denies the existence of God'. *Statistical Abstracts of the United States*

---

[351] **Larson, David B, et al.** "Systematic Analysis of Research on Religious Variables in Four Major Psychiatric Journals", *The American Journal of Psychiatry*, Vol.143, No.3 (March 1986), pp.329-334

[352] *American Journal of Psychiatry*, "Report of the Task Force on Religion and Psychiatry – Phase III", 135:6, June 1978, p.776

[353] Interview between Bruce Wiseman and Al Parides, 17th December 1993

shows that less than a half percent of the population of North America is atheist. Even if one includes persons 'professing no religion, non-believers, agnostics, free-thinkers, and de-religionised secularists indifferent to all religion', they still amount to only 7 percent of the population.

It is an odd situation. Obviously the beliefs of psychiatrists are utterly out of synchronisation with what the rest of the continent is thinking. Yet in their attempts to enlighten society, mental practitioners have gone to great lengths to convince the rest of us that we should come around to their way of viewing things." [354]

Wiseman's last point is an important one. A powerful clique, whose revolutionary sentiments represented those of only the smallest minority, were able to influence society, especially through the reporting of their agendas in sympathetic newspapers and, later, by soliciting the official stamp of approval from government and medicine.

Religion reviled

The French Revolution preceding the Napoleonic era saw the rapid transference of man's beliefs to atheism with predictable results. Historian J R Kantor writes:

"No factor in the evolution of scientific psychology stands out more prominently than the doctrines of French Materialism in the eighteenth century and German Materialism in the nineteenth century.... Materialism is essentially a non-scientific movement, a phenomenon of social transformation and change. In the religious domain, a materialist is simply an atheist." [355]

Evolution paved the way for a socially acceptable atheism. For centuries the Christian church had held sway over the morals of man, presiding over pastoral duties, counselling the sick and mentally disturbed, ideally determining, through the application of

---

[354] Wiseman, Bruce, *Psychiatry – The Ultimate Betrayal,* op. cit. p.13
[355] **Kantor, JR** *The Scientific Evolution of Psychology*, Principia Press, 1969, p.186

264

Biblical morality, what was right and wrong. The Church's many lapses into brutality, hypocrisy, simony, extortion and murder, however, along with the desire for control over the masses, had not gone unnoticed through the ages. The Catholic Church and its popes, who had intermittently for centuries carried out tortures, burnings, impalings and a wholesale slaughter of those opposed to Rome, were not the only ones to have taken the words of their prophets and usurped power to impose maniacal decrees through naked force. The Mohammedans, reformists, Protestants, Jews and a hundred diverse religions, sects and sub-sects had all vied for murderous control over their congregations down the centuries. It is an important point. Europe and the Middle East had seen Christians killing in the name of a disbelieving Jesus; Islam carrying the sword to the infidel in the name of Mohammed; Protestants killing Catholics in the name of Jesus; the Jews defending their very existence, holding before them the flickering torch of God's promise to Abraham.

By the time the era of science dawned with the Reformation, Caxton's presses were soon seeing Bibles circulating in languages other than Latin, that stranglehold of knowledge. The common citizen soon learned that the Church had no scriptural mandate for half the crimes it proclaimed as God's truth. Murder in the name of a Jesus who expressly forbade murder. The selling of salvation. The hoarding up of treasures on Earth instead of heaven. Purgatory. Simony. The most abominable acts committed by the highest echelons of an 'infallible' Church which maintained control simultaneously with assassins and the threat of hell. In 1533, England's King Henry VIII challenged the Vatican over the Holy See's refusal to grant Henry a divorce from his first wife, Katherine of Aragon. In the face of determined resistance, Henry declared his marriage to Katherine void, married Anne Boleyn, broke ties with Rome, dissolved and plundered her monasteries, and appointed himself head of a new 'Church of England'.

Henry VIII began as a highly intelligent ruler who degenerated into a brutal, flawed individual replete with hypocrisies. Aside from his famous six wives, Henry's disconcerting ability to manipulate his newly-formed Anglican Church to achieve his own earthy ends, together with his raising of the new term 'Majesty' for man, became the true paradox of his age. Yet Henry achieved something no other ruler had done before him. He had challenged the power of the Roman Church, which had held civilisation in its moral and political thrall for centuries, and Rome had lost.

The Illuminati

Another of the influential new thinkers in Europe was Adam Weishaupt, an avid follower of Voltaire and Rousseau's atheistic materialism. A brilliant professor of canon law at Ingolstadt University (Bavaria), Weishaupt had been educated by Catholic Jesuits whom he hated. Weishaupt's extreme and revolutionary sentiments entered their operational phase when, on 1st May 1776, he founded the Order of the Illuminati of Bavaria ('the Enlightened Ones'), a secret sect espousing world domination, the suppression of 'inferior' human stock, and violent anti-Christian sentiments. It is thought Weishaupt stole the name for his new cult from the Order of the Alombrados, a Spanish sect founded in 1520 and covertly supported by the Jesuit founder, Ignatius Loyola.

Weishaupt would have been dismissed as a crackpot if not for the fact that he was influenced by the leading masons of Europe – men like Massenhausen, Von Zwack, the Marquis of Constanza and Baron de Montgelas, who helped him launch his crusade. Weishaupt's political allegiances were republican and spiritually steeped in the Luciferianism of the Order of the Golden Cross and the Rosicrucians. Weishaupt realised that the quickest way to spread support of his doctrine was to infiltrate the European powerbrokers by all means possible. To Weishaupt, Masonry was where the true power and kudos resided. His order would soon have perished but for the assistance of one Baron Adolph Von Knigge, a Templar who championed Weishaupt's cause and was instrumental in persuading the Masonic orders to adopt the new fledgling organisation.

Only the cream of the crop in Weishaupt's day were initiated into the Illuminati, the latter having nine conspiratorial rings: Preparation, Novice, Minerval, Illuminus Minor, Freemason, Presbyter, Regent, Magus and Rex – the Rex, or king, being Weishaupt himself, who adopted the code-name 'Spartacus'. Those in the lower degrees were told then, as they are today, that the grand purpose of the order was: "...to make of the human race without any distinction of nation, condition or profession, one good and happy family."

G Edward Griffin writes:

"By the time the initiate had advanced to the level of 'Presbyter', or priest, his oath of absolute secrecy and obedience had become deadly serious. Only then was he allowed finally to see the ultimate goal of the order. It was the destruction of all religion, replaced by the worship of reason, or humanism, and the destruction of all independent governments, replaced by a New World Order, a world government ruled from behind the scenes by the Illuminated Ones. Needless to say, most members were never allowed to see these goals."[356]

'Spartacus' Weishaupt even poured contempt on the lower echelons of his own organisation, remarking:

"These good folks swell our numbers and fill our money-box. Set yourselves to work. These gentlemen must be made to nibble at the bait. But this sort of people must always be made to believe that the grade they have reached is the last." [357]

Weishaupt coerced key Christians into his sect by sugar-coating his manifestos with quasi-Biblical doctrines, ably put

---

[356] **Griffin, G Edward** *The Capitalist Conspiracy*, a video documentary, American Media, Westlake, CA, 1992. www.realityzone.com

[357] Ibid.

together by the tireless Von Knigge. After one leading Protestant figure joined his ecumenical efforts, Weishaupt was ecstatic:

"You can't imagine what respect and curiosity my priest-degree has raised; and, what is wonderful, a famous Protestant divine [priest], who is now of the Order, is persuaded that the religion contained in it is the true sense of Christianity. O Man, Man! To what mayest thou not be persuaded? Who would imagine that I was to be the founder of a new religion?" [358]

Weishaupt's control grew exponentially within Freemasonry. The man was a reckless braggart who incurred enemies as quickly as converts. His organisation gained control of lodges across Europe before being penetrated by agents of his enemies, the Jesuits and sectarian Rosicrucian orders. The Illuminati was briefly exposed in 1785 after one of its members, a priest named Jacob Lang, was struck dead by lightning while out walking with Weishaupt in Ratisbon. The priest's body was placed in the chapel of Saint-Emmeran where a Benedictine monk found a list of Illuminati members sewn into the clothes of the corpse. Raids carried out by the Elector of Bavaria on the home of prominent Illuminati attorney Von Zwack soon uncovered Weishaupt's conspiracy, after which the latter was banished to Saxe-Gotha where he lived under the patronage of the Duke Ernest-Louis until his death in 1812.

G Edward Griffin recounts that exposés of the Illuminati by its members have been few and the public record of Weishaupt's organisation quite thin. A few early Christian initiates who became horrified after discovering Weishaupt's hidden agenda – and indeed the ultimate object venerated within his organisation, Lucifer – spoke out and were murdered. At a secret Masonic conference held at Wilhelmsbad on 16th July 1782, terror was cast

---

[358] **Robison, John** *Proofs of a Conspiracy,* Boston: Western Islands, 1967 (orig. 1798), p.86

into some, such as the Comte de Virieu, who saw the true intent of the new organisation emerging. It is said that the assassination of King Gustav of Sweden was ordered at this Congress in full hearing of disbelieving members.[359] De Virieu, in a letter to a friend, wrote about 'tragic secrets' he had brought back with him from the conference:

"I will not confide them to you. I can only tell you that all this is very much more serious than you think. The conspiracy which is being woven is so well thought out that it will be, so to speak, impossible for the Monarchy or the Church to escape from it."

From this time onwards, says his biographer, M. Costa de Beauregard, "the Comte de Virieu could only speak of Freemasonry with horror."[360]

Weishaupt's plan for global domination was a bold stroke that appealed to those already prepared by the anti-Christian rhetoric of Voltaire and Rousseau. The Church and monarchies would be subverted and controlled, and all opposition to the plan swiftly silenced. So successful was the Illuminati penetration of established Freemasonry and the Church, that Thomas Frost, in his *Secret Societies of the European Revolution* (vol.1, p.53), has leading Mason Barruel reporting,

"...that the whole of the Masonic lodges comprised in the Grand Orient, 266 in number, were 'illuminated' by the end of March 1789..."

Weishaupt foresaw a world in which populations were controlled by an élite unrestrained by conventional values. The plan was to conquer nations economically and psychologically, leading their governments and 'cattle', as the population was termed, through different psychologically damaging steps which would eventually exhaust and break down resistance. Weishaupt's

---

[359] King Gustav III was murdered ten years later on 29th March 1792. He was shot by conspirators at a banquet in Sockholm and later died of his wounds.
[360] **Webster, Nesta H** *World Revolution*, Constable & Co., London, 1921

manifesto included the destruction of Christianity and Judaism, the abolition of private property, the abolition of inheritance, the dismantling of the family unit, the destruction of patriotism, the abolition of all national government – all in order

"…that the Luciferian ideal of totalitarianism may be imposed upon all Mankind." [361]

Communism

In 1848, wealthy Illuminati capitalist Friedrich Engels wrote a comprehensive distillation of Weishaupt's plan, which later became known as the Communist Manifesto. Karl Marx, often believed to have been the original architect, was a minor advisor whose name was only added to the document eighteen years after first publication. Marx himself rose in the constellation of the liberal atheist élite with the publication of *Das Kapital*. On the flyleaf of his manuscript, Marx attempted a dedication in the top right-hand corner which reads: 'To Charles Darwin, from a sincere admirer - Karl Marx.'

Marx saw in evolution the perfect psychological template for Communism. The man-centred, humanist philosophy preached power to the people and a clear downing of the Old Way of monarchy and religion. France had successfully shrugged off such yokes through bloody revolution. Little wonder that the doctrines of Weishaupt, Marx and Engels found immediate favour with those of a strong revolutionary bent in other nations. From 1850 onwards, a New Age or New World Order of 'freedom' was sold to the public; an order to liberate man from the shackles of royalty, poverty, moral control of the Church and its vengeful God. Nine years later, Darwin wrote his *Origins of the Species* to clamorous reviews, yet underneath the shiny exterior of this 'New Age' and man's novel ascent from the mud, a darker infamy lurked. All

---

[361] Griffin, G Edward, *The Capitalist Conspiracy*, op. cit.

aspects of the lives of citizens would be controlled for their own good down to the last detail. The wealth of nations would be aggregated into the hands of a few powerful banking dynasties, and the people's reliance on established religion and family ethics attacked and eliminated. The New World Order would be headed by a new world government, a *novus ordo seclorum*,[362] perpetually controlled behind the scenes by the all-seeing eye of Satan's 'Illuminated Ones'.

---

[362] This phrase is included on the 'Great Seal' which decorates the back of the US one dollar bill. The eye of Horus, or Satan, is depicted staring out of the top of the pyramid, replacing Christ as the capstone (Matt 21:42; Psa 118:22-23; Zech 4:7 and Rev 21:22-23). Around the edge of the seal are the words, 'Annuit Coeptis Novus Ordo Seclorum'. This variously translates as 'Announcing the Birth of the New Secular Order/New World Order/New Order of the Ages.'

VULTURES OVER EUROPE

"The world war [WW1] *was sacred to us and will remain sacred to us for all eternity. It was and is our just cause."* [363]

- **Dr Johannes Bresler, editor-in-chief of the** *Psychiatrisch-Neurologische Wochenzeitschrift*

In 1901, Britain's Queen Victoria died. For many, the passing of Britain's longest-living monarch symbolised the ending of an era. Millions had known no different, having lived and died during the period of her monumental reign. A significant passing was sensed by all – even an end to the moral austerity which had characterised the great queen's life, her magnificent funeral and the period of her empire's mourning.

When the grief passed, the British applied themselves to the new century with cautious optimism. Confronting them was an astonishing vision of constant invention, commercial travel, the first airplanes, communications, electric street lamps, magazines and the new philosophies discussed in them. Victoria's successor was her eldest son, the womaniser and profligate, King Edward VII. People relaxed and began to have fun. Britain's power was at its zenith. Merchants brought their goods to the West from the exotic lands of Kipling. The sun never set on the British empire. Excitement fired a million imaginations, the possibilities endless, and the soft but determined breeze of change caressed the cheeks of those whose faces turned expectantly towards a bright, new sophisticated age of materialism.

Promoting hate

But the new science of the mind and its evolutionist sub-philosophies were to have tragic repercussions for Europe in the

---

[363] **Bresler, Johannes** "Betrachtungen ber geistige Prophylaxe (Schlua)", *Münchner Medizinische Wochenschrift*, 1926, pp.285-288

first half of the 20th century. Psychiatry produced the flame of racism towards the end of the 1800's by pathologising into 'a disease' the hatred for others. Authors Röder, Kubillus and Burwell write:

"In 1850, psychiatrist C T Groddeck was awarded a doctorate for his dissertation entitled "The Democratic Disease – A New Form of Insanity". In Groddeck's view, every democratically inclined person was insane. In 1854 his colleague, C J Wretholm, 'discovered' the 'Sermon Disease'. Psychiatrist P J Möbius lectured shortly thereafter on the 'psychological feeble-mindedness of the woman'.

Not long thereafter, the leading proponents of psychiatry in Germany were advocating the theory that anyone who refused military service for religious reasons was abnormal and 'sick'. A psychiatrist named Adolf Hoppe characterised conscientious objection to military service as an 'unmistakable expression of ethnic inferiority'. One of psychiatry's leading figures, Richard von Krafft-Ebing, added to his list of varieties of mental disorders 'political and reformatory insanity' – meaning any inclination to form a different opinion from that of the masses. An excellent tool was thus created for politicians to denounce opponents. With the help of psychiatric classifications, it was now possible to perform the character assassination of a political enemy in the wink of an eye – anyone who disagreed was obviously insane." [364]

By 1871, the trend is in full-swing. Psychiatrist Carl Stark publishes a treatise entitled *The Psychical Degeneration of the French People*, in which he declares that the French have degenerated into mass-delusion, warmongering and delirium. Now, with being French a mental illness, others come forward. Löwenfeld discusses 'the national character of the French and its sickly excesses':

"The kind of mental abnormalities emerging nowadays belong to a borderline area which I label as psychopathy, psychopathic inferiorities, psychopathic conditions, and so on. I believe therefore that it is justified

---

[364] Röder, Thomas, Kubillus, Volker & Anthony Burwell, *Psychiatry – The Men Behind Hitler*, op. cit. p.23

273

now to talk about a 'psychopathia gallica', which should by now be obvious." [365]

Psychiatry was soon seen glorifying war and xenophobia while denouncing pacifism and the tolerance of minorities. By the first decade of the 1900's, the warmongering pronouncements of Nietzsche, Houston Stewart Chamberlain, Joseph-Arthur and Comte de Gobineau had taken firm root and primed Europe for war. The continent had become a patchwork of national treaties compelling countries to go to the aid of their treaty partners in the event that war was declared upon the partner. All that was needed was a spark.

Into the breach

On the 28th June 1914, Archduke Franz Ferdinand paid a visit to the troubled Austro-Hungarian province of Serbia and entered Sarajevo in a motorcade. As the car carrying the Archduke and his wife Sophie stopped to correct a wrong turn, Serbian nationalist Gavrilo Princip stepped out of the crowd outside Moritz Schiller's delicatessen and blasted two bullets into the vehicle, hitting the Archduke in the throat and Sophie in the abdomen.

The subsequent deaths of the Archduke and his wife set in motion the now famous catastrophic treaty landslide. On 27th July, Austria severed diplomatic ties with Serbia. The following day, spurred on by Austro-Hungarian public outrage over the shooting of Ferdinand by 'a degenerate', Austria declared war on Serbia. The Russians mobilised to the aid of their treaty partner, Serbia. Austria reacted by calling in its treaty partner, Germany. On 2nd August, Berlin demanded passage for its troops through Belgium. On 3rd August, Germany declared war on 'degenerate' France. On 4th August, Britain came to the aid of its treaty partner, France, and

---

[365] **Löwenfeld, L** *Über den Nationalcharakter der Franzosen und dessen krankhafte Auswüchse,* Wiesbaden, Germany: 1914

declared war on Germany. On 5ᵗʰ August, Austria declared war on Russia. World War 1 had begun.

The outbreak of hostilities unleashes Nietzsche's long-awaited Aryan war on a scale hitherto unseen. That this is a glorious thing is expounded upon in the unbelievable psychiatric literature of the day. Yet not even the Dantéan phenomenon of millions dead and 20 million wounded would shame psychiatry into repenting of its own role in the tragedy. By way of illustrating psychiatry's racist ethos surviving World War 1 and the implications thereof for psychiatry's involvement in a future conflict, witness Dr Johannes Bresler, editor-in-chief of the *Psychiatrisch-Neurologische Wochenzeitschrift* (Psychiatric Neurological Weekly), remarking in 1926:

"The world war [WW1] was sacred to us and will remain sacred to us for all eternity. It was and is our just cause." [366]

'War neuroses'

One of the major engagements fought in the 'Great War' was at Verdun. This battle between France and Germany began with an artillery bombardment unprecedented in ferocity. The French drew up over four miles of hub-to-hub artillery and on the opposing front, the Germans had a similar strike force waiting. It took France eight days of total national production and all their transportation facilities to haul the newly produced ammunition to the front in preparation for the opening barrage. The Germans began the attack on 21ˢᵗ February 1916.[367]

Both sides fired millions of artillery rounds before the infantry advances. Over half a million men were lost during the ten months which followed. First the Germans advanced and then the French,

---

[366] **Bresler, Johannes** "Betrachtungen ber geistige Prophylaxe (Schlua)", *Münchner Medizinische Wochenschrift*, 1926, pp.285-288

[367] **Hermann, William & Paul Bacon** *The Holocaust: From a Survivor of Verdun*, Harper & Row, New York: 1972

driving back the Germans with the help of the British, who opened up a major action on the Somme. During this four-month battle alone, the repeated engagements with artillery and machine guns claimed the lives of 600,000 Allied troops, two-thirds of them British. German losses were estimated at 450,000. All day long, soldiers were ordered out of their trenches into the line of sight of enemy machine guns and slaughtered. Many soldiers had their hearing destroyed by the artillery barrages preceding the attacks and were incapable of hearing orders above the din.

Significantly, psychiatry introduced the new concept of 'war neurotics' as unprecedented numbers of soldiers experienced fits of quivering, crying, hysteria and vomiting. Widespread desertions from frontline units alarmed the German authorities, ever promoting the 'glorious war' ethic and the struggle for 'Teutonic supremacy'. The un-German problem of the 'war neurotic' was quickly passed to the psychiatrists.

The aim was to render these soldiers fit for active duty again as quickly as possible, no matter the methods. Drastic remedies, such as electroshock therapy, sometimes galvanised 'slackers' back to the front even before treatment, due to its appalling effects and rapidly spreading, sinister reputation. Hamburg-based psychiatrist Dr Max Nonne recalls that:

"The war brought us in Eppendorf a tremendous workload. We soon got to see sad pictures of men who were amputated, half-paralysed through head wounds, paralysed down to the legs, the bladder and the rectum because of bullets in the spine, of epileptics who had seizures because of head wounds. But after a few months, we saw a sight we had rarely seen before – the sight of *hysteria virilis,* the 'manly hysteria', which had once been described to us by Charcot in Paris. We had said then: 'This only happens to the French. In Germany, hysteria of the men does not exist.' But now we saw it often and in all forms: as paralysis of the vocal cords, as dumbness, as paralysis of the upper and lower extremities, as trembling in all parts of the body, as spasms of single muscles and

276

muscle groups, as deafness, as inabilities to see and walk, and as dislocations in the most confounded forms." [368]

Less than manly

Röder et al agree that these trench problems were extremely embarrassing for the German authorities, who were eager to promote the manly virtues of war:

"Sometimes in place of war neurosis, German psychiatrists used terms like 'traumatic neurosis', 'fright neurosis', 'grenade shock' or 'war hysteria'. In other countries, such as Britain, this hysteria was described as 'shell shock', 'concussion neurosis', 'gas neurosis' or 'battle fatigue'. However in 1915, the German army medical services forbade the use of the word 'hysteria' in military psychiatric diagnosis because it was contrary to the noble concept of honour befitting a warrior. In the eyes of the army, the diagnosis of a hysterical reaction was dishonourable and, therefore, banned. No doubt the German army was offended in part by the suggestion that its soldiers might be less than 'manly'. After all, 'hysteria' comes from the Greek 'hyster', meaning 'uterus', and connotes a woman's suffering, not the illness of a soldier." [369]

Denying that soldiers were in any way 'sick' and therefore exempt from combat, German authorities used psychiatry as justification for denying the symptoms cropping up in medical offices such as Dr Nonne's. Frontline commanders were expressly forbidden from sending the 'tremblers' and 'hystericals' away from the fighting. 'Kaufmann Therapy' and firing squads awaited those who shirked battle and feigned symptoms. War neurosis was a 'constitutional, psychopathic inferiority', and those suffering from it were plainly too weak to endure the beauty of the war.[370]

---

[368] **Nonne, Max** *Anfang und Ziel meines Lebens*, Hamburg: 1971, pp.177-178

[369] Röder, Thomas, Kubillus, Volker & Anthony Burwell, *Psychiatry – The Men Behind Hitler*, op. cit. p.25

[370] **Wohlmuth, Georg**: *Feinstrom, Gavanisatoren,* catalogue 1929, p.8 (StaHH 352-3, 10 1-60)

Those undergoing Kaufmann Therapy were prepared with pre-shock suggestions. Then a strong alternating current was passed through the patient's head while the therapist repeated strong military commands in the form of 'psychic driving'. The patient was under strict enforcement that he must be healed in one session.[371] At the annual conference of the Gesellschaft Deutscher Nervenärzte in Bonn on 29th September 1917, Dr M Raether, head doctor of the Provinzial Heil und Pflegeinstitut, included a demonstration of 'Kaufmann Cure' in his lecture.[372]

Even in the eyes of the most forward-thinking psychiatrists of the day, the concept of treating shell-shock with electric shock was uncomfortably close to plain, old-fashioned torture. Though no science was presented to support the supposed efficacy of his treatments, Kaufmann and his followers were allowed to continue. 'Malingerers' were disciplined with high voltage and hauled back to the front, thereby cementing up embarrassing breaches in the honour and nobility of German military service.

An electric shock-box was also available near the front for use by psychiatrists to kill their own soldiers. Dr Emil Gelny, later a Nazi Party member from 1933, founded psychiatric electro-execution:

"Once a patient went unconscious from the effects of the electricity, the caretakers then had to attach four other electrodes to the hands and feet of the patient. Dr Gelny ran high voltage through them and after ten minutes at the most, the death of the patient would set in." [373]

In spite of psychiatric measures like Kaufmann's being couched in pseudo-scientific terminology and passed off as 'cutting-edge medicine', there were those in the scientific community who saw their psychiatric colleagues "…sinking back

[371] **Kaufmann, Fritz** *Münchener Medizinische Wochenschrift,* 1916
[372] **Riedesser, Peter & Axel Verderber** *Aufrüstung der Seelen. Militärpsychologie und Militäpsychiatrie in Deutschland und Amerika,* Freiburg: 1985, pp.15-17
[373] Röder et al, *Psychiatry – The Men Behind Hitler,* op. cit. pp.207-208: f/note 12

into the barbarism of the Middle Ages." Röder et al report that psychiatry had an ingenious answer to its attackers at the time:

"It took considerable courage to denounce the psychiatric movement of the era because critics were liable to be labelled with an unfavourable diagnosis by the very subjects of their criticism. This was no idle fear. In 1927, a professor of psychiatry from Hamburg named Ernst Ritterhaus actually came up with the diagnosis of 'mass psychosis of hostility toward psychiatry' for all critics of the psychiatric movement. In other words, 'if you disagree with us or challenge our methods, you are insane.'

The same diagnosis was applied to a large number of journalists, doctors, officers, legislators, manufacturers and law professors as well as the victims of psychiatry who had dared to challenge the utility and ethics of inhuman therapies. By then, it was almost impossible to argue logically against psychiatry – psychiatry was too irrational to allow for it." [374]

By 1899, leading psychiatrist P J Möbius was elevating psychiatry to the post of 'Judge of all Human Things' – a position still occupied in the minds of many by God himself:

"The psychiatrist should be the judge about mental health, because only he knows what 'ill' means. If one views psychiatry in this way, then it turns from a servant into a ruler, and becomes what by nature it should be. The psychiatrist then becomes the judge of all human things, a teacher of the lawyer and theologian, a leader of the historian and the writer."

By the turn of the 20th century, German psychiatry saw itself poised to influence the legislature, the media, religion and even history itself in its design for control of the new society. The tools to enforce such control were by this time nearing completion:

"The formula was as simple as it was chilling in its implications. Beneath a shroud of a few impressive-sounding, Greek- and Latin-based words, and cloaked with the presumed authority of a medical science, to

---

[374] Ibid. p.28

shut up your critic, simply pronounce him or her insane and do so from the point of view of the omniscient expert." [375]

The cauldron rising – between the wars

As the seeds of Weishaupt's and Engels' great plan were watered into growth by Marx, Trotsky and Lenin, their roots spread out across Tsarist Russia. Elsewhere, other peoples, dissatisfied with the old imperialism, examined ways in which atheistic Communism could be applied to their own nations.

That 'Spartacus' Weishaupt's original thesis still formed the underpinning of Communism well into the 20th century is clearly seen with the formation of German Communist revolutionaries in the chaotic aftermath of World War 1. Known as 'Spartacists', their leaders included Rosa Luxemburg and Karl Liebknecht, who were later hunted down by German Chancellor Friedrich Ebert and shot. In Hungary, Communist revolution broke out under Béla Kun in March of 1919, resulting in the establishment of a Communist satellite state. Kun himself later resigned and moved to Moscow, where he ironically became one of the hundreds of thousands of loyal Communists shot during Stalin's purges.

'Life unworthy of living'

For many, the horrors of the Great War had put paid to any notion of a loving God. Comrades crushed under the tracks of tanks. Brothers buried in the filth of artillery craters. Nietzsche was right. Life was madness and suffering, and the world was pointless. European psychiatry, however, survived World War 1 in rather better shape. With their fig leaf of indefatigable science, the mental sciences offered their own explanations for why man did the things he did. Studies in genetics, ongoing since the turn of the century, were redefining in the public mind the haphazard nature of man. Eugenics stated that any perceived physical or mental

---

[375] Ibid. p.29

abnormality in the population was evidence of a genetic trait that must be eradicated to prevent proliferation. Into this context came the first mention of the concept of 'life unworthy of living'.

Today, many attempt to process the horrors of the Second World War without understanding the framework behind *why* the atrocities happened. Many times we read of the incongruity of the Nazi officer – a cultured and educated man, lover of Wagner and the arts, at the same time capable of committing acts of genocide with an everyday banality of spirit. Yet it is precisely the explanation behind this paradox, so studiously avoided in Spielberg's *Schindler's List*, that gives the real reason why so many in Europe went along with the policies of the SS and their enforcers, Reinhard Heydrich and Adolf Eichmann.

The German people have been sold on evolution, on the superiority of the Aryan race, and the need to sterilise or kill those whose lives are deemed 'of no value'. They have bought the utter conviction of a New Order which will haul Germany from the ashes of her First World War humiliation. Though Hitler's *My New Order* espouses these very concepts, the underlying groundwork providing the cultural acceptability of these fatal philosophies had been laid down by the eugenicists, psychiatrists and Darwinists of the previous fifty years. Bruce Wiseman writes:

"Alfred Hoche, a professor of psychiatry, and Karl Binding, a German jurist and retired professor of Wundt's *alma mater*, the University of Leipzig, published 'The Release of the Destruction of Life Devoid of Value' in Leipzig in 1920. It went a step further than the recommendation of mere sterilisation. It advocated the outright killing of mental defectives, 'euthanasia' as it was called: 'For the idiots… the continuation of life for society as well as for the person himself has no value.'

By 1922, at a psychiatric congress in Dresden, Germany, a proposal was put forward requesting legalization of euthanasia. The psychiatric social experiment called Eugenics had embarked on a road from which there was no turning back." [376]

Throughout the 1920's and '30's, the language grew increasingly sinister as German proponents of racial hygiene and eugenics faced scant opposition. Germany was in turmoil following the humiliation of Versailles after World War 1. Upon signing the Treaty on 28th June 1919, English premier David Lloyd George was asked what had been accomplished. He replied, "Gentlemen, I have just signed the document which guarantees war in 20 years." These words were repeated in Lloyd George's memoirs, published after his administration in 1923.

Lloyd George's extraordinary admission can be understood when one appreciates that Versailles left Germany with nothing, not even the wherewithal to rebuild its economy and physical infrastructure from within. Fifteen years later, Japan would encounter the same problem. Faced with such a future, a nation must go to war to free itself, and this is the platform Hitler used in the late 1920's to increase his appeal after the financial collapse of the Weimar Republic. Germany's hardships provided the ideal fodder for the supremacist philosophies of Darwin, Malthus, Weishaupt, Wundt, Galton and Kraepelin. Someone was to blame for the Fatherland's woes. And Germany wanted to feel clean, redeemed and efficient. In charge again.

Ernst Rüdin

By 1930, rising psychiatric luminary Ernst Rüdin was articulating on the urgent need for Germany to:

"...do something about the positive and negative eugenics before it is too late. For the negative, the sterilisation of the genetically sick has to be closely looked at.... It would be a blessing to know that genetically incompetent, unhappy people would not be produced anymore. Much

---

[376] Wiseman, Bruce, *Psychiatry – The Ultimate Betrayal,* op. cit. p.63

more national expansion would be created through positive eugenics than we can imagine.

The fertility rate of the genetic undesirables is so great today that we have every reason in the interest of humanity to address ourselves to the prevention of the genetically weak. The increase of the hereditarily healthy that is so necessary to us as a nation today will cause less of a headache in the future." [377]

The significance of the above statements, from the man who would become the key player in implementing the Nazis' racial hygiene policies, is stark when one considers that these ideas were fully formed by psychiatry *a full three years* before Hitler even came to power. Thus the Nazis were not the creators of the eugenics program which underpinned the Holocaust but German psychiatry. And it would be psychiatrists also who, in the dark and hopeless years to follow, would draw up and implement the murderous policies to rid the Reich of its 'mental defectives', political opponents, habitual criminals, the 'genetically weak' and those deemed 'unworthy of living'. In 1933, when Hitler gained power, a legal brief describing a new law gives a chilling insight into the appalling turn Germany was about to take:

"With the passing of the Law for the Prevention of Genetically Diseased Children, the German Nazi government took an important step for the future of our nation. Because of their nature, our previous government could not come to a decision, since German parliamentarianism has generally shown itself to be incapable of innovative steps for the salvation of our nation... Only the Nazi world view has reoriented us to the future, we have again remembered the learning of our lives, the purpose of the state, the fight for survival and life of our families, the species and the race! Hitler writes in his book 'Mein Kampf': 'Who is not healthy bodily or mentally is not allowed to perpetuate his malady in the body of his child....' Therefore, this Act is a

---

[377] **Von Gruber, Max** *Docent Ernst Rüdin*, Fortpflanzung, Verebung Rassenhygiene, Munich: 1931, p.279f.

complete break from the small-mindedness of an outdated philosophy of life and the overblown and suicidal charity of past ages." [378]

[378] **Gött, Arthur, Ernst Rüdin, Falk Ruttke** explaining *Gesetz zur Verhülung erbkranken Nachwuchses vom 14. Juli 1933*, Munich: 1934, p.5

DELIVER THOSE YOU CANNOT HEAL!
Germany descends into the abyss

"I am sure it would be sensible to restrict as much as possible the work of these gentlemen [psychiatrists], *who are capable of doing an immense amount of harm with what may very easily degenerate into charlatanry."* **– Winston Churchill, December 1942**

"Since sterilisation is the only sure thing to prevent further transmission of mental illness and serious hereditary afflictions, it must therefore be viewed as an act of charity and precaution for the upcoming generation." **– Prof. Ernst Rüdin, Director of the Kaiser Wilhelm Institute for Psychiatry, Munich, Germany, 1936**

"We should make a law which helps nature have its way. Nature would let a creature which is not equipped starve to death. It would be more humane for us to give it a painless, mercy killing. This is the only option which is proper in such cases and it is a hundred times more noble, decent and humane than the cowardice that hides behind the idiocy of humanitarianism and which burdens both the creature with its own existence, and the family and the society with the burden of supporting it." **– Das Schwarze Korps (The Black Corps), 18th March 1937**

No bleaker insight into the marriage of evolution and Nazism can be seen than the above Black Corps declaration, which illustrates why Hitler's National Socialists wish to 'cleanse' Germany of its undesirables. Psychiatry is deemed the 'science' which has the expertise and will to determine who is desirable for the Fatherland and who should be removed from it. Psychiatry plays the defining role in selecting undesirables for processing under laws soon to be drafted. Clearly the measures that follow – measures forever seared into the post-war psyche of a horrified world citizenry – can never, by any stretch of the imagination, be categorised as 'a hundred times more noble, decent and humane'.

The path to the gas chambers began with the evolutionary attitudes and bogus science promulgated decades before in the mad dash for acceptance, and gradualism took care of the rest. Germany's perceptions of man's place in the cosmos were not unique in their transition. Elsewhere in the world, a wholesale shift in attitudes was underway to where 'might was right' whatever the circumstances. Stalin was flexing his might in Russia. The Communist Mao Zedong was rising in China. Survival in a brave new world demanded new attitudes where the unthinkable eventually became thinkable. Soon you did not love your enemy, nor did you treat with him. You took a spade and buried him in the forest. And the second one next to him. And the third after that.

Not just Nazi Germany

In Germany's case, the road to hell was paved with bad intentions. Insanity was initially frowned upon and locked away from the public to be monitored by those in charge. Later, 'mental disorders', and those exhibiting the growing list of them, became Kraepelin's 'heavy burden for our nation'. The evolutionary beliefs of Darwin, Lyell and Galton formed the bedrock for the desire to 'perfect evolution' by breeding out 'undesirable traits' and 'feeble-mindedness' in different races. Such beliefs were not restricted to those of the German psychiatric community but held by many 'forward-thinkers' elsewhere. By 1914, mental illness was professionally regarded as 'hereditary' in the United States. The American Medico-Psychological Association (forerunner to the modern-day American Psychiatric Association) stated that:

"… a radical cure of the evils incident to the dependent mentally defective classes would be effected if every feeble-minded person, every imbecile, every habitual criminal, every manifestly weak-minded person, and every confirmed inebriate were sterilised." [379]

Lewis M Terman, professor of psychology at Stanford University, USA, believed in 1916 that:

"...if we would preserve our state for a class of people worthy to possess it, we must prevent, as far as possible, the propagation of mental degenerates." [380]

Houston Stewart Chamberlain was born in Britain in 1855 and married the daughter of composer Robert Wagner, becoming a German citizen in 1916. Chamberlain's works lionised Aryan philosophy, denigrated Jewish influence as negative and inferior, and promoted German supremacy. Chamberlain remarked that

"...moderate talent... is frequently the character of bastards; one can easily observe this daily in cities where, as in Vienna, the various peoples meet each other; at the same time one can also notice a particular laxity, a lack of character, in short, the moral degeneration of such people." [381]

A young Adolf Hitler echoed these sentiments in 1925:

"...those who are physically and mentally unhealthy must not perpetuate their suffering in the body of their children." [382]

By 1933, after the Nazis gained power, Hitler busied himself with the implementation of The Nazi Act for Averting Descendants Afflicted with Hereditary Diseases. Within six years, 375,000 forced sterilisations were carried out. Even the physically 'unfit' were not exempt.

---

[379] **Castel, Robert, Castel, Francoise & Anne Lovell** *The Psychiatric Society*, (Translated by Arthur Goldhammer), Columbia University Press, New York: 1982, pp.46-47. Source for quote is **MacDonald, Carlos F** "Presidential Address", *American Journal of Insanity*, July 1914, 71:9

[380] Lapon, Lenny, *Mass Murderers in White Coats*, op. cit. p.78

[381] Röder et al., *Psychiatry – The Men Behind Hitler*, op. cit. p.19

[382] **Hitler, Adolf** *Mein Kampf*, translated by Ralph Manheim, Houghton Mifflin & Co., Boston, USA: 1971, p.255

Psychiatrist Ernst Rüdin was the catalyst and organiser of the operational phase of Nazi eugenics. With the credibility of his professorship at Munich University to drape his acts with the requisite legitimacy, Rüdin was fêted for his fidelity and unswerving loyalty to the Reich. Upon his sixty-fifth birthday, the Munich psychiatrist was honoured for having:

"…just recently received the Goethe Medal for the Art and Science from the Führer 'in recognition of his achievements in the development of German Racial Hygiene'."

Fellow racial hygiene advocate Dr Alfred Ploetz continued at the festivities to announce that:

"…the Reichminister of the Interior, Dr Frick, sent him [Rüdin] the following telegram: 'To the indefatigable champion of racial hygiene and meritorious pioneer of the racial hygiene measures of the Third Reich, I send my sincerest congratulations on his 65th birthday'." [383]

Professor of Evolutionary Biology, M Rose of the University of California, Irvine, comes clean:

"The case for Darwinism cannot be based on any edification that is supposed to come from its truths. Through eugenics, Darwinism was a bad influence on Nazism, one of the greatest killers in world history. Darwinism probably contributed to the upsurge of racism in the latter part of the nineteenth century, and thus it helped foment twentieth-century racism generally. Darwinism was also used to exacerbate the neglect of the poor in the nineteenth century. All things considered, Darwinism has had many regrettable, and sometimes actually vicious, effects on the social climate of the modern world. Modern Darwinism does not offer any guarantee of unending progress. It is understandable that so many hate Darwin and Darwinism. It is often a bitter burden to live with Darwinism and its implications. Unlike so many doctrines,

---

[383] Quoted in Schreiber, B, *Geheime Reichssache: Die Manner Hinter Hitler: Eine Deutsche Warnung an Die Welt*, op. cit. p.18

288

religions, and ideologies, it certainly isn't intellectual opium. No one can make a case for Darwinism based on moral hygiene."[384]

Euthanasia

The concept of sterilisation was soon to have another sinister bedfellow – euthanasia. The murder of those whose lives were deemed 'devoid of human value' commenced with a landmark episode in 1938. Dr Werner Catel, Professor of Neurology and Psychiatry at Leipzig University, advised the father of a deformed child that he should write to the Führer requesting permission to end the child's life. In response, Hitler sent his personal physician, Professor Karl Brandt, to discuss the matter with Catel. The significance of a father requesting a mercy death for his own son fascinated the German public. The child was subsequently killed.

Such an event was to have major repercussions in the realm of public psychodrama:

"A group of physicians was called to the Reich Chancellory to form a Euthanasia Committee. Dr Herbert Linden, psychiatrist and ministerial advisor for health in the Reich Ministry, was appointed its director. Of the four other doctors on the committee, two were psychiatrists, including the influential Dr Werner Catel. Shortly, another seven psychiatrists were added.

In 1939, the following document was signed and released by Hitler: 'Reichleader [Philipp] Bouhler and Karl Brandt MD are charged with the responsibility of enlarging the authority of certain physicians to be designated by name in such a manner that persons who, according to human judgment, can upon most careful diagnosis of their condition of sickness, be accorded a mercy death.'" [385]

---

[384] **Rose MR** *Darwin's Spectre: Evolutionary Biology in the Modern World*, Princeton University Press, Princeton NJ, 2000, p.210

[385] Wiseman, Bruce, *Psychiatry – The Ultimate Betrayal*, op. cit. p.64; also Schreiber, B, *Geheime Reichssache: Die Manner Hinter Hitler: Eine Deutsche Warnung an Die Welt*, op. cit. p.41

Journalist Joseph Harsch makes an important point concerning the above ruling by Hitler:

"Those who proposed [the plan for euthanasia] are understood to have asked Hitler for a written edict or law which would officially authorise them to proceed with the 'mercy killings'. Hitler is represented as having hesitated for several weeks. Finally, doubting that Hitler would ever sign the official order, the proponents of the project drafted a letter for him to sign which merely expressed his, Hitler's general approval of the theory of euthanasia as a means of relieving incompetents of the burden of life. While this letter did not have the character of the law, it was adequate in Nazi Germany. The Führer had expressed approval of the practice. It went ahead." [386]

Europe explodes

Meanwhile, throughout the first seven months of 1939, German industry churned out weaponry, tanks, aircraft, submarines and warships. In spite of Hitler's assurances to Neville Chamberlain that England and Germany were not in danger of war, events inexorably built during the spring and summer. In the second week of August, Hitler ordered German troops to mass along the border with Poland. Late on the night of 31st August 1939, Hitler's government informed the world that Polish troops had stormed a German radio station in Upper Silesia. After murdering the technicians there, they apparently broadcast an appeal to the Polish people inciting them to war with Germany. Historian Martin Gilbert writes of the tragic farce that followed:

"No such Polish provocation had taken place. The Polish troops were Germans dressed up as Poles. The dead German – for there was indeed one – was a common criminal taken from a concentration camp and killed by his fellow Germans to give credence to the tale of a Polish attack. The incident was a crude fabrication, but in the early hours of 1st September, citing this bogus incident as the reason, Hitler ordered

---

[386] Harsch, Joseph, *Pattern for Conquest*, quoted from Schreiber, B, op. cit. p.45

German troops to cross into Poland.... On 3rd September 1939, Britain and France declared war on Germany." [387]

Cleaning up the human detritus

By 1939, a telling documentary was circulating Germany entitled *Existence Without Life* ('Dasein ohne Leben'). Featured in the 1991 documentary 'Selling Murder', the German piece was designed to influence public opinion on the controversial subject. All the latest film techniques were used, says Wiseman, to give the project every chance of success:

"The main character was a professor... used 'to add spurious scientific respectability' to the film. The documentary explains, 'The [film's] script demands that demonically mad faces arise like a spectre out of the scene.... Unedited film shows the techniques used such as sharp, underneath lighting to make the patients appear grotesque.... His [the professor's] lecture, scripted by psychiatrists.... first claims that care for the sick has become indiscriminate and too costly.'

The professor closes the movie with a dramatic appeal to all: 'We call upon a merciful destiny to liberate these regrettable creatures from their existence without life.... Allow me to close with a few purely human and personal remarks and so extend the framework of this lecture. If I knew that I – and this could happen to anyone – would be struck down by the disaster of some incurable mental illness and that such an existence without life would lie before me, I would do anything for this not to happen. I would rather die. I am convinced all healthy people think like this. But I am also convinced that every incurable mental patient or idiot, if he could recognise his position, would prefer an end to such existence. No sensible human being could deny him the right to die. Is it not the duty of those [psychiatrists] who care for the incapable - and that means total idiots and the incurable mental patients – to help them exercise their rights? Is that not a sacred demand of charity? Deliver those you cannot heal!'" [388]

---

[387] **Gilbert, Martin** *History of the Twentieth Century,* HarperCollins, 2001, p.263
[388] Wiseman, Bruce, *Psychiatry – The Ultimate Betrayal,* op. cit. p.65; **Burleigh, Michael** *Selling Murder*, directed by Joanna Mack, Domino Film Productions, 1991

T4 and the 'mercy killings'

The deliverings are carried out under the organisation of the infamous T4 centre, so named for its Berlin address at Tiergartenstrasse 4.[389] According to Nuremburg Trial transcripts, some 275,000 mental patients are murdered between 1939 and the cessation of hostilities in 1945 under Operation *Gnadentod* (Operation *Mercy Killing*). Even before the killing centres have been set up and tested, psychiatrists are rounding up patients from institutions in Meseritz, Pomerania (Poland) and shipping them into the forests. Here they are executed by SS firing squads and buried. Later in the war, these bodies, some 3,500 of them, are hastily exhumed and burned by the SS to prevent their discovery by the approaching Russian Army.

Two of the first killing facilities are set up at Castle Grafeneck and Brandenburg by T4 under control of 'politically reliable' psychiatrists, doctors, nurses and orderlies who oversee the murders. Psychiatrist Werner Heyde moves from Würzburg to Berlin to head up T4. Heyde's job is to oversee the Reich's euthanasia program and supervise its consulting staff of approximately 30 physicians, most of whom are psychiatrists. The T4 psychiatric team will 'evaluate' patients and decide their fate.

"The systematic 'treatment' of Jews under T4 began in April 1940, with a proclamation from the Reich Interior Ministry that within three weeks all Jewish [mental] patients were to be registered. In June, the first gassing of Jews took place: 200 men, women and children were killed in the Brandenburg facility; they had been transported to the killing centre in six buses from the Berlin-Buch mental institution." [390]

The original method of murder was carbon monoxide gas, chosen for its obvious lethality and lack of smell. Specially

---

[389] T4 was originally known as 'The Working Association of Sanitaria and Caretaking Facilities of the Republic'.

[390] "Medical killings led Nazis to mass murder", *Los Angeles Daily News*, 28th September 1986

constructed 'shower rooms' lured the unwary victims inside. The gas was then pumped in until all visible movement ceased. After the gas was extracted, the bodies were removed to the nearby crematoria for incineration. Later, the appalling plumes of smoke cause many local inhabitants to complain to the authorities. In time, as the nefarious purpose of these facilities became known, public complaints about the centres themselves became a cause for the arrest and deportation of 'troublemakers'.

Author and psychiatrist Dr Frederic Wertham describes a student tour of one of the facilities involved in Operation *Mercy Killing*:

"In the fall of 1939, a group of psychology students were given a tour of the state psychiatric institution Eglfing Haar in Nazi Germany. Dr Hermann Pfannmüller, a psychiatrist and director of the institution, explained the 'euthanasia' or 'mercy killing' program that was being used on the inmates. In the children's ward, twenty-five children were being starved to death. They ranged in age from one to five years. Pfannmüller lifted up one emaciated child who was near death and told the students that food is withdrawn gradually, not all at once. 'With this child,' he said, 'it will take another two or three days.'" [391]

Ludwig Lehner, one of the students attending that visit to Dr Pfannmüller's institution, commented in a sworn statement at Nuremburg:

"I shall never forget the look of that fat, grinning fellow with the whimpering little skeleton in his fleshy hand, surrounded by the other starving children." [392]

At first, only the 'mental defectives' were killed. As these 'deliverings' proceeded, however, the criteria for selection were steadily widened. Psychiatrist Dr Wertham writes:

[391] **Wertham, Frederic** *A Sign For Cain: An Exploration of Human Violence*, Robert Hale Ltd, London: 1966, p.180

[392] **Mielke, F** *The Death Doctors*, Elek Books, London: 1962, p.248

"It has been stated that psychiatrists were merely following a law or were being forced to obey an order. Again and again we read – as if it were historical fact – of Hitler's secret order to exterminate those suffering from severe mental defect or disease.... There was no law and no such order. The tragedy is that the psychiatrists did not have to have an order. They acted on their own. They were not carrying out a death sentence pronounced by someone else, they were the legislators who laid down the rules for deciding who was to die; they were the administrators who worked out the procedures, provided the patients and the places, and decided the methods of killing; they pronounced a sentence of life or death in every individual case; they were the executioners who carried the sentences out, or – without being coerced to do so – surrendered their patients to be killed in other institutions; they supervised and often watched the slow deaths." [393]

By the middle of 1941, the killing of the mentally ill was well underway throughout the Reich. T4 expanded the definition of victims and a full training program was launched to coach officials in the skills of mass extermination. Dr Wertham, an accomplished authority on the mental health system of Nazi Germany, writes:

"The 'material' for all this training was mental hospital patients. On them the methods were tried out and tested before they were later applied to Jewish and other civilian populations of the occupied countries. Technical experience first gained with killing psychiatric patients was utilised later for the destruction of millions.

Towards the end of 1941, the gas chambers in the death institutions were dismantled, transported to the east, and then freshly erected for their new tasks in concentration camps.... Some were the same psychiatrists who selected patients in hospitals, went to concentration camps and selected death candidates there. Heinrich Himmler had the idea of having the inmates of these camps examined to 'comb out' those to be eliminated. He needed suitable physicians, so the central bureau of the 'euthanasia' program [T4] supplied him with 'experienced psychiatrists'.... In 1941, a commission of five went to the concentration

---

[393] Wertham, Frederic, *A Sign For Cain: An Exploration of Human Violence*, op. cit. pp.164-165

camp at Dachau to select prisoners to be transferred to Mauthausen to be killed. All five men were psychiatrists, and their chief was a professor of psychiatry at the University of Berlin." [394]

Branching out the program

The success of the euthanasia program spurred more imaginative ways to dispose of the mentally ill. New facilities were opened in occupied Poland, equipped with 'shower rooms' and machine guns. Specialised gassing trucks were painted to look like 'Kaiser's Coffee' delivery vehicles. Carbon monoxide gas was fed from steel canisters into the interior while the vehicles drove to the disposal sites to deliver the bodies for cremation.

There was money in the killing. Questionnaires were submitted to T4 from the mental institutions for each patient to be evaluated. Psychiatric consultants, under the guidance of T4 chief Heyde, reviewed the questionnaires and, on the basis of the information learned, placed a red mark on the form for those to be killed and blue for those spared. By October 1940, a psychiatrist working as a euthanasia consultant was receiving 100 marks per patient evaluation up to a total of 500 questionnaires. Bonuses were also being earned: 200 marks per evaluation up to 2,000 questionnaires, 300 marks up to 3,000 and 400 marks for all questionnaires above that.

Records show, for instance, that the above-mentioned Dr Hermann Pfannmüller completed 2,000 registration forms in only three weeks, while another, Dr Schreck, 'very conscientiously' completed 15,000 in nine months, according to his own testimony. One witness, states researcher Ernst Klee:

"even worked while drinking wine in a public restaurant." [395]

---

[394] Ibid. pp.181-182

[395] **Klee, Ernst** *'Euthanasie' im NS-Staat*, Frankurt am Main, 1989, testimony of an eyewitness (Mauthe) on 18th October 1948, pp.120-121

And then a strange thing happened. On 24th August 1941, Hitler called a halt to the T4 killings. Some say the Führer had become politically uncomfortable as the public learned the truth. A psychiatrist named Menneckes, involved in the killings in the Rhenish Eichberg Institute, later declared in an open session of the Eichberg proceedings on 3rd December 1946:

"One day when Hitler was travelling on his special train from Munich to Berlin, it had to make a stop at a station at Hog. To find out why, he went to the window and was spotted by a crowd standing outside that had been witnessing the shipment of mentally ill patients. When the crowd saw Hitler at the window, they became irate, as they knew what would happen with the patients. This demonstration of dissatisfaction against Hitler prompted him to call off what had been going on until then." [396]

Other surviving documentation demonstrates that Hitler's policy of distancing himself from the carnage was being recognised at staff level. One physician, giving testimony after the war, states:

"The discontinuation of the extermination program was skilfully exploited, according to a physician of the Weissengau Institute, by spreading a whisper campaign that it had happened because of Adolf Hitler, who prior to that had not been aware of the killing." [397]

But researchers Röder, Kubillus and Burwell surmise another, more prosaic explanation for Hitler's order to cease the euthanasia program. In their *Secret Activities of the Third Reich*, the authors show with research that by August 1941, T4 has actually reached its quota of 70,000 persons euthanized. In fact, it had exceeded its target by exactly 273 persons. Having achieved its target, the program was being terminated. Were the Nazis calling in a breathing space while those in charge decided what to do next?

---

[396] Ibid, p.341
[397] Dr Bischoff, 10th December 1945, quoted by Klee, E, *'Euthanasie' im NS-Staat*, op. cit. p.341

Reinhard Heydrich

By 1942, a new plan to expand the slaughter of the mentally ill into the conquered territories had been drawn up by Himmler's deputy, Reinhard Heydrich. The criteria were to be widened to include Jews, gypsies, homosexuals, habitual criminals and other political undesirables. On 20th January, Heydrich convened a meeting of 15 senior Nazi officials at the beautiful lakeside retreat of Wannsee, ostensibly to examine the options of ridding Europe of 'parasitic Jewry'.

Heydrich was Himmler's *Wunderkind* - an operations genius who had just been appointed 'Reich Protector' of Bohemia and Moravia in September 1941. Heydrich's career with the Nazis had hitherto been meteoric. Having organised the entire Nazi secret police and intelligence services (SS and SD) even before his party gained power, Heydrich was trusted by Hitler and Himmler for his incredible capacity for organisation on a large scale. It was Heydrich who removed Nazi opponents quietly and effectively to Dachau, near Munich. It was Heydrich who, by 1934, had all the political police of the Reich under his control. It was Heydrich who organised four special task forces to follow Operation *Barbarossa* into Russia to liquidate Communist officials, saboteurs, agitators and Jews as the Germans advanced. By the time Wannsee was convened, wholesale murder of the Jews in Russia was routine. Historian Sir Martin Gilbert writes:

"From the first days of the German invasion of the Soviet Union, the SS Special Task Forces took Jews out of their homes to the nearest wood or ravine and shot them down. Tens of thousands of Jews were murdered in the first few weeks; hundreds of thousands in the months ahead; as many as a million by the end of the year. As the executions spread from town to town and village to village, babies and small children were thrown into the deep pits in which their parents had been shot." [398]

In spite of his brutality, there is evidence that Heydrich, born in Prussian Saxony the son of a music director and minor composer, was secretly disgusted by the scale of the worst tasks he was called to perform. Less well known were the social reforms Heydrich introduced into Czech society through his own initiatives, realising the carrot and the stick were both of use in maximising the productivity of conquered peoples brought into the Reich. For example, Heydrich discovered that Czech farmers had been holding out on the true number of cattle to be registered. He ordered all surplus animals slaughtered and the meat added to the rations of the factory workers. On Labour Day 1942, Heydrich distributed thousands of free cinema, theatre and football tickets to the workers to reward them for their endeavours. New national insurance cover, pension rights, new wage levels and holiday entitlements were agreed with the Czech trade unions. Ignoring the safety risks, Heydrich often toured the factories of his protectorate, telling the dumbfounded workers to their faces what an inspiration they were, even to the Nazis.

Wannsee – murder over cigars and cognac

It is this Heydrich, part monster, part operations genius, who seats himself at the conference table at the villa at Wannsee in January 1942 to discuss what must be done with the inferiors, mental degenerates, habitual criminals and Jews across the empire. Heydrich's mind has no moral conflict with the task at hand. He has instructed his subordinate, Oberstürmbahnführer Adolf Eichmann, to attend and record the event, and the minutes of this

---

[398] Gilbert, Martin, *History of the Twentieth Century*, op. cit. p.276

meeting have survived. From them we can piece together a chilling montage of what was agreed with Hitler's approval.

Clear was the fact that Hitler himself would issue no such order for the murder of eleven million Jews, though the mass exterminations could never have gone ahead without the Führer's approval. Ernst Klee writes that Hitler's quandary and subsequent refusal to issue a written order appears to be centred on the fact that it is still illegal at this time in Nazi Germany actually to murder people:

"Everyone involved knows that Hitler rejects a legal ruling for political reasons." [399]

Heydrich makes this clear at Wannsee when some of the incredulous attendees, upon hearing of Heydrich's proposal for the extermination of the Jews, timidly request the whereabouts of an official written order from the Führer. Heydrich pointedly reminds them of the need to purge Germany of undesirables. He is counting on their unanimous support to overcome the logistical problems of ceasing the propagation of 'inferior stock'.

In his book, *The Villa, The Lake, The Meeting: Wannsee and the Final Solution*, British scholar Mark Roseman uses the minutes from the infamous meeting to paint an almost unbelievable portrait of cultured men gathering in a stately, picturesque location, eating superb food, smoking cigars and sipping cognac, discussing the fate of such 'mental degenerates' as remain, along with the removal of 11 million Jews from European society. The meeting, conducted in cultured tones, begins with the question of deportation of undesirables. References are made to the success of the previous T4 euthanasia program.

Although sterilisation is openly discussed in connection with the desire to prevent 'inferior races' from breeding, it is evident that Heydrich is dissatisfied with the costs and manpower

---

[399] Ibid. p.86

associated with such an operation. At Wannsee, we see the efficient Heydrich presenting the top brass with a *fait accompli* with his *Endlösung*, his Final Solution for the Jews - a package of measures already planned, costed down to the last detail, and bearing the Himmler stamp of approval.

Setting up the Final Solution

There are historians who attempt to minimise Hitler's involvement in, and cogniscence of Heydrich, Eichmann and Himmler's plan, but clearly from documentation and later testimony at Nuremburg, Hitler is in the loop and always in overall command. Roseman agrees, reporting that within weeks of Wannsee, the random massacres of 'degenerates' throughout the empire, including thousands of Russian prisoners of war falling into German hands during *Barbarossa*, give way to highly organised and documented industrial extermination.

Psychological propaganda is all-important in breaking the will of the Soviets, regarded by leading Nazis as sub-human animals. But some Wehrmacht commanders are shocked at the savagery that has by now overtaken the regular soldiers under their command. On 26th June 1941, four days after the launch of *Barbarossa*, General Lemelsen, commander of the 47th Panzer Corps, is protesting to his subordinates about the 'senseless shootings of both prisoners-of-war and civilians'. Yet the savagery on both sides continues unchecked both within the Soviet Union and across occupied Europe. A war between millions, not of conquest, but of annihilation.

At dinner with Himmler and Heydrich on 25th October 1941, Hitler reminds his guests of his 'prophecy' in 1939 that a world war would result in the complete destruction of European Jewry. He adds:

"Let no-one say to me, we cannot send them into the swamp.... It is good if our advance is preceded with fear that we will exterminate Jewry."[400]

This is one of many examples illustrating that Hitler was sanctioning the continued murder program and was aware the SS were drowning Jewish women and children in the Pripet marshes. Just ten days after the Wannsee meeting, while Hitler is celebrating the ninth anniversary of his accession, he reminds a huge crowd in Berlin:

"The war will not end as the Jews imagine it will, namely with the uprooting of the Aryans, but the result of this war will be the complete annihilation of the Jews." [401]

The war widens

Worsening relations with America and a deteriorating war with Russia eventually cause the Nazis to abandon their original idea of sending European Jews on 'luxury ships' to any nation which would have them. And then the Japanese attack the US Pacific Fleet in Pearl Harbor on 7th December 1941 and pound US airfields in the Philippines. On 11th December, believing with elation the Japanese will score a quick victory over the United States, Hitler declares war on America. The Führer is relieved to receive the Japanese boost to his endeavours. Operation *Barbarossa* has bogged down in Russia with a shocking winter with temperatures as low as -35ºC. Though Stalingrad is the turning point of the war, it is one of the tragic ironies that, at precisely the time when it is dawning on the more prescient of Hitler's staff that the war may be lost, Hitler embarks on his full-scale war on the Jews.

---

[400] **Roseman, Mark** *The Villa, the Lake, the Meeting: Wannsee and the Final Solution*, Allen Lane, 2002

[401] Gilbert, Martin, *History of the Twentieth Century*, op. cit., p.281

At Wannsee, Heydrich is speaking with the voice of Hitler. Adolf Eichmann, Heydrich's operations chief, records in his memoirs and later 1961 trial in Israel that Heydrich's proposal for genocide of the Jewish people is enthusiastically and unanimously endorsed by all attendees at Wannsee. The Wannsee protocol is specific in its evolutionary stance. Any Jews surviving the attempt to work them to death for the benefit of the Reich:

"…will have to be dealt with appropriately, because otherwise, by natural selection, they would form the germ cell of a new Jewish revival."[402]

The death camps

Meanwhile the psychiatrists at T4 were experimenting with new, more efficient forms of annihilation. Decrying the increased costs of firing-squad ammunition and the shipping of carbon monoxide to the extermination facilities in Poland, arrangements were made for the off-the-shelf pesticide gas, Zyklon B, to be manufactured on-site by chemical giant I G Farben's subsidiary DEGESCH, an acronym for the German Corporation for Pest Control. In the purpose-built extermination facilities in Poland, the gassing of Russian prisoners of war proceeded apace, together with the continuous stream of victims provided by T4 psychiatrists from the KZs (concentration camps) across the empire. The Polish camps at Belzec, Sobibor and Treblinka, according to reliable estimates, carried out the murders of over 1.7 million alone. Approximately one hundred T4 psychiatrists were transferred from the Berlin headquarters to the Polish extermination sites to supervise and implement Heydrich's *Endlösung*. The original gas chambers were built to contain 500 people. At the height of the extermination program, up to 1,500 people were herded into the rooms at a time

---

[402] Ibid.

to prepare for what camp guards referred to sarcastically as 'the peaceful sleep'.

Nazi psychiatrist Ernst Rüdin's racial hygiene program reached its appalling denouement between 1942 and 1945 as further extermination facilities sprang up across occupied Europe. Numerous eyewitness accounts testify to the brutality of Heydrich's hated SS, who presided over the genocide with ruthless efficiency:

"After the arrivals were taken to the location next to the crematorium, they had to undress entirely because they were told they would have a shower. They were then chased – often with beatings – by the SS into the so-called bath, which in reality was a gas chamber...." [403]

"[in the dressing room of the crematorium], people's bloodstained and battered heads and faces proved that there was scarcely anyone who had been able to dodge the truncheon blows of the yard. Their faces were ashen with fear and grief.... Hope and illusions had vanished. What was left was disappointment, despair and anger.

They began to bid each other farewell. Husbands embraced their wives and children. Everybody was in tears. Mothers turned to their children and caressed them tenderly. The little ones... wept with their mothers and held on to them....

After a while, I heard the sound of piercing screams, banging against the door, and also moaning and wailing. People began to cough. Their coughing grew worse from minute to minute, a sign that the gas had started to act. Then the clamour began to subside and to change to a many-voiced dull rattle, drowned out now and then by coughing...." [404]

On 8th May 1945, the war ends in Germany. In the camps however, the killing continues, masked by the uncontrolled chaos of a Nazi empire in ruins. The mental institutions also appear to be functioning as before. Röder el al report:

---

[403] Among eye-witness accounts documented by **Lifton, Robert Jay** *The Nazi Doctors*, Basic Books, 1986, p.170

[404] Ibid.

"In the extermination institutes, they either kept on killing, or let the patients starve to death. As late as 29th May 1945, a four-year-old feeble-minded boy was murdered in Kaufbeuren, and on 7th July, a Munich newspaper made a horrifying discovery which proved that the loss of World War 2 had had no effect on the overall intentions of those who still operated the human slaughterhouses.

On 2nd July 1945, Robert E Abrahams walked into the district hospital of Kaufbeuren to find the warm, swinging body of a physician who was junior only to the director. He had hanged himself. Twelve hours earlier, the last adult had died. In Irsee, soldiers found the bodies of men and women who had died just hours earlier, most of them through starvation." [405]

The final hours

As often in the tragedy of war, a retrospective look at the most destructive conflict in human history yields a million tales of brutality, courage and fatal heroism. The march of the Allies across Europe and eventual fall of Berlin to the Soviets finally ends the mass killings, aerial bombings, artillery and tank battles, the firing squads in the forests, as well as the emotional torment of the populations under Nazi rule. The smoke of a thousands fires from Dresden to Hamburg, from Warsaw to Normandy, show the world the funeral pyre that is German National Socialism. Hitler kills himself with a pistol in his Berlin bunker on 30th April 1945. His mistress, Eva Braun, whom he has just married, takes poison. Hitler's propaganda and psychology chief, Josef Goebbels, arranges for his six children to be given a lethal injection by an SS doctor. He then has himself and his wife Madga shot by an SS orderly. While others attempt to flee Berlin to escape the retribution of the Russians, the Allies frantically attempt to account for all the major human rights violators in the chaos that is Europe at the end of the Second World War.

---

[405] Röder et al, *Psychiatry – The Men Behind Hitler,* op. cit. p.70

A spring day in Prague

But SS-General Reinhard Heydrich was to survive only a matter of months after Wannsee. On 27th May 1942, the SS chief was assassinated in Prague by two British-trained Czech agents, Kubis and Gabcik, as he took the beautiful drive from his villa at Panenske Brezany to his headquarters in the capital. As his Mercedes slowed to negotiate a hairpin bend in the Prague suburbs, Kubis and Gabcik attacked the vehicle with a Sten gun that jammed, and a specially prepared fragmentation mine that did not. Heydrich sustained wounds to his spleen, a lung and diaphragm, blasted through by shrapnel containing cloth and leather fragments from the vehicle's upholstery. Heydrich actually managed to give chase to Kubis on foot with a pistol before sagging to the road a few hundred yards later. He was taken to Bulovka hospital where he appeared to rally from an emergency operation to save his life. By the time Himmler paid him a visit on 2nd June, however, Heydrich's condition had worsened and he appeared reconciled to his fate.

"The world is just a barrel-organ which the Lord God turns Himself. We all have to dance to the tune which is already on the drum."[406]

After Himmler left, Heydrich slipped into unconsciousness and was pronounced dead two days later from septicaemia at the age of 38. An investigating police official, Dr Bernherd Wehner, later remarked that as Heydrich passed, his facial expression betrayed an

"...uncanny spirituality and entirely perverted beauty, like a Rennaissance cardinal."[407]

---

[406] **MacDonald, Callum** *The Killing of SS-Obergruppenfuehrer Reinhard Heydrich,* NY, 1989

[407] **Hohne, HZ & R Barry** *The Order of the Death's Head: The Story of Hitler's SS,* Penguin, 2001

Wagner and pageantry

Heydrich was buried with all Nazi honours in the Veteran's Cemetery in Germany's capital. The Berlin Philharmonic Orchestra played Wagner's funeral march. Heydrich's state funeral, designed to be broadcast to the world as a show of Nazi solidarity and power, featured the entire Nazi leadership and thousands of black-uniformed SS guarding the pageantry of the procession. Hitler gave an emotional eulogy of the dead man. Himmler praised Heydrich as a –

"…gentleman of breeding and bearing" who had been "feared by lower racial types and sub-humans, hated and defamed by Jews and criminals." [408]

As Heydrich's coffin, draped in the swastika, was drawn by four jet-black horses in procession towards the Veteran's Cemetery, the retaliation began hundreds of miles to the south in Czechoslovakia. The Führer was beside himself with rage. Hundreds of Czechs of doubtful allegiance were rounded up and shot. The entire village of Lidice, thought to have sheltered Heydrich's assassins at some point during their five-month preparation, had its entire male population machine-gunned and its women and children driven away to concentration camps.

The assassins were tracked down to an Orthodox church in Ressel Street, Prague. Hundreds of SS surrounded the building while their officers decided how to finish the stand-off. Finally, the pride of Heydrich's officer corps ordered the Prague fire department to pump water from the River Vltava into the crypt to drown out 'the vermin'. Later the bodies of the priests, assassins and collaborators were recovered. All were found to have died either fighting or having shot themselves with the last of their bullets before the water reached them.

---

[408] **Garbutt, Paul** *Assassin!* Ian Allan Ltd., England, 1942, p.87

EVOLUTION'S HALL OF SHAME

"If the race is to be freed from its crippling burden of good and evil, it must be psychiatrists who take the original responsibility."
– **G Brock Chisholm, President of the World Federation for Mental Health**

"From the days of 'Spartacus' Weishaupt, to those of Karl Marx, to those of Trotsky,… this world-wide conspiracy for the overthrow of civilisation… has been the mainspring of every subversive movement during the nineteenth century, and now at last has gripped the Russian people by the hair of their heads and has become the undisputed master of that enormous empire."[409] – **Winston Churchill**

Thousands of books have been written on Hitler and the Second World War, yet few have examined the period through the prevailing evolutionary ideology since this would pose too many awkward questions into practices that go on to this day. Thus atheists find themselves on the back foot with Hitler. Many deny his evolutionary beliefs. Others maintain Hitler was even a Christian. Only through exposing evolution for its socio-political fallout can the spectre of cultured Nazis seated around the dining table smoking cigars and plotting genocide be fully understood. Martin Brookes writes in *Science:*

"Since Darwin's death, all has not been rosy in the evolutionary garden. The theories of the Great Bearded One have been hijacked by cranks, politicians, social reformers and scientists to support racist and bigoted views. A direct line runs from Darwin, through the founder of the eugenics movement – Darwin's cousin, Francis Galton – to the extermination camps of Nazi Europe."[410]

---

[409] *Sunday Illustrated Herald,* London, 8th February 1920
[410] **Brookes, Martin** in "Ripe old age", Review of *Of Flies, Mice and Men* by **Francois J**, Harvard University Press, 1999. *New Scientist,* vol. 161, No. 2171, 30th January 1999, p.41

Hitler's *Mein Kampf* ('My Struggle') goes strong on the evolutionary process, especially in its relevance to a master race.[411] We read:

"If nature does not wish that weaker individuals should mate with the stronger, she wishes even less that a superior race should intermingle with an inferior one; because in such cases all her efforts, throughout hundreds of thousands of years, to establish an evolutionary higher stage of being, may thus be rendered futile."[412]

And: "The Germans were the higher race, destined for a glorious evolutionary future. For this reason it was essential that the Jews should be segregated, otherwise mixed marriages would take place. Were this to happen, all nature's efforts 'to establish an evolutionary higher stage of being may thus be rendered futile.'"

Evolutionist Sir Arthur Keith saw "… Hitler devoutly convinced that evolution produces the only real basis for a national policy. The means he adopted to secure the destiny of his race and people was organised slaughter, which has drenched Europe in blood … it is consistent with evolutionary morality. Germany reverted to the tribal past and demonstrated to the world, in her naked ferocity, the methods of evolution."

Those closest to Hitler were completely clear about his views on the subject. David Robertson cites Traudl Junge's book, in which Junge, Hitler's personal secretary, writes:

"Sometimes we also had interesting discussions about the church and the development of the human race. Perhaps it's going too far to call them discussions, because he [Hitler] would begin explaining his ideas when some question or remark from one of us had set them off, and we just listened. He was not a member of any church, and thought the Christian religions were outdated, hypocritical institutions that lured people into them. The laws of nature were his religion. He could

[411] Hitler, Adolf, *Mein Kampf*, op. cit., vol.2, ch.4
[412] www.billmuehlenberg.com/2008/09/15/a-church-apology-to-darwin/

reconcile his dogma of violence better with nature than with the Christian doctrine of loving your neighbour and your enemy.

'Science isn't yet clear about the origins of humanity,' he once said. 'We are probably the highest stage of development of some mammal which developed from reptiles and moved on to human beings, perhaps by way of the apes. We are a part of creation and children of nature, and the same laws apply to us as to all living creatures. And in nature the law of the struggle for survival has reigned from the first. Everything incapable of life, everything weak is eliminated. Only mankind and above all the church have made it their aim to keep alive the weak, those unfit to live, and people of an inferior kind." [413]

Evolutionist Stephen J Gould writes: "Ernst Haeckel was the chief apostle of evolution in Germany.... His evolutionary racism; his call to the German people for racial purity and unflinching devotion to a 'just' state; his belief that harsh, inexorable laws of evolution ruled human civilization and nature alike, conferring upon favored races the right to dominate others; the irrational mysticism that had always stood in strange communion with his brave words about objective science - all contributed to the rise of Nazism." [414]

Immersed in Darwin as a young revolutionary, Hitler would have read:

"At some future period, not very distant as measured by centuries, the civilised races of man will almost certainly exterminate, and replace, the savage races throughout the world. At the same time the anthropomorphous apes, as Professor Schaaffhausen has remarked, will no doubt be exterminated. The break between man and his nearest allies will then be wider, for it will intervene between man in a more civilized state, as we may hope, even than the Caucasian, and some ape as low as a

---

[413] Per Robertson, David, *The Dawkins Letters*, op. cit. **Junge, Traudl** *Until the Final Hour: Hitler's Last Secretary*, Weidenfeld and Nicolson, 2003

[414] **Gould, Stephen J** *Ontogeny and Phylogeny*, Belknap Press: Cambridge MA, 1977, pp.77-78

baboon, instead of as now between the negro or Australian [Aborigine] and the gorilla."[415]

The few books that deal with evolution and mass-murder won't be found in your local library. They include: **Edwin Black,** *War against the Weak: Eugenics and America's Campaign to Create a Master Race* (Four Walls Eight Windows, 2003); **Stefan Kuhl,** *The Nazi Connection: Eugenics, American Racism, and German National Socialism* (Oxford University Press, 1994); and **Richard Weikart,** *From Darwin to Hitler: Evolutionary Ethics, Eugenics, and Racism in Germany* (Palgrave Macmillan, 2004).

Ex-SS officers testified that throughout basic training, not just weapons instruction was hammered into them but evolution, the foundation of their creed and justification for barbarity. Oddly, many of the Nazi inner staff were born Catholic like Hitler and acknowledged God, yet maintained the pagan belief that they were descended from Aryan Hittites who inhabited the mythical ice paradise of Hyperborea in the wastes of the frozen north. This strange belief was in stark contrast to the regular patriotic fervour exhibited by most of the Wehrmacht and other branches of the German armed forces (with the exception of the SS), who grew to view their leadership's exotic fancies with more than a little trepidation. Such belief schisms planted the seeds for Claus Von Stauffenberg's attempted assassination of Hitler at the Wolf's Lair on 20th July 1944.

The lists still survive which Eichmann, Himmler and Heydrich used to determine racial purity, and those who would live and those destined for slaughter in Auschwitz, Treblinka, Bergen-Belsen and other camps. Segregation and internment policies for the *Untermenschen* (half-humans) were hammered out to purge the Fatherland of unwanted detritus. Jews were regarded as pure ape.

---

[415] **Darwin, CR** *The Descent of Man and Selection in Relation to Sex,* John Murray, London, 1922, pp.241-242

Blacks, gypsies, Asians, Slavs and homosexuals were only marginally 'more evolved'. At the top of the list was the blond-haired, blue-eyed, 'racially pure', hyperborean Aryan – the Hitlerite ideal.

We should not make the mistake of believing Hitler's reign of terror was an aberration. Karl Marx used Darwinism to underpin Communism. The fact that both Nazism and Communism had evolution as their bedrock is an irony lost on most today, since the two were antagonistic. Today, we refer to Communism and fascism to allude to either extremist doctrine – left or right – yet both wings are, and always have been, gilded with the featherwork of Lyell and Darwin. Both systems seek to control. And they seek to destroy those who oppose that control.

The great red stain

Following the 1848 production of the Communist Manifesto by Illuminist and capitalist Friedrich Engels, Communism was destined to produce successive generations of political strongmen who would hold that strength, survival and success were the dominant human dynamics. Because of their evolutionary beliefs, none of the major Communist leaders tolerated weakness or vacillation in their subordinates. Thousands of army officers who committed the unthinkable and showed the slightest compassion to the helpless found themselves at the business end of a firing squad.

Communism took evolution to new heights as a belief. Lenin, Trotsky and later Stalin institutionalised it as a political way of life. The question of morality, right and wrong, good and bad became redundant with the most barbaric of results. The Institute of Christian Research's (ICR) article, *Stalin's Brutal Faith*, records a telling incident during the young Stalin's school years:

> "At a very early age, while still a pupil at ecclesiastical school, Comrade Stalin developed a critical mind and revolutionary sentiments. He began to read Darwin and became an atheist.

A boyhood friend of Stalin's relates, "I began to speak of God, Josef heard me out, and after a moment's silence, said:

"You know, they are fooling us. There is no God."

I was astonished at these words. I had never heard anything like it before.

"How can you say such things, Soso?" I exclaimed.

"I'll lend you a book to read. It will show you that the world and all living things are quite different from what you imagine. All this talk about God is sheer nonsense." Josef said.

"What book is that?" I enquired.

"Darwin. You must read it," Josef impressed upon me."[416]

Josef Stalin had originally been a Christian studying in T'bilisi Theological Seminary in 1894 until a friend handed him a copy of Karl Marx's *Das Kapital* and, later, Darwin's *On The Origin of Species*. After reading both, Stalin's perspective changed. The result of that paradigm shift was 60 million slaughtered during the twenty-five years of terror that followed.

In September 1939, Stalin pushed west into Poland in violation of the Polish-Soviet Non-Aggression Pact while the Germans attacked from the south. Stalin abruptly found himself in possession of 14,700 Polish officers and 11,700 auxiliaries who became his prisoners of war. On 5th March, Stalin and the Politburo signed the order for their execution. After 3rd April 1940, the killings began at the hands of Lavrentiy Beria's NKVD. Though the episode has come to be known as the Katyn massacre, the murders were carried out over a wide area. Wikipedia records:

"Those who died at Katyn included an admiral, two generals, 24 colonels, 79 lieutenant colonels, 258 majors, 654 captains, 17 naval captains, 3,420 NCOs, seven chaplains, three landowners, a prince, 43 officials, 85 privates, and 131 refugees. Also among the dead were 20 university professors; 300 physicians; several hundred lawyers, engineers, and teachers; and more than 100 writers and journalists as well as about

---

[416] www.icr.org/article/stalins-brutal-faith/

200 pilots. In all, the NKVD executed almost half the Polish officer corps. Altogether, during the massacre the NKVD murdered 14 Polish generals… A mere 395 prisoners were saved from the slaughter… They were taken to the Yukhnov camp and then down to Gryazovets. They were the only ones who escaped death….”[417]

One by one, 14,700 Polish officers had hoods put over their heads by Beria's NKVD, ropes bound around their wrists behind their backs and then arms jacked up to the backs of their necks until the bones cracked. Each was led to the edge of a large, rectangular pit in the forest and shot once in the back of the head. Elsewhere:

“Detailed information on the executions in the Kalinin NKVD prison was given during the hearing by Dmitrii S. Tokarev, former head of the Board of the District NKVD in Kalinin. According to Tokarev, the shooting started in the evening and ended at dawn. The first transport on 4 April 1940 carried 390 people, and the executioners had a hard time killing so many people during one night. The following transports were no greater than 250 people. The executions were usually performed with German-made Walther PPK pistols supplied by Moscow, but Nagant M1895 revolvers were also used. Vasili Mikhailovich Blokhin, chief executioner for the NKVD, personally shot 6,000 of those condemned to death over a period of 28 days in April 1940.

The killings were methodical. After the condemned's personal information was checked, he was handcuffed and led to a cell insulated with a felt-lined door. The sounds of the murders were also masked by the operation of loud machines (perhaps fans) throughout the night. After being taken into the cell, the victim was immediately shot in the back of the head. His body was then taken out through the opposite door and laid in one of the five or six waiting trucks, whereupon the next condemned was taken inside. The procedure went on every night, except

---

[417] http://en.wikipedia.org/wiki/Katyn_massacre

for the May Day holiday.[418] Near Smolensk, the Poles, with their hands tied behind their backs, were led to the graves and shot in the neck."[419]

Records relating to these massacres were only recently released by Moscow to the West. Under the world spotlight after the war, Soviet authorities at first tried to blame the Germans and even erected a black memorial honouring 500 bogus Russians who were supposedly executed by the SS. Later the Kremlin came clean. Stalin had done the unthinkable and, as usual, subordinates had enforced their master's wishes.

Pol Pot

Pol Pot, dictator of Cambodia, slaughtered one third of his own population (3-4 million people) between 1975-1978. Pot was an avid evolutionist whose Khmer Rouge brainwashed new recruits with evolution. Imagine the president of the United States murdering 90 million Americans in four years. Imagine Tony Blair executing 20,000,000 Brits, hauling them out of their homes, dragging them into the woods and shooting them. Inconceivable. Yet Pot was purging his country of the 'undesirable' elements of humanity (ethnic cleansing) in exactly the same way Hitler and Stalin did, and later the Serbs would do under Ratko Mladić at Srebenica and elsewhere. Pot's behaviour actually earned him an entry into the Guinness Book of Records as the man responsible for the highest population percentage of humans slaughtered in the shortest period of time.

Aftermath

If you believe in evolution, how do you know what is right and wrong? Where does your moral code come from when compassion,

---

[418] Adam Weishaupt's revolution day. Key events occurring on 1st May are thought by some to be connected to this revolution.

[419] http://en.wikipedia.org/wiki/Katyn_massacre

love and understanding are antithetical concepts to the survival of the fittest? In evolution, why should lying, cheating, raping and murder be wrong at all?

It is the incredible survival and indeed future prosperity of the hundreds of key figures involved in the Nazi extermination program which provides the true scandal of the post-war 'clear-up'. Psychiatry not only survives the war but takes its eugenics and racist philosophies into the decades of the 20th century to follow. Witness the following 1949 German court ruling four years after the cessation of hostilities:

> "The criminal court… is not of the opinion that the extermination of the mentally dead and the 'empty human husks', as Hoche has called them, is absolutely immoral per se. There can be extremely differing opinions about this. Long ago, the removal of 'life unworthy of living' went without saying.… All these details… lead us to the conclusion that the question of the shortening of life unworthy of living is, of course, a highly contested problem, but that its execution can in no way be called a measure which conflicts with the general moral code."
>
> *Criminal Court 1 of the District Court*
> *of Hamburg on the issue of child*
> *euthanasia, 19th April 1949*

The above ruling was used as justification for freeing twenty Nazi psychiatrists from war crimes indictments. Hoche's 1920's tract espousing eugenics and the weeding out of 'empty human husks' during the Nazi era had been expanded to absurd and devastating proportions, as we have seen. Röder et al comment on the above:

> "The court's opinion represents the post-war marriage of the psychiatric and official authorities who had initiated and advocated mass extermination being quoted as justification of why the mass extermination could not automatically be condemned even in retrospect. It was in fact the only official reason why the court of Hamburg

exempted the twenty accused Nazis from prosecution for war crimes, four years after Hitler was defeated." [420]

Scot free

Psychiatrist Werner Heyde, Erstwhile head of T4, escaped after his 1947 arrest and resumed work as a 'Dr Sawade'. Acting as a consultant for the courts of the Schleswig-Holstein district of Germany, it seems incredible that Heyde was not only able to continue work as a well-renowned psychiatrist, *but carry out his assignments within Germany itself.* The well-known serpentine secrecy among former Nazis assured that records went missing, aliases were maintained, and eyes studiously turned the other way when unwelcome questions were asked. Ernst Klee remarks that:

"…numerous professors, the Director of the Social Court, a district court councillor, a Social Court counsellor, two presidents of the Senate and even a federal judge all knew that Professor Heyde was also Dr Sawade." [421]

That silence was the unspoken code of secrecy among psychiatrists is amply demonstrated when ex-Nazi eugenicist Dr Hans Bürger-Prinz told a parliamentary investigation into Dr Heyde/Sawade in 1961:

"With the exception of the clergymen, I do not believe that there exists a profession in which silence plays as big a role as with us [psychiatry], and by this, I mean with respect to everything.… Silence is very important to us and is not limited to the legal requirement concerning confidential medical communication.…" [422]

Bürger-Prinz's involvement with Nazi atrocities has never fully come to light, such is the misty web of disinformation that shrouded such characters after the war. He is the same Bürger-

---

[420] Röder et al, *Psychiatry – The Men Behind Hitler*, op. cit. 84-85

[421] Klee, Ernst, *'Euthanasie' im NS-Staat*, op. cit. p.414

[422] **Klee, Ernst** *Was sie taten – was sie wurden. Ärzte, Juristen und andere Beteiligte am Kranken – oder Judenmord*, Frankfurt, 1988, p.146

Prinz though, quoted in a *Der Spiegel* article in 1988, who reminded his colleagues in 1935 to 'register' young children 'afflicted with a hereditary disease' before 'fertility' in order to 'pick them out and exclude them from procreation.' The *Der Spiegel* article continues:

"[Bürger-Prinz] became an ordinary professor in Hamburg! Konrad Lorenz, who would later win a Nobel Prize, stood up in 1940, demanding the 'more stringent eradication of ethical inferiors', only to concern himself after the war with writing bestsellers, only generally about the 'so-called evil', not about his own past.

Johannes Heinrich Schulz, the father of 'autogenic training' and a no-nonsense expert on hereditary disease and homosexual behaviour, sent homosexuals to the concentration camps if they could not have intercourse with a woman while he watched. After 1945, Schulz became one of the most popular medical educators in the country. The professor died in 1970, as old as Methuselah and highly honoured.

Hans-Joachim Rauch, who, as court psychiatrist was very active in Stammheim, was for decades afterwards a full professor in Heidelberg. During the Nazi era, he was a pathologist who dissected the brains of gassed children. The small patients were brought to the killing institute of Eichberg, near Heidelberg. This institute thus satisfied Rauch's desire for their freshly slaughtered organs." [423]

Denazification programs carried out after 1945 were thwarted at every turn. The occupying powers often allowed entire infrastructures of the German judiciary to return to office due to an absence of qualified, German-speaking personnel to administer the devastated nation. Röder et al describe the astonishing result:

"Given the amount of complicity in high positions in Germany, the post-war halls of justice were every bit as polluted with Nazis as were the halls of academia. The courts held a plethora of judges and prosecutors whose tenures were interrupted, but not concluded, by military defeat. It is therefore not surprising that Germany's justice system did little to overcome Germany's bloody past in the days following the Third Reich's

---

[423] Spiegel-series 1988; *Die Mörder sind noch unter uns* ['The murderers are still among us'], issue 25, p.116

decline. The truth is that many Nazis returned to positions as judges and prosecutors with little or no scrutiny from those supposedly responsible for supervising the administration of justice." [424]

The *Der Spiegel* series on this subject concurs that most professional Nazis experienced but a momentary hiccough in their careers:

"Most of the murderers were only overcome through the advance of time, through their own old age. After the founding of the Federal Republic of Germany, they advanced again to the ranks of head physicians, medical officers and professorships, respected as academics and college teachers, and finally woven back into the political fabric of justice, bureaucracy and archives, protected by their old comrades.... The Nazi idea... was forgotten, suppressed and glossed over, right from the start." [425]

The list of Nazi psychiatrists, especially those who were actively involved with T4 either as staff or consultants, reads as a *Who's Who* of post-war psychiatry, especially those who eventually ended up as presidents of the German Society for Psychiatry and Neurology (GSPN):

Ernst Rüdin (1874-1952)

President of GSPN 1935-1945 – former head of the Nazis' sterilisation, euthanasia and racial hygiene program, Rüdin was still being lionised by the prestigious Max Planck Institute in 1992 for "...following his own convictions in 'racial hygiene' measures, co-operating with the Nazis as a psychiatrist and helping them legitimise their aims through pertinent legislation." [426]

---

[424] Röder et al, *Psychiatry – The Men Behind Hitler*, op. cit. p.84

[425] *Spiegel-series* 1988, op. cit. p.116

[426] Acknowledgement of Ernst Rüdin in the Institute's publication: "75 Years of the Max Planck Institute for Psychiatry, Munich 1917-1992".

Ernst Kretschmer (1888-1964)
President of GSPN 1948-1951

Nazi psychiatrist and eugenicist who advocated sterilisation of the mentally ill to avoid their reproduction. Kretschmer also included "drunkenness, criminality and epilepsy" within the "more or less unspecified lot of degenerations" which are the "actual great sphere of action for eventual eradication".[427]

Werner Villinger (1887-1961)
President of GSPN 1952-1954

Nazi psychiatrist and one of mental hygiene's most outspoken advocates. Listed as a T4 consultant. Villinger was involved with the drafting of the post-war Sterilisation Act that was enacted with the approval of American occupation forces by the Health Committee of the Stuttgart Council of the Länder.

Friedrich Mauz (1900-1979)
President of GSPN 1957-1958

Nazi psychiatrist, T4 consultant and mental hygienist. Mentored by Ernst Kretschmer. Klee comments: "In the list of consultants for T4, some famous people are recorded. Besides professors Heyde and Nitsche, we can also find the names of professors Polisch and Panse (Bonn), Carl Schneider (Heidelberg), Erich Straub (Kiel), Friedrich Mauz (Konigsberg), Berthold Kihn (Jena)... while Villinger (Breslau), as we have seen, was involved for much longer." [428]

Honoured for his 'special accomplishments' on 17th May 1980 a year after his death, Mauz incredibly surfaced in London in 1948 as a participant in the International Congress of Mental Hygiene. During this conference, the World Federation of Mental Health was founded. One of Mauz's 'special accomplishments' was the

---

[427] Kretschmer, Konstitutionslehre und Rassenhygiene in Rüdin: *Erblehre und Rassenhygiene im völkischen Staat*, Munich, 1934, p.186
[428] Klee, E, *'Euthanasie' im NS-Staat*, op. cit. p.227

development of a law in 1940 'ending the suffering' of the 'incurably ill'.

Hans Bürger-Prinz (1897-1976)
President of GSPN 1959-1960

Nazi psychiatrist Bürger-Prinz, as the military district psychiatrist in charge of the Neuropathy Clinic in Hamburg from 1937 to 1970, never distanced himself from what happened to the mentally ill during the Nazi period. Bürger-Prinz's post-war career was characterised by a desire to continue his work, unsobered by the foreign occupation of his country. Strong evidence exists that Bürger-Prinz may have been trained in the killing activities of the mentally ill and attempted to profit from them.[429]

Heinrich Kranz (1901-1979)
President of GSPN 1961-1962

Twins researcher who, although less radical than his colleagues Rüdin and Luxenburger, bowed to pressure during World War 2 and joined in enforcing the compulsory sterilisation laws and commitments to asylums. Later these inmates were transferred to the killing institutions.

Friedrich Panse (1899-1973)
President of GSPN 1965-1966

Nazi military district psychiatrist and T4 consultant. Panse became infamous for applying 'Pansing' techniques on battle-shocked soldiers who were suspected of malingering and 'pension-neuroses'. This involved electroshock treatment, reminiscent of Kaufmann's methods during World War 1. Acquitted of atrocities through lack of evidence, Panse rose in honour and prestige in post-World War 2 psychiatry.

---

[429] Ibid.

* * * * *

Robert Felix – The US NIMH

With its infamous role during World War 2 played down, and its psychological warfare benefits promoted to government and the public as an essential national asset, psychiatry now entered a new and significant era. In the post-WW2 world, the mental hygiene movement was able to 'institutionalise' itself in open society when, in 1946, the United States National Institute of Mental Health (NIMH) was formed with psychiatrist Dr Robert Felix as its first director. The ambitious Felix outlined the new strategy and goals of his institution, which were to establish community mental health programs aimed at fostering 'the prevention of mental illness' before it occurred.[430] Felix exhorted colleagues to become involved with,

"....education, social work, industry, the churches, recreation and the courts" so that "mental health services" could be "fully integrated into, and a regular and continuing part of, the total social environment." [431]

Henceforth the promises made by psychiatry became profuse. Authors Foley and Sharfstein write:

"The extravagant claims of enthusiasts – that new treatments were highly effective, that all future potential victims of mental illness and their families would be spared the suffering, that great economies of money would soon be realised – were allowed to pass unchallenged by the professional side of the professional-political leadership." [432]

---

[430] **Shrag, Peter** *Mind Control*, Pantheon Books, 1978, p.42

[431] **Sharkey, Joe** *Bedlam: Greed, Profiteering, and Fraud in a Mental Health System Gone Crazy*, St Martin's Press, New York: 1994, p.174; **Felix, Robert** *Mental Health and Social Welfare*, Columbia University Press, New York: 1961, p.21

[432] **Foley, Henry & Steven S Sharfstein** *Madness and Government*, American Psychiatric Press, Inc., Washington DC: 1983, p.25

321

G Brock Chisholm

G Brock Chisholm, one of the 20th century's most influential mental health advocates and former president of the World Federation for Mental Health, chillingly verifies the collective aim of his profession to continue in its original aim of freeing man from the chafing constraints of righteousness:

"The reinterpretation and eventually eradication of the concept of right and wrong which has been the basis of child training, the substitution of intelligent and rational thinking for faith in the certainties of the old people, these are the belated objectives of practically all effective psychotherapy…. The fact is, that most psychiatrists and psychologists and other respectable people have escaped from these moral chains and are able to observe and think freely." [433]

Chisholm's position of influence would confirm to society and his peers the notion that mental doctors and "other respectable people have escaped from these moral chains". One of the most profound influencers of post-WW2 global psychiatry remarkably goes on to quote Satan in Genesis, declaring:

"We have swallowed all manner of poisonous certainties fed us by our parents, our Sunday and day school teachers, our politicians, our priests, our newspapers and others with a vested interest in controlling us. 'Thou shalt become as gods, knowing good and evil', good and evil with which to keep children under control, with which to prevent free thinking, with which to impose local and familial and national loyalties and with which to blind children to their glorious intellectual heritage….

If the race is to be freed from its crippling burden of good and evil, it must be psychiatrists who take the original responsibility."[434]

All the more incredible are Chisholm's words with the ashes of war-torn Europe still smouldering in testament to the unhinging of

---

[433] **Chisholm, G Brock** "The Re-establishment of Peacetime Society – The William Alanson White Memorial Lectures, Second Series', *Psychiatry: Journal of the Biology and the Pathology of Interpersonal Relations*, February 1946, p.9

[434] Ibid. pp.7-9

society from traditional moral precepts. Chisholm defends his beliefs with the following ironic words which prefigure the future:

"The pretence is made, as it has been made in relation to the findings of any extension of truth, that to do away with right and wrong would produce uncivilised people, immorality, lawlessness and social chaos." [435]

After the war, psychiatry moves into the current era, its modalities intact, its racist and eugenics philosophies undented, many of its most barbaric practitioners vaunted and honoured. American psychiatrists increased tenfold in number over the forty years following World War 2.[436] Government-funded research increased more than a hundredfold during the same period. In fact, psychiatry would earn the distinction of being the only medical profession regularly to receive US federal funding for the education of its members – training grants increasing eightyfold from 1948 to 1972.[437] Around the world, governments and their citizens would remain somnolent and largely unaware of the wolf that had taken up residence in their midst. Progress was science. Time to look forward to a fresh start and a new age in which to begin it. Everyone understood the war now. Those who weren't dead were a little older, a little wiser. Here was peace. A time to lay the ghosts to rest.

---

[435] Ibid.
[436] **Torrey, E Fuller** *Nowhere to Go*, Harper & Row, New York: 1988, pp.163-164
[437] Ibid.

A MAD, MAD WORLD

"The technetronic era involves the gradual appearance of a more controlled society. Such a society would be dominated by an élite, unrestrained by traditional values." **– Zbigniew Brzezinski, National Security Advisor to Carter and four other US presidents, in** *Between Two Ages*

On 1st May 1997, Tony Blair and the British Labour Party were elected to power with a crushing majority.[438] The extraordinary thing about this election, however, was not the unanimity of Mr Blair's victory but the symbolism it represented. The Old Britain that trudged despairingly to the polls on 1st May was the dying Christian Britain of Kenneth More and Sir John Mills; of *Land of Hope and Glory* and *The Last Night at the Proms*; of Mr Churchill and Bernard Montgomery; the sort of Britain reflected in the *Cruel Sea*, *The Dambusters* and other black and white TV films still playing on a rain-swept Sunday afternoon. The New Britain that powered to victory that spring day was chiefly state-educated and -employed, atheist or agnostic, trendy, hip and gay, who scorned, or were deeply offended by the patriotism and empire espoused by the Old Order.

The roots to the ultimately fatal attack on Britain go back many decades but could be discerned after the war in many other countries. After two global conflicts, the world citizenry was suffering a delayed moral and spiritual fatigue. For Britain, it happened because the empire was dying anyway, and having limped herself to victory with her allies, Old Britain found a quiet corner to gather some peace before she passed. In any case, a nation grown weary of attacks at any moment, of slaughter on a Herculean scale, ironically faced its greatest threat in the deceptively safe anti-climax of the post-war period. More deadly

---

[438] *Coincidentally* on Adam Weishaupt's revolution day?

than a flotilla of Scharnhorsts, more insulting to her traditionalists than the crash of ten thousand jackboots up Whitehall, Weishaupt's liberal-socialist revolution ambushed the Old Order from a direction it least expected.

Who could have predicted such a colossal upheaval of British society not even two wars were able to provoke? The atheist counter-culture revolution which characterised the 1960's shocked many, not only because of its flaunted open sexuality and anti-authoritarian signature, but through the sheer speed with which the old institutions, morals and customs disintegrated which had sustained society for centuries. Who had seen the like?

George Orwell saw the writing on the wall in 1941. In *The Lion and the Unicorn,* he wrote:

"In intention, at any rate, the English intelligentsia are Europeanised. They take their cookery from Paris and their opinions from Moscow. In the general patriotism of the country, they form a sort of island of dissident thought. England is perhaps the only great country whose intellectuals are ashamed of their own nationality. In left-wing circles it is always felt that there is something slightly disgraceful in being an Englishman, and that it is a duty to snigger at every English institution, from horse racing to suet puddings. It is a strange fact, but it is unquestionably true that almost any English intellectual would feel more ashamed of standing to attention during 'God Save the King' than of stealing from a poor box."

Arts and media

The postmodern revolutionaries hijacked the arts and media, traditionally conservative, patriotic and loyal. This mighty cannon was then turned on its own country and what was left of the empire. Many of the intelligentsia of which Orwell spoke were themselves burrowed deep in the arts and well positioned to carry out their *coup d'état* on the BBC, leading broadsheets and radio. Many were already familiar if controversial figures to the public. The self-deprecating British, happy to grin indulgently at the lampooned images they began to see of themselves, were simply having another good laugh at their own expense. At first, nothing subversive was sensed in this comic relief. Few understood the implications of laughter until it was too late.

Religion, morality, patriotism and literature took a complete beating. The 1960's revolution caricatured and poured scorn on the Church, state, monogamy and chastity, as well as the classics. The new pop culture wrote countless songs damning existing civilisation as warmongering, sexually repressed and a danger to everyone. Targets considered sacrosanct, especially Jesus and the Christian faith, were particularly juicy targets. The atheists set to with a will, strafing the very icons that judged their way of life. *The Life of Brian* lampooned traditional stories of Jesus and his disciples, for centuries hallowed ground for millions. An initial frisson of horror at Monty Python's blasphemy soon gave way to gales of cathartic laughter as British households recognised with relief that it was all just fun, that God must have a sense of humour, and no harm was meant by any of it.

This Was the Week that Was (TW3), Benny Hill and a hundred other programs from the 1960's onwards poked fun at the institutions, politics and mores of the Old Order, but these were tame to what would follow. The revolution changed human values through gradualism and the relativist view that what was true for you was not necessarily true for anyone else. Stanley Grenz writes:

"The postmodern worldview operates with a community-based understanding of truth. It affirms that whatever we accept as truth and even the way we envision truth are dependent on the community in which we participate."[439]

The fallout has been spectacular. To those not adhering to the absolutes of the Mosaic Commandments, the possibilities were

---

[439] **Grenz, S** *A Primer on Postmodernism,* Eerdmans, Grand Rapids, USA, 1996, p.8

endless. Cynicism and satire suffocated everything, even the loss of thousands of RAF aircrew who had paid the ultimate price during the war years. A Peter Cook and Jonathan Miller sketch ran as follows:

"Perkins! Sorry to drag you away from the fun, old boy. War's not going very well, you know!"

"Oh, my God!"

"We are two down and the ball's in the enemy court. War is a psychological thing, Perkins, rather like a game of football. And you know how in a game of football, ten men often play better than eleven?"

"Yes, sir."

"Perkins, we are asking you to be that one man. I want you to lay down your life, Perkins. We need a futile gesture at this stage. It will raise the whole tone of the war. Get up in a crate over to Bremen, take a shufti, don't come back. Goodbye, Perkins. God, I wish I was going too."

"Goodbye, sir. Or perhaps it's au revoir?"

"No, Perkins."

No doubt a *frisson* of shame was felt by many at the mocking of areas hitherto regarded as hallowed ground, yet most indulged in it anyway. The new television personalities like Miller and Cook, Michael Palin, John Cleese and Alan Bennett, were astonishingly different from anything the public had seen before. Those who complained came in for the Perkins treatment. The working class was given the first forbidden freedom of saying, doing, swearing and feeling whatever it wanted. According to John Lennon, God was dead, and a world without God was a world without judgment and man strapped in the driver's seat.

Mass hypnosis

The Rolling Stones typified the counter-culture revolution. Never far from the news, Mick Jagger et al popularised the revolt with their raw music, outrageous exploits and enough drugs to kill a rhinoceros. In an interview with Keith Richards, the famous guitarist was asked, *"Do you think of yourselves as servants of Satan?"* Richards replied:

"Kenneth Anger [Satanist and disciple of Crowley] told me I was his right-hand man. It all depends whether you've got that good and evil thing together. Left-hand path, right-hand path. How far do you want to go down? Once you've started, there's no turning back. And where it leads is another thing.... It's something everybody ought to explore. There are a lot of possibilities there. A lot of people have played with it and it's inside everybody. [pause] Everybody's Lucifer." [440]

One of their more stirring songs goes as follows:

Sympathy For The Devil
Please allow me to introduce myself
I'm a man of wealth and taste
Been around for a long, long year
Sold many a man's soul and fate
I was around when Jesus Christ
Had His moment of doubt and pain
Made damn sure that Pilate
Washed his hands and sealed His fate
Pleased to meet you, baby
Hope you guess my name.... [441]

The Rolling Stones typify Crowlianism. Mick Jagger and Keith Richards led high-profile public lives of unrepentant rebellion and an 'anything goes' attitude. Today *The Stones* are still prophets to millions with their albums and songs, which include *Bridges to Babylon, Goat's Head Soup, Their Satanic Majesty's Request, Tattoo*

---

[440] **Dalton, David & Mick Farren** *The Rolling Stones: In Their Own Words*, Omnibus Press, 1995

[441] The Rolling Stones, *Sympathy For The Devil*, from the movie, *Gimme Shelter*. This song was performed live at the Altamont Speedway in December 1969. Three people were killed during the concert. Mick Jagger's recorded comment after singing this song and hearing of the deaths in the crowd: *"Something funny always happens when we start that number."*

You, Through the Past, Darkly (a Bible misquote), *Voodoo Lounge* (also the name of their London nightclub in Leicester Square), *Saint of Me* and *Out of Control*. *The Rolling Stones* were undeniably marketed as the 'bad boys of rock', but the following group was supposed to be the one your mother preferred.

All you need is love

On the cover of *The Beatles'* Sgt. Pepper Lonely Hearts Club Band album, we find the Fab Four surrounded by a crowd of historical figures. Apart from the revolutionaries in evidence, from Jung to Marx to, apparently, Adolf Hitler before his face was removed because of protests; top left, second face in, we find the bald head of Aleister Crowley.

In the *Playboy* interviews, John Lennon sums up *The Beatles'* philosophy thus:

"The whole Beatle idea was <u>to do what you want</u>, right? To take your own responsibility and try not to harm other people, right? <u>Do what thou wilst</u> as long as it doesn't hurt anybody."

In the biography, *The Lives of John Lennon*, author Albert Goldman tells how Yoko Ono journeys to South America to make a pact with Satan for a number of things, including John Lennon's career:

"Finally it was time to consummate all these spells by making a living sacrifice and signing a pact with the Devil. For Lena was not a white witch, she was the real thing - a practitioner of black magic. There was no knowing what she planned to do to seal the bond with Lucifer. All she would say was that the witch's moon was nigh and she had to make ready the sacrifice." [442]

Goldman goes on to tell how they sacrificed an animal and Ono paid the witch, Lena, $60,000 for her trouble. Goldman

---

[442] **Goldman, Albert** *The Lives of John Lennon*, St Martin's Press, 1984

explains away this event and others linked with it by stating that John Lennon was grappling with psychiatric disturbances and peer-pressure gremlins.

A more detailed study of Lennon, however, reveals the musician to have been profoundly antichrist. Often described as a man 'with peace on his lips but war in his heart', John Lennon was undeniably the spiritual force behind *The Beatles,* eclipsing the more moderate and parent-friendly McCartney. Lennon was their most progressive spokesman. When he made his infamous comment, *"The Beatles are bigger than Jesus Christ",* most wrote it off as sensationalism and hype. However, in the same interview with the *San Francisco Chronicle*, Lennon goes out of his way to declare that *"Christianity will vanish."* In his book, *John Lennon: In His Own Write*, Lennon openly blasphemes Jesus Christ and the Holy Spirit: *"I forgive them by the Father, the Sock and Mickey Most."* (Most was a famous record producer in the sixties).

Thus Rebel John made no secret of his disdain of religion, yet his flagship tune, *Imagine,* is a veritable ode to the religion of atheism:

Imagine
Imagine there's no heaven (*Let's take God out of the picture*)
It's easy if you try (*There's nothing to it*)
No hell below us (*No judgment on wrong-doing*)
Above us only sky
Imagine all the people
Living for today... (*Imagine the whole world embracing the core philosophy of Satanism: "Life is the great indulgence. Death is the great abstinence. Therefore make the most of life here and now."* Book of Satan 4:1)
Imagine there's no countries (*Let's break down national boundaries*)
It isn't hard to do (*It's a snap*)
Nothing to kill or die for (*Let's do away with patriotism*)

And no religion too (*Remove religion and replace it with man's reason (humanism)*)
Imagine all the people
Living life in peace... (*People will live in peace without God*)
Imagine no possessions (*Imagine Communism. Nobody owns anything*)
I wonder if you can
No need for greed or hunger
A brotherhood of man (*A Big Brother human government feeding and caring for us all*)
Imagine all the people
Sharing all the world... (*Let's have worldwide Communism*)
You may say that I'm a dreamer
But I'm not the only one (*There are lots of people out there who think the same way I do*)
I hope some day you'll join us (*Because you aren't with us at the moment*)
And the world will be as one. (*Welcome to the New World Order*)
(John Lennon, *Imagine*, EMI Blackwood Music, Inc.)

Revolution was all part of *The Beatles* appeal. 'Love', 'peace' and *Yesterday* were thrown in just so your mother did not cough up a hairball. *All You Need is Love* proved somewhat of a stumbling block, however. When *The Beatles* broke up, they hated each other for years afterwards.

Sold out

In the midst of such spiritual upheaval, the Anglican Church found itself slack-jawed, on the back foot and starved of an answer. Resorting to compromise, vicars began popping up who tried to be trendy by not believing the Bible was the Word of God or that Jesus was his Son. "**In the beginning God created the heavens and the earth**" suddenly wasn't so simple. Grandfather was now a monkey but Jesus still loved you. The pews emptied. Windows were smashed. Someone made a living stripping the lead off church roofs and selling it on for scrap. On Sundays, everyone went down the pub instead.

Stripped of the need for deference, forelock-tugging and subservience, working-class Britain preferred the better-looking socialist version it saw of itself. Wronged by the ruling class, flexing their industrial muscle to negotiate on their own terms, the unions fought for their own interests rather than died in the dirt for others. The media provided a steady diet of sex, beer, cars, sex, football, drugs, working-class heroes, sex, rock and roll, swearing, sex, drugs, crime, cigarettes and more sex. The television, still a recent enough reminder of the Old Way to carry the *imprimatur* of authority, now seemed to be saying that inflaming the animal within was cool, that it was OK, that it was not that bad.

The British middle-class was given a consistent, abrasive, hypocritical version of itself to contemplate on TV. Through the cynical lens of the camera, the middle class truly became the class caught in the middle. Sex-obsessed and ridiculous, unfaithful and rudderless on an ocean of banality, destined to die without ever having really lived. Twitching lace curtains. Suburban dwellers to be pitied. Hen-pecked husbands washing their Capris on Sunday morning, the symbol of their fading virility. Wives attempting a genteel snobbery, inviting the laughter of the upper class. Five hundred completely silent souls on the 8:10am to Charing Cross. Those garden boundary wars.

Today it's *Mock the Week* with Russell Howard napalming the Surrey set, Andy Parsons rubbishing creationism and Frank Boyle insulting the Queen. You can watch *Sex in the City, Shameless, Little Britain* or MTV to the strains of *The Bloodhound Gang*:

You and me, baby, ain't nothin' but mammals,
So let's do it like they do on the Discovery Channel.

But the upper class, with its tweed and grouse-shooting, got both barrels of the satire Purdy. So sent up and savaged did the posh set become that it lost the moral bottle to govern. Laughter was one of the chief weapons used because there was no known defence against it. The *Spitting Image* puppets achieved what the Messerschmitts couldn't – the destruction of any respect the British had left for their leaders. What power could be harnessed in the presence of comedy! What harm in laughter and fun! After the dreadfulness of the previous fifty years, Britain started guffawing again, and to the many for whom the previous decades had held precious little to laugh about, it was a wonderful if alien sensation.

Putting the safeties on

Mockery was the prerogative of the cultural left, but when this weapon was turned against them, it became the most powerful agent for their own demise. Thus the revolutionaries ensured, where possible, the path was mined behind them to avoid friendly fire.

The Old Order winced at the mauling it got in programs such as *TW3*, *Monty Python*, *Beyond the Fringe* and *Forty Years On*. The New Order ensured that it would not suffer the same fate. To safeguard against return lampooning of its own position on humanism, abortion, casual sex, homosexuality or immigration, a careful web was spun to ensure its beliefs were protected by law and its enemies stigmatised. The public's perception of sex, marriage, humour, duty, fidelity, language, customs, religion and art were all put through their turbulent transformations, while the TV, now in every home, reassured the public that this was the progressive, liberating thing to do.

The first contraceptive pill, Envoid, came onto the market in the 1960's, for the first time allowing women control over their reproduction. The new Baby-Boomers, too young to remember the Doodle Bugs, bomb shelters and bacon rationed to one ounce, found themselves increasingly isolated from, and suspicious of their parents. Baffled by the quaint moral reserve and sense of duty; insulted by their disapproval of the freedom espoused by Lennon's atheism, they harboured the revolution's contempt for the faith which had sustained their parents through unimaginable horrors. Peter Hitchens writes:

"As the war generation grew old, they found themselves living on an alien landscape where their traditional morals and values were increasingly mocked and derided by each generation which followed…. The society they now lived in, where the word of television was law, suddenly allowed only one point of view to be expressed openly, and it was not theirs…." [443]

Violence and the videodrome – the effects

Since Tony Blair's election, the revolution has shifted gears. The all-pervasive MTV videodrome now beckons children with 24 hours of near naked sado-masochism. By the time a child is 16, he will have seen 300,000 acts of gratuitous violence, torture, mutilation, suicide and murder on television and video. The Comedy Channel has us laughing at euthanasia, adultery, God, blasphemy and death in a way that makes it funnier than hell. The Hollywood liberals have taught us how to enjoy the 'buzz' of sin without the aggravation of accountability, in much the same way Richard McDonald showed us how to enjoy a Big Mac without the aggravation of the abattoir.

After being presented with five volumes of scientific data showing that sex and violence on TV had a significant effect on society, American ABC TV executives issued a statement denying that televised imagery affected real-world behaviour in any way. Film critic Michael Medved was outraged:

"Now if ABC TV believes that, then it better start refunding billions of dollars in advertising revenues. Because if televised imagery does not

---

[443] **Hitchens, Peter,** *The Abolition of Britain*, Quartet Books, 1999

affect real-world behaviour in any way, what are they doing selling ad time?"

The double mind

The rest, as they say, is history. The atheist revolution has triumphed. We are a society today that can moralise about rape, murder and sex abuse when we read about them in the newspapers, but have no problem accommodating the latest Quentin Tarantino rape, demon, murder and sex abuse movie advertised on the very next page. England wept like babies during the serial run of *Hearts of Gold*, seeing all those ordinary folk doing good deeds for one another, dissolved into sentimental goo. But the following day it was 'Hearts of Lead' as we cussed out the kids, gobbled down the porridge and carved up the grannies on our mad dash into work.

The double mind is a form of social insanity pushed by atheism. It's 'a mind profoundly at war with itself and ignorant even of that fact'.[444] Morals are relative, truth elastic. The confused individual is left in Nietzsche's world of no sense, no justice, and no hope but to defer to 'authority' to feed and deliver him. The following editorial from Britain's bestselling newspaper is a good example:

WRECKED LIVES

"There's one thing at which we [Britain] DO lead the world. And we should hang our heads in shame: Britain has the highest rate of unmarried teenage mothers - nine times worse than Japan. Why is Britain so different? Not because we don't teach children about contraception. Just the opposite – we teach them too much and in the wrong way.

The more sexually aware our children become at too early an age, the more they are tempted. Tragically, it has become unfashionable to drum into children the word 'No'. We are paying the price in wrecked lives."

---

[444] **Hoffman Michael** *Secret Societies and Psychological Warfare,* Wiswell Ruffin House, 1992, p.90

This from *The Sun*, 15th May 1998, page 8. Turn five pages back and you find the daily, half-page photograph of a teenage girl stripped to the waist in provocative pose, earning her pocket-money as the latest 'model' to break onto the scene.

Atheism cause and effect

In 1976, the number of reported child abuse cases in America was 670,000. By the early 1990's, this figure had risen to nearly 3 million. 25% of the movies rented in the US in 1998 were pornographic. *Christ for Nations Magazine* reports that:

> "In Washington D.C., within blocks of the Department of Justice, there are 37 'adult' bookstores, 8 X-rated theatres and 15 topless bars."

A published Pentagon telephone audit showed that $300,000 of taxpayers' money had been spent on 1(900) sex lines.

Today, trashy teen magazines and social-climber periodicals deify sex, promiscuity, adultery, drunkenness and the occult. MPs fiddle their expenses and wonder what the fuss is about. In Britain, drug abuse is now so widespread in our nation's towns and cities, when the Metropolitan Police randomly searched a cross-section of club-goers in London's King's Cross in July 1998, 100% of them were found to be carrying, or under the influence of illegal drugs.

Many of the famous have owned up to needing psychiatric drugs to get by, reflecting the unspoken devastation of millions of ordinary citizens of little newsworthy note. Singer Del Shannon (Charles Westover) thought the Prozac prescribed by his psychiatrist would *"…help me over the hump I'm in."* His wife LeAnne *"…watched him turn into somebody who was agitated, pacing, had trembling hands, insomnia and couldn't function."* On 8th February 1990, after taking Prozac for just 15 days, Charles Westover shot himself in the head with a .22 calibre rifle.

Princess Diana and Sarah Ferguson both admitted using the 'liquid sunshine' drug, Prozac, and Diana became the subject of huge media speculation over her drug use. Royal author Andrew Morton's *Diana: Her New Life* detailed her catastrophic mood-swings and alleged suicide attempt on board a royal flight, in which she attempted to slash her arms and smear blood over the walls before being restrained.[445]

Lady Brocket, Libby Purves, Al Pacino, Roseanne Barr and Mariella Frostrup are others who have been some-time users of Prozac. The flagship drug is routinely prescribed for depression. Its side-effects include depression, suicidal tendencies and the propensity for sudden, unthinking violence. INXS pop-frontman Michael Hutchence died in November 1997 in an apparent hanging while playing a sex game. His song-writing partner, Andrew Farriss, attributed his death to Prozac and alcohol. Australian acting star Heath Ledger died in January 2008 from a toxic combination of psychiatric drugs.[446] The actor/comedian Chris Farley died aged 33 after a four-day alcohol and drug binge. Prozac was found in his blood. Michael Jackson died of a drugs overdose in 2009, which included anaesthetic and antidepressants. Don Simpson, co-producer of Hollywood blockbusters such as *Beverly Hills Cop, Top Gun* and *Crimson Tide*, died in 1996 aged 52. Police searching Simpson's Bel Air estate discovered thousands of pills lined up neatly in alphabetical order in his bedroom closet. They later discovered Simpson had obtained over 15,000 psychiatric amphetamines, tranquillisers and sedatives from 15 doctors and 8 pharmacies. Steve Simmons, a senior investigator for the California Medical Board, stated:

"Everybody understands how lethal street drugs like heroin are, but it takes a prescription overdose by someone famous like Don Simpson to

---

[445] "Di's Hooked on the Happy Drug", *Daily Record*, 7th November 1994, p.26

[446] *Los Angeles Times*, "Heath Ledger's Death Ruled Accidental Overdose", 7th February 2008

drive home the fact that pharmaceutical medications are just as deadly."[447]

Can't keep hold of this good feeling

Elizabeth Wurtzel's book, *Bitch*, is one example among thousands of how popular literature has sustained the revolt. The author's celebration of a life devoid of traditional mores becomes a lament to spiritual abandonment and bondage. James Crowley reviews Wurtzel's book:

"…If she has a thesis, it is that women can find freedom only through aggressive self-assertion ['Girl Power'], by wilfully flouting convention, by being entirely bad even. 'I intend to scream, shout… throw tantrums and confess intimate details about my life,' she writes. 'I intend to do what I want to do and be what I want to be and answer only to myself.' Can she be serious?"

"…Wurtzel has certainly embraced the dark side. *Prozac Nation* [her previous novel] told of her battles with depression and drug abuse, of her suicide attempt and chaotic sexuality and of the misery of a Manhattan childhood marred by her parents' messy divorce…. Over lunch, Wurtzel told me that she was indeed miserable. Her twenties were, in effect, a chain of successes, a staff job on *The New Yorker magazine,* a best-selling book that defined the spirit of the age, fame and wealth [traditionally Lucifer]. 'I have so much good fortune, and everything is so glorious, yet there's this shadow hanging over me. I just can't keep hold of this good feeling.'" [448]

Today's children's books may include *Daddy Has a Roommate* and *Heather Has Two Mummies*. Bestselling children's author Philip Pullman's new foray is entitled *The Good Man Jesus and the Scoundrel Christ*. Britain's *Daily Mail* writes:

"The book, due to be published next Easter, accepts there was a holy man called Jesus but says the idea of such a divine link came from the

---

[447] "Buying Off the Drug Traffic Cop", *Freedom*, Vol.30, Issue 1, Los Angeles, CA

[448] *The Times*, London, 21st May 1998

'fervid imagination' of the apostle St Paul. Pullman has already been condemned by the Vatican for the allegorical trilogy *His Dark Materials*, which has been described as anti-Christian."[449]

The evolution effect on law and order

From the 1960's onwards, British justice was fed through the mangler. After the abolition of capital punishment, robbers no longer searched each other for weapons before going on a raid. Criminality began to be excused on grounds of diminished responsibility and treated with drugs rather than punished. A steady rise in serious crime resulted. The police, traditionally unarmed and viewed as the gentle protectors of the community, were branded 'racist' or 'right-wing' and reorganised. Home Office targets could now be met by pursuing soft targets who did not fight back. Muggers and thieves walked free under new European human rights legislation while citizens were arrested for defending themselves. Today, the British bobby wears a stab-proof vest and hangs out in police vans with Kevlar-clad SWAT cops who call everyone 'civilians'. Britain is the most surveilled nation on Earth, possessing 20% of the world's CCTV cameras to spy on its citizens, yet only one crime is solved each year for every 1,000 cameras. 1 in 78 Britons is now under surveillance. 3,500 new criminal offences have been brought in since Tony Blair came to power in 1997.

The destabilising effect this mad, mad world has had on public morale has been deliberate and calculating. Nothing makes sense and that's the whole point. Release the 'Libyan bomber' on compassionate grounds. Fine the public for leaving their wheelie bins out an extra day. Send the British army to Afghanistan with poor equipment, then, when soldiers are injured, claw back their compensation. While you are doing that, import all the Afghan youths you can and let them claim benefits.

---

[449] *Daily Mail*, 7th September 2009

"Mrs Withers [81] had just finished her lunchtime sandwich and rather than throw away the morsels that remained, she decided to throw them to the birds. Having done that, she even put the bag in the nearest litter bin. The wardens demanded her name and address, told her she was breaking the law and threatened her with a £2,000 fine. Two days later she received a fixed penalty notice in the post, alleging that she had been 'seen emptying the contents of a bag to feed the pigeons.' She said the birds cleared up the crumbs in the time it took for the wardens to take down her details." [450]

Richard Littlejohn writes:

"Some people complain that all this is very un-British. Sorry to shatter your illusions, but this is very British indeed. Very new Labour British. As British as shopping your neighbours for breaking the hosepipe ban and as British as Eastbourne Council fining shopkeepers £75 if a seagull tears open their rubbish bags…. Punishment is always the weapon of first resort. It's about showing us who's boss."[451]

The madder the better. Today we have a Gay Police Association,[452] a National Black Police Association,[453] a Pagan Police Association[454] and a Trans(gendered) Police Association.[455] In fact, as Colin Rossini from Bradwell laments:

"Pagan cops, gay cops, lesbian cops, patriotism-free cops… Everything except tough street cops in Labour's lunatic landscape of lost values."[456]

At the time of writing, the Red Cross has ordered 430 of its stores to take down Christmas decorations for fear of offending British Muslims. The BBC is producing a documentary in time for Christmas, portraying the pregnant Virgin Mary as a rape victim.

[450] **Littlejohn, Richard** *Littlejohn's Britain,* Arrow Books, 2007, p.31
[451] Ibid.
[452] www.gay.police.uk
[453] www.nbpa.co.uk
[454] http://news.bbc.co.uk/1/hi/uk/8154812.stm
[455] www.ntpa.org.uk
[456] *Daily Mail,* 4th August 2009, p.55

Another friend of Tony Blair's, Lord Justice Keene, has won a plum job which carried heavy influence over what is left of the British legal system. Lord Woolf, another Blairite, has ordered judges and magistrates to cease jailing burglars who are up for the second offence, who steal expensive goods and jewellery, who raid in a gang, or who harass and rob the elderly. The day after Woolf's pronouncement, drug addict and serial robber Danny Coulson, 28, who pleaded guilty to two night raids on commercial premises and asked for a further 16 robberies to be taken into consideration, walked free from court, grinning at the prospect of something called 'community treatment'. Another crack-addict, Lee Skinner, who admitted to 90 crimes ranging from burglary to auto-theft to shoplifting, was let off twice from prison after the judge followed Woolf's guidelines. Another criminal with a string of convictions was spared jail because the judge believed he had a promising career as a poet.

The Un-naming of evil

A culture which teaches its young they are nothing but animals should not be surprised when they start behaving like animals.

TEENAGE 'COLUMBINE COPYCATS' PLANNED 'BEST MASSACRE EVER... TO KILL THOUSANDS' IN ATTACKS ON SCHOOL AND SHOPPING CENTRE

Matthew Swift, 18, and his friend Ross McKnight, 16, both loners with a grudge against society, hoped 'to kill thousands' in an attack on schoolmates and a shopping centre, it was alleged. The younger boy even wrote an essay describing how he carries out a shooting at his school in which ten die, including himself and Swift....

The court heard Swift's notepad contained a CCTV still of Harris and Klebold during the Columbine massacre next to which he had written: "My favourite picture in the world. To most just a CCTV shot. I perceive so much more, I see depression, sadness, rage, hate, deceit. Most of all I see two kids enraged by the corruption of this world. The image is beautiful."[457]

In his book *The Death of Satan*, author Andrew Delbanco addresses the issue of society's 'un-naming of evil' with a simple change of vocabulary. Vance Packard, the author of numerous works on subliminal advertising, makes the observation in *Hidden Persuaders* that, in order to gain the moral/political/philosophical high ground in a given debate, your chances are improved considerably by pre-empting the opening vocabulary. To do this you need political correctness and more laws to hamstring dissent.

Delbanco shows that, until quite recently, society had a clearly defined idea of 'moral evil'. Today, the words 'moral', 'sin', 'ethics', 'wickedness' and 'evil' are sneered at for their religious connotations, yet never has 'evil' been more ubiquitous than today. The problem, says Delbanco, is that:

"…we feel something that our culture no longer gives us the vocabulary to express."

Does evil exist? Two French students are butchered to death in New Cross, London. Laurent Bonomo and Gabriel Ferez, both 23, are trussed up and tortured with knives for two hours to extract their PIN numbers. The pair are then stabbed a total of *244 times* in 'an orgy of bloodletting' at Bonomo's flat in south-east London.[458]

Or perhaps Tracey Connelly standing by while her sadistic neo-Nazi lover and his brother torture her 17 month-old toddler over a period of months. Baby Peter is eventually found dead in his bloodsplattered cot with a broken back, fractured ribs and fifty other injuries. Tracey Connelly views her three-year sentence as an annoyance and says she's looking forward to seeing Baby Peter in heaven one day.

---

[457] *Daily Mail,* 3rd September 2009
[458] Ibid, 29th April 2009

"Like the Moors murderess, Connelly aided and abetted a brute she was sexually in thrall to. She put her own pleasure before her baby's pain. And with what cunning did she smear chocolate onto the sores and bruises on Peter's face so that a dozy social worker would not guess the child was being battered by his mother's lover.

While Barker was 'entertaining himself' by putting Peter on a stool and spinning it round until he flew off and hurt himself, where was the woman that bewildered little boy looked to for protection? She was watching pornography. Or boasting in an internet chat room that she was 'madly in love with the most amazing guy'. That would be the same amazing guy who allowed his rottweiler to bite Peter on the head. The teethmarks were clearly visible on the dead child."[459]

Such crimes find a natural home in a nation devoid of decency, and Cool Britannia has long since ceased being decent.

'INHUMANE' MOTORISTS DROVE OVER AND AROUND HIT-AND-RUN VICTIM AS HE LAY DYING IN THE STREET

"Motorists who left a cyclist to die in the road after he was knocked over by a stolen car were described as inhuman yesterday. Instead of stopping, they simply swerved around him, and detectives believe that one may even have driven over the badly injured Stephen Wills, breaking both his legs. By the time a passer-by finally raised the alarm, Mr Wills, 55, who had been riding home from a dinner, was already dead."[460]

Sociologists sharpen their pencils to find out why it happened. Could it be because the timeless laws which gave us protection have been buried in the shifting sands of atheist relativism? Laws like 'love thy neighbour as thyself' (not drive over his legs while he's lying in the road), 'thou shalt not murder', 'thou shalt not lie, steal, take the name of the Lord in vain, or sleep with thy neighbour's wife'? Today you can murder if the baby's not wanted, commit fraud and get away with it, cheat on thy MP's expenses, blaspheme Jesus on *Live at the Apollo* if it raiseth a laugh, and sleep with thy neighbour's wife the way they do on *Desperate Housewives*.

---

[459] Ibid, 13th August 2009
[460] Ibid, 17th April 2008

None of this is 'modern liberalism'. This rebellion against common decency is as old as man himself and typified by the insane society.

The Dark Lord

Most atheists are unaware of the theological ramifications of their beliefs because they do not concern themselves with 'religion'. The problem is, even if one professes no belief in God or anything else, that's still a belief. The atheist seeks random causes for man's existence and thereby no ultimate accountability for his actions. Man is at the top, self-deified and ruling the roost. In theological terms, this is known as atheistic Satanism, the most prominent today of the Luciferian beliefs. American occultist Anton LaVey, who founded the worldwide Church of Satan in San Francisco, explained it thus:

"And he must, as a Satanist, knowing this, realising what his human potential is, eventually, and here is one of the essential points of Satanism, attaining his own godhood in accordance with his own potential. Therefore, each man, each woman, is a god or goddess in Satanism."[461]

Peter Gilmore, who took over as 'high priest' after LaVey's death in 1997, writes:

"Satanists do not believe in the supernatural, in neither God nor the Devil. To the Satanist, he is his own God. Satan is a symbol of Man living as his prideful, carnal nature dictates. The reality behind Satan is simply the dark evolutionary force of entropy that permeates all of nature and provides the drive for survival and propagation inherent in all living things. Satan is not a conscious entity to be worshipped, rather a reservoir of power inside each human to be tapped at will. Thus any concept of sacrifice is rejected as a Christian aberration—in Satanism there's no deity to which one can sacrifice."[462]

---

[461] **Holmberg, Eric** *The Allure of Rock,* Amercian Portrait Films, 1999
[462] http://www.churchofsatan.com/Pages/Feared.html

As opposed to *theistic* Satanism, which is the worshiping of the Devil as God, involving the practice of magic(k), arcane ritual and sometimes animal sacrifice.

Atheistic Satanism then, according to LaVey and Gilmore, is not worshiping the Devil at all. It is egotism (pride), acknowledging no higher power above you, not even Satan. It is spirit-led. It's the serpent's hiss in the Garden. The Devil's desire to **'be like the Most High'**. Man liberated to become his own god, to be who he wants to be and do what he wants to do with no singeing of the conscience. Aleister Crowley's *"Do what thou wilt shall be the whole of the law"* is the endgame, along with *"Life is the great indulgence. Death is the great abstinence. Therefore make the most of life here and now."* (Book of Satan 1:4).

Atheistic Satanism sees the Devil as the icon of man's inherent sin nature. The goal is rebellion against God's order and the unchaining of the Christ conscience. To the evolutionist, God is the spoiler of pleasures, the unwelcome rulebook and mythical judge of a world which, in fact, made itself. The atheist recognises only human and 'natural' law. Man is the supreme animal.

Some of the most popular channels, serials and soaps on UK TV continually push these themes: *The Discovery Channel, Virgin Media, Sex in the City, Sexcetera, Coronation Street, The History of Porn, EastEnders, Brookside, Buffy the Vampire Slayer, Planet of the Apes, Hellboy, Supernatural, Primeval, Big Brother, Shameless, Men Behaving Badly, South Park, Married with Children, Absolutely Fabulous*, and so on. How about *Star Trek*? For example, the episode when Kirk and his intrepid crew go off in search of God and ultimately find him as they gaze up at a projection of themselves.

'Cult classics' like the *Lion King, Mad Max, The Matrix, The Terminator, Wanted, the Devil's Advocate* and *Beauty and the Beast* are all about teaching us the 'morality of violence' and 'the beautiful side of evil'. *The Lord of the Rings* and *Harry Potter* speak to our children of the enchantment of spells, witchcraft and potions, complete with goblins, trolls, hobbits and devils, which of course fall under our control so long as we know the right words. The poster of *Beauty and the Beast* depicts a devil figure holding a rose. The poster for Al Pacino's *The Devil's Advocate* has the caption, *"Evil Has Its Winning Ways."*

In the movie *The Silence of the Lambs*, Anthony Hopkins plays cannibalistic psychiatrist Hannibal Lecter, who admonishes Jodie Foster's politically correct FBI officer for pathologising his wickedness:

"Nothing happened to me, Officer Starling. I happened. You can't reduce me to a set of influences. You've given up good and evil for behaviourism, Officer Starling. You've got everyone in moral dignity pants – nothing is ever anybody's fault. Look at me, Officer Starling. Can you stand to say I'm evil?"

Wendy Wallace, in her *Four Horsemen of the Apocalypse*, remarks:

"Other films push 'Messiah' themes to replace Jesus as traditional Redeemer, such as *The Day the Earth Stood Still* (the ET is handsome and his name is Carpenter [Jesus]). *ET* (grey aliens as gods), and television series such as *V* and *The Intruders* (mate with a reptile and produce a magical child who'll save the world) play against Streiber's *Communion* (these things are nasty, but you can't help but love them) and *Fire From the Sky, Signs* and *Aliens* (these things are nasty, and you can't help but fear them)."[463]

To Richard Dawkins, to whom atheism is 'a liberating experience', the Satanism moniker will be unwelcome. Then again, what better title for a Satanist's *magnum opus* than *The God Delusion?* In ignorance of the real battlefield he's blundering across, Dawkins lends his support to the atheist Camp Quest outings to get the message across to the children. Peter Hitchens writes:

---

[463] Wallace, Wendy, *The Four Horsemen of the Apocalypse,* op. cit.

"Some unfortunate children are being subjected to an Atheist Summer Camp. I hope it rains and rains and rains. But they have another problem. Professor Richard Dawkins is said to be in favour of this.

Yet Professor Dawkins said recently: 'What I really object to – and I think it's actually abusive to children – is to take a tiny child and say "You are a Christian child" or "You are a Muslim child". I think it is wicked if children are told "You are a member of such and such a faith simply because your parents are."'

Why then is it all right to tell a child it should be an atheist?" [464]

Pamela B McCullum writes:

"[Dawkins'] Atheist Summer Camp takes me back to my childhood in the Thirties. As a niece of Dora and Bertrand Russell, I was 'privileged' to attend their boarding school, and if ever there was brainwashing, it happened in this so-called progressive and enlightened establishment. Library books were vetted for the main theme – the glorious Russian revolution and its heroes, Lenin and Stalin. No religious or material relating to any faith was evident. Indeed when the children – mostly from the professional and academic world – wrote their own plays, the words of the characters were put into their mouths by the staff, such as "We don't think much of God." So the attempted indoctrination of vulnerable youngsters is nothing new. The greatest sin in the Russell's book was to question the 'truth' of what they were trying to instil.

The atheists and secularists insist only their [beliefs] are valid. The irony is that they would not need to go to such lengths with their conditioned-thinking agenda but for one obvious drawback – the spiritual hunger in our society."[465]

Rock of ages

Christian faith was important to the Old Order, not because the British were outwardly deep about their religion at that time – they were not. But Christianity recognised man's inherent evil and was a brake against the worst excesses of which he was capable. God was a moral compass in the bad times and the certainty that your

---

[464] *Daily Mail,* 2nd August 2009
[465] Ibid. 5th August 2009

strivings and labours were for the forces of good. A blanket of comfort in the trenches. An angel on your shoulder in the flak-torn skies over the enemy. The assurance that if you lost your life for a righteous cause, God would forgive your sins and raise you to glory on the last day.

The Christian belief once lent enchantment to the British and their countryside. Every village had an active church and the minister was the heart of the community before television morphed him into a paedophilic degenerate. The vicar gave the parish peace, order, dignity and a steadfast example to follow. He was God's man and the Old Order backed him unflinchingly. They tramped along to church every Sunday, scrubbed clean and dressed to the nines, mumbled their way through the catechism, shuffled their feet through the sermon, raised their voices to 'Nearer My God to Thee', then shook the vicar's hand as they left. That was the deal the Old Order had with God. Be good, turn up, do the business, and "OK. I'll be off, then." And in return, God agreed to remain unobtrusive, dependable, willing to listen and undeniably British.

Me, myself and I

In times of terror, religion is an insurance policy few allow to lapse completely. In times of peace and plenty, God is forgotten. In the months following 9/11, churches across Britain reported record attendance. Eight years on, the churches are empty.

Today our religion is the religion of 'me' and our god is gold. We're working hard at our naughtiness. We're proud of our lawlessness. We celebrate them in our mindless soaps. We lift them up in our toe-curling pop videos. We idolise them in the zoo media and those mawkish, camp celebrity quiz shows. Surely we deserve some reward for all the abhorrence we've honed into fine art. An effigy of Jesus Christ in a bowl of urine? Why stop there? As the posters for British comedian Dennis Pennis proudly proclaim above his gravestone, *"Rest in P*ss."*

Once we had churches, now we have glass cathedral malls decked out with all the latest retail outlets to satisfy that spiritual yearning. Once we went to church on Sundays to worship with the family. Today on Sundays we take the family to worship at B & Q and Bluewater. Instead of being given a song sheet at the door, we're given a loyalty card application. Instead of lining up at the rail for communion, we queue impatiently at the checkout. Instead of leaving our sins at the feet of Christ, we heave our shopping into our Volvo. We worship our Harley Davidsons instead of our heavenly David's Son. We celebrate our greed with our sons instead of confessing it before the Son. We cry in anger at the cost of spirits instead of weeping in thanks for what we cost the Spirit.

Today you no longer need to watch TV, you can date one. You no longer have to drink Coke, you can snort it. You no longer marry the heroine, you can freebase her. When we contemplate divorce we're so hardened, our only definition of 'a crying shame' is a plane full of lawyers crashing and burning with two empty seats.

Forget the kids. Our teenage boyz don't know whether to lead or follow on the dance-floor. Our teenage gurlz are obscene and not heard. With divorce proceedings going out at £100 an hour and half their worldly estate, have married men come to the conclusion the cheapest sex is the sex they can pay for?

Rupert Murdoch, thank you for your digital TV revolution. Now we have a porn channel for every psalm:

THE TWENTY-THIRD CHANNEL
The TV is my shepherd,
I shall not want,
It makes me lie down on the sofa,
It leads me away from the faith,
It destroys my soul,
It leads me in the path of sex and violence

349

For the sponsor's sake.
Yea, though I walk
In the shadow of Christian responsibilities,
There will be no interruption,
For the TV is with me,
Its cable and remote,
They comfort me.
It prepares a commercial for me
In the presence of all my worldliness.
It anoints my head with
Humanism and consumerism,
My coveting runneth over.
Surely laziness and ignorance
Shall follow me
All the days of my life.
And I shall dwell in the house
Watching TV forever.

A newspaper cartoon depicts a man arriving in hell, faced with the Devil and a TV.

"Wow!" exclaims the man. "I didn't know there'd be TV down here!"

The Devil replies, "There's nothing but TV down here."

THE DOCTOR WITHIN

"Let no one who has the slightest desire to live in peace and quietness be tempted, under any circumstances, to enter upon the chivalrous task of trying to correct a popular error." – **William Thoms, deputy librarian for the House of Lords, c. 1873**

Today's brave new world is in trouble in another area. In all the sources studied for the preparation of this book, little to no mention was made of the effect evolutionary philosophy has had on medicine. Of the sources that do tackle the subject, the area chiefly covered is the aforementioned treatment of the 'mentally ill'.

Psychiatry pronounces that children are nothing more than stimulus-response animals to be controlled pharmaceutically. Millions of the most vulnerable members of society have been hooked on highly destructive medications for bogus diseases such as ADHD and Obsessive Compulsive Disorder, for which there is no scientific evidence, nor one *bona fide* medical test. Medical science in general, following evolutionary precepts, eschews nutrition and lifestyle changes in favour of man-made drugs to treat symptoms in diseased individuals. Never mind the bafflement of getting from amino acids to the first protein, the human cell is regulated by a further universe of DNA/RNA, minerals, vitamins, enzymes, fats, sugars and hormones which interact in ways science is only just beginning to discover.

Evolution's scorn of nutrition is evident today in the medical establishment's refusal to train its doctors in nutrition. The miracle of every cell in our body comes from what we eat yet, incredibly, drugs, radiation and surgery are the only options for cancer. Millions have died because of this catastrophic wrong turn.[466] In

---

[466] **Day, Phillip** *Health Wars,* Credence, 2007; also **Day, Phillip** *The ABC's of Disease,* Credence 2004

Australia and the United States today, doctors can be struck off and sent to jail for using nutrition and lifestyle changes instead of chemotherapy to treat cancer. Others have found themselves the baffling target of pernicious witchhunts to stamp out unorthodox 'quackery', yet how unorthodox is food in the matter of a person's health? Dr Albert Schweitzer once remarked:

> "I'll tell you a secret. We doctors do nothing. We only help and encourage the doctor within."

Yet to the FDA, BMA, TGA, MHRA and everything else that ends in an 'A', the Doctor Within is an importunate profit-wrecker. Drugs are the only empiricism. The game has big stakes and the public are the chess pieces.

Bedside manner

Through ignorance of the biophysical effects of bad news on the immune system, doctors think little today of condemning a patient to death. "Well, Mr Smith, we've examined the scans and the cancer has spread. You have four months." Few show any interest in the patient's state of nutrition, or whether they are toxic, deficient, stressed or dehydrated. In the rush to intervene with human brilliance, Mr Smith ends up so full of carcinogenic chemotherapy and radiation, his loved ones can find him in the dark. Surgery confirms what the doctor knew all along – that the cancer cannot be stopped, not with these tools at any rate, which wreck the patient's immune system and often finish him. "If doctor says I'm done for, then I'm done for," rues Mr Smith, and shuffles off to the bus, with nothing to do but go home now and weep with his wife and dog. Or check himself into a Dignitas clinic. Ernst Rüdin's old friend, state-sanctioned euthanasia, is back. Miss C Morton is outraged.

"What is our country coming to when nurses may now discuss suicide with their dying patients but may not mention God?"[467]

Why not mention the Doctor Within, who has other plans for Mr Smith if the patient is willing? For 26 years as a health reporter, I have covered the progress of nutritional research and lectured on the subject around the world. I've seen patients with no right to live even another two months take control of their situation and turn it around with lifestyle changes. I've written a dozen books on how you are what you eat, drink, slap on your skin, breathe in, look at and listen to, yet the studies validating this approach are ignored because the answers don't pay. It's the Doctor Within or the Doctor at £100 an Hour. Money talks. People die. Welcome to 21st century allopathic medicine, the third leading cause of death in the Western world.

Hopeless

We've made some great advances in medicine and all credit where due, but it serves the public to know what doctors are good at doing and where they are hopeless. Doctors are very good at putting you back together after a car accident. They are good at infant survivability at birth. They are good at pain management, prosthesis, transplants and A&E trauma medicine. They are hopeless at disease, both physical and 'mental', borne out, for example, by the five-year or better survival rates for almost all forms of cancer, which are largely unchanged for the past forty years in spite of the billions spent.

And what of the billions of dollars' worth of bypass surgery carried out around the world to this day? Heart disease still kills 1 in every 3 of us, and in 50% of those deaths, the first symptom *is* death.[468] Few GPs are trained in the Doctor Within. They were

---

[467] *Daily Mail*, 3rd August 2009
[468] www.doctoryourself.com; www.orthomolecular.org

taught doctor-intervention, man-centred, evolutionary biochemistry (pharmacology) in the pharma-sponsored medical schools in which they were trained. Not a hoot was paid to nutrition. They swallowed the idiocy that food is good enough to make every cell in their body (40 trillion of them), but not good enough to fix them when they are sick. Philip Binzel MD laments:

"Most of my first patients were those who had all of the surgery, radiation and chemotherapy they could tolerate and their tumors were still growing. I did for these patients the best I knew to do. My biggest problem at the time was understanding nutrition. In four years of medical school, one year of Family Practice residency, I had not had even one lecture on nutrition."[469]

Dr James Le Fanu writes:

"The commonest misunderstanding in medicine is why doctors should "treat the symptoms and not the cause", to which the response can only be that, regrettably, the cause of virtually every illness in the medical textbooks, from asthma and arthritis all the way to Zoons balanitis, is quite unknown. Thus the best we can hope for is to "treat the symptoms" as effectively as we can."[470]

We don't know what causes disease? Apparently not. So patients with cancer, osteoporosis, arthritis, heart disease and diabetes are stuffed full of chemicals with scant concern for why they fell ill in first place. There is no money in the 'why', only in the 'what'. Greed places profits over patients with devastating consequences. Threats are invented which scare the public to death. The saviour pushed is always man with his life-saving medicines:

PLAGUE ATTACK – The horrifying spectre of terrorists turning themselves into walking biological weapons on Britain's streets was raised by doctors. Fanatics could be given smallpox and walk amongst us infecting people, yet we only have a vaccine for one in three. **Express Newspapers, 6th March 2003**

---

[469] **Binzel, P E** *Alive and Well*, American Media, 2000
[470] *Sunday Telegraph,* 22nd October 2006

SMALLPOX KILLS! Smallpox kills about 30% of those infected with the disease. There is no cure but there is a vaccine. If given before exposure, the vaccine will prevent the disease from appearing. *But is there enough for everyone?* **BBC NEWS, 13th January 2003**

TUBERCULOSIS! NEW SPECTRE OF THE WHITE DEATH - We had it beaten, but TB is back and deadlier than ever.... Anyone who refuses inoculation is a danger both to society and to himself. **Daily Mail, 30th March 2001**

MEASLES! Public health officials have stressed the severity of the situation. The Government is now urging parents to take heed of this warning and allow their children to be immunised with the MMR jab before an epidemic sweeps the nation. **Readers Digest, January 2001**

FIRMS INVENTING DISEASES TO
BOOST PROFIT, CLAIMS REPORT

'Pharmaceutical companies have been accused of deliberately creating diseases to boost profits, with many of their marketing strategies turning healthy people into patients, a leading journal has claimed. The Public Library of Science Medicine has said that the drugs industry is promoting non-existing illnesses or exaggerating minor ailments. It lists female sexual dysfunction, Attention Deficit Hyperactivity Disorder (ADHD), osteoporosis and restless legs syndrome as some of the complaints targeted by unscrupulous pharmaceuticals.' – **Irish Examiner, 12th April 2006, p.10**

Today, it's swine flu. Tomorrow, who knows? Today, if you refuse certain drugs for your family, child protection services will be unleashed. If you refuse chemotherapy for your child on the grounds that it's carcinogenic poison, your child can be removed and forcefully poisoned to death 'to preserve their human rights'. If you *don't seem right,* you can be sectioned and placed into padded confinement and a drug regimen enforced. Such actions are all the more sinister when carried out with the best of intentions. You can be sincere, and you can be sincerely wrong.

The reality is, almost all drugs are an unqualified failure with disease. Then there are the side-effects, ruinous cost and the potential for litigation. Banishing symptoms is not the same thing as curing disease. The conclusion is unwelcome, un-man-centred, so the Doctor Within is excluded. There's no money in it, and to admit that the body has an innate intelligence far beyond our own is to yield man's control to the molecules. So four thousand more women run around Mote Park, Maidstone in their *brassières* to raise money for breast cancer to develop more drugs to continue to follow the wrong course with the maximum of precision.[471] Years pass and we get more cancer, more strokes and more heart attacks despite the knowledge gained, fortunes spent and 'wars' declared. MPs wonder how to save the National Health Service while the brightest and best wander the corridors of our pharmaceutical corporations with unlimited budgets. Miracle drugs are daily touted. With some, the cure turns out to be worse than the disease. With others, the cure *is* the disease. Andrew Saul PhD, assistant editor of the *Journal of Orthomolecular Medicine,* is fed up.

"I have seen the foolishness of conventional disease care wisdom. I have seen hospitals feed white bread to patients with bowel cancer and hospitals feed Jello to leukemia patients. I have seen schools feed bright red Slush Puppies to 7 year-olds for lunch and I have seen children vomit up a desktop full of red crud afterwards. And, I have seen those same children later line up at the school nurse for hyperactivity drugs.

I have seen hospital patients allowed to go two weeks without a bowel movement. I have seen patients told that they have six months to live when they might live sixty months. I have seen people recover from serious illness, only to have their physician berate them for having used natural healing methods to do so. I have seen infants spit up formula while their mothers were advised not to breast-feed. I've seen better

---

[471] **Deutscher, W** *Social Problems*, University of Manchester Institute of Science and Technology course handout

ingredients in dog food than in the average school or hospital lunch. And I have seen enough."[472]

The right gas in the machine

In the documentary *Food Matters,* directors James Colquhoun and Laurentine ten Bosch gather the evidence. 250,000 Americans lose their lives annually to doctor-induced (iatrogenic) action.[473] On the other hand, thousands of studies reveal the benefits of comprehensive nutrition, stress reduction, exercise and lifestyle changes. This was known half a century ago after work was carried out among a dozen indigenous peoples who routinely lived beyond 100. They survived off the land, ate their own produce and lived to great ages in low-stress environments. These folks are rarely mentioned in the press because they don't live like we do and don't use Western medicine.

Dr Samuel King Hutton wrote:

"Some diseases common in Europe have not come under my notice during a prolonged and careful survey of the health of the [Labrador] Eskimos. Of these diseases, the most striking is cancer." [474]

Remarking on his interview with Joseph Herman Romig, dubbed 'Alaska's most famous doctor', Dr Weston A Price claimed that,

"...in his [Romig's] thirty-six years of contact with these people, he had never seen a case of malignant disease among the truly primitive Eskimos and Indians, although it frequently occurs when they are modernized." [475]

---

[472] www.doctoryourself.com

[473] *Journal of the American Medical Association,* vol.284, July 2000

[474] **Hutton, Samuel King** *Among the Eskimos of Labrador,* London and Philadelphia 1912

[475] **Price, Weston A** *Nutrition and Physical Degeneration,* London and New York, 1939

The stories are similar wherever non-Westernised tribes were encountered and food not a problem. Lack of degenerative diseases in another indigenous culture led famous explorer Roald Amundsen to comment in 1908:

"My sincerest wish for our friends the Nechilli Eskimos is, that civilization may never reach them." [476]

The *Ecologist* writes:

"Sir Robert McCarrison, a surgeon in the Indian Health Service, observed "a total absence of all diseases during the time I spent in the Hunza valley [seven years]... During the period of my association with these peoples, I never saw a case of... cancer." [477]

Dr Alexander Berglas sums up his own findings about our man-polluted environment:

"Civilization is, in terms of cancer, a juggernaut that cannot be stopped.... It is the nature and essence of industrial civilization to be toxic in every sense.... We are faced with the grim prospect that the advance of cancer and of civilization parallel each other." [478]

The good news

Upon embarking on a study of longevity, you don't get very far before encountering the Hunzakuts. This isolated culture of north-eastern Pakistan, located in the Himalayan foothill valleys, was not discovered until the 1920's when British Army engineers traversed the mountain passes and came into contact with them for the first time. One practitioner on the expedition, Dr Robert McCarrison (later Sir Robert McCarrison), was able to document in some detail the astonishing people he encountered.

The Hunzas were open, warm and friendly and had a tremendous sense of community. McCarrison noticed the lack of

---

[476] **Amundsen, Roald** *The Northwest Passage*, London and New York, 1908
[477] *The Ecologist,* vol. 28, No. 2, March/April 1998, p. 95
[478] Ibid.

diseases and fine condition of the people. In their indigenous environment, the Hunzas exhibited near perfect physical and mental health. There was no sign of cancer, heart disease, diabetes, ulcers, colitis, diverticulosis, high blood pressure or childhood ailments. Neither was there any juvenile delinquency or crime. Respect for age was ubiquitous and the tribe's sense of community made it clear that if one was to succeed, all had to succeed. The happiness with which Hunzas executed their daily chores produced peace of mind and a lack of strife. They had no police, no jails, no judges and no doctors or hospitals.

Their teeth were in the finest condition – perfect dental arches with no disfiguration, caries or tarnishments common to Westerners. Some of their population were estimated to be older than 100, fathering children over this age, with some of the most vital apparently surviving to 120. Hunza womenfolk experienced few birth problems and the matriarchs of 80 looked the equivalent of 40, with fresh and remarkably unblemished complexions.

McCarrison later became Director of Research on Nutrition in India and Chairman of the Post-Graduate Medical Education Committee at Oxford University. He was so taken by these people, he spent years writing at length of their 'secrets'.

"These people are unsurpassed by any other race in perfection of physique. They are long-lived, vigorous in youth and age, capable of great endurance and enjoy remarkable freedom from disease in general." [479]

Renee Taylor studied the Hunzas and was told by their King, the Mir:

"The idleness of retirement is a much greater enemy in life than work. One must never retire *from* something, one must retire *to* something." [480]

---

[479] **French, Roger** *The Man Who Lived in Three Centuries*, Natural Health Society of Australia, 2000, p.29

[480] **Taylor, Renee** *Hunza Health Secrets*, Keats Publishing, 1964

The Hunza workload is prodigious. Author Roger French remarks that it is common for a tribesman to walk the 200km round-trip to Gilgit in neighbouring Pakistan, carrying a heavy load over mountain passes and dangerous terrain without stops other than meal breaks. The men regularly play vigorous games including volleyball and polo. The young men aged 16 to 50 play against the elders who are well over 70 and, as observed in one game, included a man thought to be 125 years old. Hunza polo is ferocious and teeth are often lost. As the Mir remarks:

"The men of 100 feel no more fatigue than the men of 20." [481]

McCarrison attributed the Hunza success to super-nutrition and the absence of a toxic, industrial environment. He proved how diet was a major contributing factor by taking rats and feeding them a staple Hunza diet – fresh fruits and vegetables, dried fruits, legumes, wholegrain foods and goat's cheese and butter. Meat was a rarity and the meat and dairy components of their diet were low in contrast to Westernised diets today.

The water used by the Hunzas was highly mineralised with a spectrum of nutrients derived from mountain streams and glaciers. The tribesmen also irrigated their crops with this mixture, benefiting the food which they later consumed. Hunzas ate a high percentage of their meals raw. Biochemist Ernst Krebs, along with other researchers, also remarked that the Hunzakuts, proud farmers of apricots, always consumed the seeds (kernels) of their fruits along with the pulp. This practice is widely condemned in the West today due to a supposed danger of cyanide poisoning, yet Krebs discovered the active cyanide component in seed kernels and forty-five other foods was not only not harmful in moderation, but conferred strong anti-cancer properties to the consumer. Today this food group is known as the nitrilosides.

---

[481] French, Roger, *The Man Who Lived in Three Centuries*, op. cit. p.30

You are what you eat

McCarrison conducted experiments with rats, feeding different groups a variety of diets to adjudge the effects. Rats fed the Hunza staple were extremely long-lived and almost completely free of disease. Their condition was sleek, childbirth was easy and free of complications and the young ones were gentle, good-natured and healthy.

Another group was fed the diet of the poor of the Bengal/Madras region: pulses, rice, old vegetables, condiments and a little milk, together with city water. As described in his book, *Studies in Deficiency Diseases*, McCarrison's Bengal/Madras rats were not happy rodents. The list of diseases afflicting them included those of the ear, nose and throat, lungs and upper respiratory tract, gastrointestinal diseases, skin diseases, reproductive problems, cancer of the blood and lymph, heart disease and oedema.

McCarrison fed a third sample of rats the same diet consumed by the working-class Englishman of the day. Man-food. Refined, white bread and sugar, margarine, sweetened tea, boiled vegetables, tinned processed meats and jams. The same rash of diseases as previously reported with the Bengal/Madras group broke out among the rats, this time with severe additional complications; namely nervous diseases and pronounced delinquency among the rodents, which bit their attendants constantly and finally, by the 16th day of the experiment, began turning upon their own, killing each other and cannibalising the weaker among them.[482] McCarrison summarised as follows:

"I know of nothing so potent in producing ill-health as improperly constituted food. It may therefore be taken as a law of life, infringement of which shall surely bring its own penalties, that the single greatest factor

---

[482] For more information on the effect of diet on emotional and mental health, please see **Day, Phillip** *The Mind Game*, Credence Publications, 2002

in the acquisition of health is perfectly constituted food. Given the will, we have the power to build in every nation a people more fit, more vigorous and competent; a people with longer and more productive lives, and with more physical and mental stamina than the world has ever known." [483]

Biochemist Ernst Krebs remarks:

"There are many chronic or metabolic diseases that have challenged medicine. Many of these diseases have already been conquered. What proved to be their solution? By solution we mean prevention and cure. What really cures really prevents. Let us think of some of these diseases that have found total prevention and hence cure.

At one time, the metabolic disease known as scurvy killed hundreds of thousands of people, sometimes entire populations. This disease found total prevention and cure in the ascorbic acid or vitamin C component of fruits and vegetables. Similarly, the once fatal diseases so aptly called pernicious anemia, pellagra, beriberi, countless neuropathies, and the like, found complete cure and prevention in specific dietary factors, that is, <u>essential nutrients in an adequate diet</u>." [484]

Not the faintest idea

Confront a doctor about any of this and he'll mumble that not enough studies have been done, or say nothing and stare at his shoe-laces. The studies were done decades ago but the answers don't pay. If you don't want to be sick, you learn to be healthy and eat God's good food, not the perverted alternative. Nutrition and lifestyle are the primary strategies for good health and the Doctor Within takes care of the rest. That's not to say sensible drugs and medical care can never be used, but *we* don't fix anything.

Consider that Richard Dawkins is nothing more than a collection of chemicals worth 40p, and yet something has arranged them in so precise a fashion that Dawkins is able to live and breathe today and give vent to his spleen. When he cuts himself

---

[483] French, Roger, op. cit. p.32
[484] **Krebs, Ernst T** *Journal of Applied Nutrition*, vol.22, Numbers 3 & 4, 1970

with the blade of his wit, something heals him. Richard breathes air which so happens to be the precise mixture required to trigger countless reactions to give voice to his wrath. His proteins fold and lock without error. Enzymes zip across his cells to their docking points unerringly. Fats form Richard's cell walls, vitamins catalyse his reactions, and 400-800 species of micro-flora inhabit Dawkins' gut, providing 80% of his immune function and a myriad of vitamins, hormones and substrates for his diatribes. Anyone can look up 'gut flora' in Wikipedia and read:

"Research suggests that the relationship between gut flora and humans is not merely commensal (a non-harmful coexistence), but rather is a mutualistic, symbiotic relationship.[485] Though people can survive with no gut flora,[486] the microorganisms perform a host of useful functions, such as fermenting unused energy substrates, training the immune system, preventing growth of harmful species, regulating the development of the gut, producing vitamins for the host (such as biotin and vitamin K), and producing hormones to direct the host to store fats."[487]

Steinhoff's paper is entitled, "Who controls the crowd?" I bet his grant flew out of the window. Charlie Campbell cites other miracles which convinced him the human body was a design project:

"It has an amazingly complex nervous system, cardiovascular system, reproductive capability, skeletal system, muscle system and the ability to heal itself and fight off diseases. I find it difficult to believe that the human body could have come into existence by some mindless process, apart from an incredibly intelligent designer, even given millions of years.... And yet atheists believe that a human being with 206 bones, 640

---

[485] **Sears CL** "A dynamic partnership: celebrating our gut flora", *Anaerobe* 11 (5): 247–51, October 2005
[486] **Steinhoff U** "Who controls the crowd? New findings and old questions about the intestinal microflora", *Immunol.* Lett. 99 (1): 12–6, June 2005
[487] www.wikipedia.org

muscles and a heart that beats over 100,000 times a day is the product of a random series of accidents. This is foolish."[488]

Evolution's effect on health

But in Alice's Wonderland, watchdogs declare that organic food is no more nutritious than other food.[489] Joanna Blythman covers the cancerous conspiracy to put people off real grub in favour of processed, genetically modified fare which has been smothered in chemicals.[490] With man at the helm, it's what we'd expect. Nature is weak and needs a helping hand. The problem is, even the chickens found out.

CHICKENS NOT FOOLED BY GM CROPS

Chickens refusing to eat the maize they had been fed has led to the discovery that their feed had been genetically modified to include a well-known weed and insect killer. Strilli Oppenheimer's indigenous African chickens were refusing to eat the mealies in the chicken feed bought from a large supplier. Concerned that the birds may be ingesting genetically modified maize, she had the maize tested. The results confirmed Oppenheimer's initial suspicion -- the maize had been genetically engineered to produce proteins that are toxic to certain insects and weeds. About her chickens' refusal to eat their maize, Oppenheimer said: "They're smart."[491]

But real food doesn't make the medical system billions, and neither do healthy people. So our health czars promote cow's milk formula instead of breast milk. Statins rather than telling us how to be healthy. Diabetic medication rather than telling us how to be healthy. HRT drugs rather than telling us how to be healthy. Joint replacement surgery rather than telling us how to be healthy. Got pregnant 'by mistake'? They can fix that too.

---

[488] www.alwaysbeready.com
[489] *Daily Mail,* 30th July 2009
[490] Ibid. 3rd August 2009
[491] www.gmwatch.org, 3rd August 2009

Millions of babies can now be killed by doctors in defence of 'a woman's right to choose....' Let's complete that sentence: 'A woman's right to choose whether to murder her baby for lifestyle reasons.' After all, pregnancy is just evolution at work, so there's no judgment, it's just tissue, and it's apparently not human until 23 weeks old, so no remorse.

No remorse? In the film, *The Silent Scream,* Dr Bernard Nathanson shows the true horror of abortion with the help of ultrasound technology. Dr Nathanson should know. He once headed the world's largest abortion clinic in the US.

"Viewers are stunned to see a 12-week-old 'foetus' becoming desperate while attempting to escape the abortionist's suction curette. The tiny baby's heart rate doubles during the 'procedure' that ends its life."

The abortion war continues between liberals and religious conservatives. The death toll so far in America is several abortionists and 44 million babies – more than the entire population of Canada. Reported global abortions, broken down by country, are 945 million babies, or 13% of the current world population killed. The true figure is far higher.[492] Forget Helmand or Mogadishu, the most dangerous place to be on Earth today is in the womb of an American mother, where you have a 1 in 4 chance of being murdered.[493]

God is nowhere – God is now here?

Of all the creatures, humans have the capacity to reason and be wrong. Dawkins' brain, which he has never seen, operates in the physical to form 'mind' in the ethereal. How do chemicals form Richard's 'mind'? To Dawkins, it's chance. He does not satisfactorily explain the origins of man's personality, emotions,

---

[492] http://www.johnstonsarchive.net/policy/abortion/wrjp337sd.html
[493] **Missler, Chuck** *The Origin of Evil,* www.khouse.org

will and intellect other than through the evolution of genetic information. There's a big problem with this, according to Dr Marciej Giertych, a population geneticist for the European Union:

"Darwin assumed that the increase in information comes from natural selection. But natural selection reduces genetic information, and we know this from all the genetic, operational studies that we have."[494]

To unbiased science, however, Richard is a sentient human only by dint of an intelligence which replicates his cells, fires up his synapses and digests his lunches. When pushed by Ben Stein on a design inference for the origin of life, Dawkins intriguingly states the following:

"It could come about in the following way. It could be that at some earlier time, somewhere in the universe, a civilisation evolved by probably some kind of Darwinian means to a very, very high level of technology, and designed a form of life that they seeded onto, perhaps, this planet. Now that is a possibility, and an intriguing possibility. And I suppose it's possible that you might find evidence for that if you look at the details of biochemistry, molecular biology, you might find a signature of some sort of designer...."[495]

So Richard concedes that *aliens* could have seeded Earth if design there be, just not the God Alien.[496] Notice he does not dispute the power and code in the molecules. When asked what he might say if he ran into the Almighty after he died, Dawkins quotes atheist Bertrand Russell:

"Sir, why did You take such pains to hide Yourself?"[497]

Is the Designer hidden? The Bible answers in somewhat sterner terms:

---

[494] Stein, Ben, *Expelled – No Intelligence Allowed,* op. cit.
[495] Ibid.
[496] Ibid.
[497] Ibid.

"For the wrath of God is revealed from heaven against all ungodliness and unrighteousness of men, who hold the truth in unrighteousness. Because that which may be known of God is manifest in them, for God hath shewed it unto them. For the invisible things of Him from the creation of the world [Greek: *kosmos*] are clearly seen, being understood by the things that are made, even his eternal power and Godhead, so that they are without excuse.

Because that, when they knew God, they glorified Him not as God, neither were thankful, but became vain in their imaginations, and their foolish heart was darkened.

Professing themselves to be wise, they became fools, and changed the glory of the incorruptible God into an image made like to corruptible man, and to birds, and fourfooted beasts and creeping things. Wherefore God also gave them up to uncleanness through the lusts of their own hearts, to dishonour their own bodies between themselves. Who changed the truth of God into a lie, and worshipped and served the creature more than the Creator, who is blessed for ever. Amen." (Rom 1:18-25)

"Or speak to the Earth, and it shall teach thee: and the fishes of the sea shall declare unto thee. Who knoweth not in all these that the hand of the LORD hath wrought this?" (Job 12:8-9)

Next time you go for a walk, stand in front of a garden and examine the flowers in detail. What maintains each bloom? Renews every leaf? Gives life to even the tiniest creatures in the cycles of the seasons? All seems part of a whole with benevolent will, gently prompting us to experience its abundance. And what of our thoughts, operating in dimensions we can only surmise? Flashes of brilliance. Scenes of sheer ugliness. Capable of producing the greatest beauty or the basest of crimes. Our minds are plugged into the Great Beyond and there are two channels broadcasting. People grow sick when their thoughts become dark. Stress affects biochemistry and suppresses immune function. Placebo boosts health. Nocebo wrecks health. We are not out of the starting gate with any of this. We are still Newton:

"I do not know what I may appear to the world. But to myself, I seem to have only been like a boy playing on the sea shore, diverting myself, now and then, in finding a smoother pebble or prettier shell than the ordinary, while the great ocean of truth lay all undiscovered before me."

FORGIVE US!

"Yes, there are two paths you can go by but in the long run, there's still time to change the path you're on. And it makes me wonder."
– Led Zeppelin, *Stairway to Heaven*

Today, man is spiritually hungry. As of 2009, there are more registered witches and fortune-tellers in Britain than Anglican ministers. Of the latter, the reduced numbers now include lesbian and homosexual clergy and priests who blush at a virgin birth and Resurrection, not to mention the Creation and Flood. Then, as only Anglicans can, they trip over each other in their haste to apologise for the wrong sin:

CHURCH SAYS SORRY TO CHARLES DARWIN

"The Church of England will make an official apology to naturalist Charles Darwin for criticising his famous theory of evolution. Coming 126 years after his death, the church's apology will focus on how wrong it was for senior bishops in the past to misunderstand and attack Darwin's theory about man being descended from apes.

Senior church officials will post the apology in the form of an article written by the Reverend Dr Malcolm Brown on the church's website tomorrow. "Charles Darwin, 200 years from your birth (in 1809), the Church of England owes you an apology for misunderstanding you and, by getting our first reaction wrong, encouraging others to misunderstand you still," the article says, according to extracts printed by *The Mail on Sunday* newspaper.

…Dr Brown says everyone makes mistakes, the church included. "…It is important to think again about Darwin's impact on religious thinking, then and now." <u>Dr Brown said there was nothing incompatible between Darwin's scientific theories and Christian teaching</u>." [498]

---

[498] www.news.com.au, 14th September 2008

The Catholic hierarchy has similarly lost its bottle:

POPE BENEDICT 'BELIEVES IN EVOLUTION'

"Pope Benedict has aired his views on evolution for the first time - and says he partially believes Darwin's theories. The Pontiff said science had narrowed the way life's origins are understood and said Christians should take a broader approach to the question. However, he did not adopt a strictly scientific view of the origins if life, believing instead that God created life through evolution."[499]

POPE SACKS ASTRONOMER OVER EVOLUTION DEBATE

"Pope Benedict XVI has sacked his chief astronomer after a series of public clashes over the theory of evolution. He has removed Father George Coyne from his position as director of the Vatican Observatory after the American Jesuit priest repeatedly contradicted the Holy See's endorsement of 'intelligent design' theory, which essentially backs the 'Adam and Eve' theory of creation."[500]

Islam is a different story. No one dares tell Muslims they are wrong except, of course, our old friend from Oxford:

ATHEIST RICHARD DAWKINS BLAMES MUSLIMS FOR 'IMPORTING CREATIONISM' INTO CLASSROOMS

"Devout Muslims are importing creationist theories into science and are not being challenged because of political correctness, one of the country's most famous scientists said tonight.

Professor Richard Dawkins argued that as a result teachers were promoting the 'mythology' of creationism over the science of evolution.

Professor Dawkins, a geneticist and author of the best-selling book *The God Delusion*, said: 'Islam is importing creationism into this country.'"[501]

The *New York Times* reports:

"Fifty-four percent [of Americans] can't name the authors of the gospels. Sixty-three percent don't know what a gospel is. Fifty-eight

---

[499] *Daily Mail*, 12th April 2007
[500] Ibid, 23rd August 2006
[501] Ibid, 5th August 2008

370

percent can't name 5 of the 10 Commandments. Ten percent think Joan of Arc was Noah's wife."[502]

International cult expert Caryl Matrisciana writes:

"75% of all children raised in Christian homes who attend public schools will reject the Christian faith by their first year of college." [503]

In an article entitled "Three Cheers for Our Secular State", P Blanchard writes:

"I think that the most important factor moving us toward a secular society has been the educational factor. Our schools may not teach Johnny how to read properly, but the fact that Johnny is in school until he is sixteen tends toward the elimination of religious superstition. The average American child now acquires a high school education, and this militates against Adam and Eve and all other myths of alleged history."[504]

But Dr Colin Patterson, Senior Palaeontologist at the British Museum of Natural History, thinks integrity is the science casualty. He told an august group in America in 1981:

"The question is: Can you tell me anything you know about evolution, any one thing that is true? I tried that question on the geology staff at the Field Museum of Natural History and the only answer I got was silence. I tried it on the members of the Evolutionary Morphology Seminar in the University of Chicago, a very prestigious body of evolutionists, and all I got there was silence for a long time and eventually one person said, 'I do know one thing - it ought not to be taught in high school.'"[505]

A member of the American Civil Liberties Union (ACLU), a group not renowned for its Christian sympathies, writes:

---

[502] *New York Times,* 7th December 1997

[503] *Let My People Go*, video presentation, www.jeremiahfilms.com

[504] **Blanchard, P** "Three Cheers for Our Secular State," *The Humanist,* Jan/Feb 1983

[505] Patterson, C. Keynote address at the American Museum of Natural History, New York City, 5th November 1981

371

"For the past five years, I have closely followed creationist literature and have attended lectures and debates on related issues.... Based solely on the scientific arguments pro and con, I have been forced to conclude that scientific creationism is not only a viable theory, but that it has achieved parity with (if not superiority over) the normative theory of biological evolution. That this should now be the case is somewhat surprising, particularly in view of what most of us were taught in primary and secondary school.

In practical terms, the past decade of intense activity by scientific creationists has left most evolutionist professors unwilling to debate the creationist professors. Too many of the evolutionists have been publicly humiliated in such debates by their own lack of erudition and by the weaknesses of their theory."[506]

Gunning for the young

In law and order terms, 'three cheers for our secular state' might be somewhat premature. Fifty years ago, British children almost never killed. Today, the young routinely go large with extreme violence.

"In Greenwood, South Carolina, James Wilson loads the small .22 calibre shells into his rifle and works the bolt, driving the first tiny bullet into the breach. Minutes later the 19-year-old walks into the elementary school cafeteria and begins shooting screaming children and a teacher, before working his way through the school, systematically selecting his targets. He kicks open the door to a girls' restroom where he shoots another teacher, moving next to a third-grade classroom, where he shoots more children. Two children die and seven are wounded in the killing spree."[507]

James had been taking psychiatric drugs for years, prescribed to him by Greenwood psychiatrist Willie Moseley. These included Xanax, Valium, Vistaril, Mellaril, Thorazine, Tofranil and Halcion. James Crossen, program director of the Chemical Dependency

---

[506] **Smith, Robert E** "Origins and Civil Liberties", *Creation Social Sciences and Humanities Quarterly*, 3 (Winter 1980): pp.23-24
[507] **Day Phillip** *The Mind Game*, Credence, 2003

Recovery Unit at the Medical Center of North Hollywood, California, commented:

"That that young man should have been on drugs all his life, since he was fourteen, is ghoulish. The drugs would be a major contributing factor in such a surprising and sudden act of violence – a major contributor."[508]

Two years previously, on 20th November 1986, 14-year-old Rod Matthews went on the rampage in Canton, Massachusetts. He beat a classmate, Shawn Ouillette, to death with a baseball bat in the woods near his home. The academically gifted Matthews had been fed Ritalin since nine and was withdrawing at the time of the killing.[509] Matthews had told a teacher in the weeks leading up to the crime that he had an urge to kill somebody. The teacher merely replied that murder was a felony.

Nine months before that, young Timmy Becton, 10, used his 3-year-old niece as a shield while wielding a shotgun at a sheriff's deputy, who had visited the Becton residence with a truant officer. *"I'd sooner shoot you than go to school!"* Timmy yelled. The month before, he had been taken to see a psychiatrist to help him with his hatred of school. The psychiatrist prescribed Prozac. His parents described how their son suffered personality changes when the dosage of the drug was increased. They reported violent mood swings, during which Timmy would get 'really angry'.

On 25th May 1997, 18-year-old Jeremy Strohmeyer raped and murdered a 7-year-old girl in the ladies' room of a casino a week after commencing the drug Dexedrine.

On 21st May 1988, 14-year-old Kip Kinkel began his brief rule of terror. Kip's problems started when he was diagnosed with dyslexia and placed on Ritalin. His problems persisted. He

---

[508] "Prescription for Murder – Psychiatric Drugs Create Killer", *Freedom*, November/December 1988, pp.16-17

[509] CCHR, *Psychiatry – Betraying and Drugging our Children*, Los Angeles, 2002, p.17

attended 'anger control' classes and was additionally prescribed Prozac. Kip later went berzerk, entered his Springfield, Oregon high school and opened fire, killing two and injuring 22. Police discovered he had also shot his parents to death.

On 20th April 1999, Eric Harris, an 18-year-old senior at Columbine High School in Colorado, went on a murder rampage, killing 12 students and a teacher, injuring 21 others. Both Harris and his partner, Dylan Klebold, took their own lives after the event. Blood samples confirmed that Harris had been taking Luvox, a mind-altering drug in the same class as Prozac. Luvox (fluvoxamine) and Prozac (fluoxetine) are known as 'selective serotonin re-uptake inhibitors' (SSRI's), so named because they block the brain's absorption of the neurotransmitter serotonin, responsible for mood stabilisation. Luvox's manufacturers even warn that Luvox is 'sometimes fatal' to those who take it, and can activate mania and impair judgment. Nicholas Regush, producer of medical features for ABC News, stated:

"This is a widely recognised feature of antidepressants, as documented by their very own manufacturers. These drugs are also associated with bouts of irritability, hostility and aggression. Exactly how all this behavioural change is processed in the brain and how long-lasting it might be is poorly understood. Contrary to the big shows of knowledge by psychiatrists, there is a whole lot of guessing going on." [510]

Eight years before Harris and Klebold's massacre, Columbine had been the subject of a 1991 ABC *20/20* documentary for its controversial 'death education' class, in which students discussed such macabre topics as how they wanted to look in their caskets. Both Harris and Klebold had a well-documented obsession with violence, Satanism and weapons, and had been arrested for burglary in 1998 and placed into 'anger management'. Both were

---

[510] "The Hidden Hand of Violence", *Freedom*, op. cit. p.8

fans of the Satanist pop-star, Marilyn Manson. Eric's website should have rung alarm bells:

"I am the law. If you don't like it, you die!" and *"You all better... hide in your houses because I am coming for EVERYONE soon, and I WILL be armed to the ... teeth, and I WILL shoot to kill and I WILL... KILL EVERYTHING."*

On 16th April 2007, Seung-Hui Cho opened fire at Virginia Polytechnic Institute in Blacksburg, Virginia, killing 32 people and wounding many others. He later took his own life. Mike Adams confirms the suspicions behind why Cho acted without mercy.

"New revelations about the mental 'treatment' of Virginia Tech shooter Seung-Hui Cho are surfacing today after the surprise discovery of his mental health records in the home of the former university psych doctor who treated him. These mental health records, which have not yet been made public, have been missing since the shooting took place. Dr. Robert C Miller, we now know, took the records home and secretly kept them there, avoiding telling police about their location. They were only found during a document discovery phase of a pending trial."[511]

In Britain, cases involving James Bulger, the Menendez brothers, Rhys Jones and Damilola Taylor shocked many, yet more were to come:

On 17th December 2007, fifteen-year-old schoolboy Edward Belben smashed his 59 year-old father on the head with a hammer and then pounded his head to pulp 30 times before knifing what was left. He had been taking Prozac for depression. He also attacked his 43 year-old mother, stabbing her in the face with some scissors before she escaped.

BOY OF SEVEN 'LYNCHED' BY GANG OF SCHOOLCHILDREN WITH 'HOMEMADE NOOSE'

A gang of schoolboys tried to 'lynch' a seven-year-old with a home-made noose in a park in a chilling echo of the James Bulger case. Bradley

---

[511] www.naturalnews.com, 23rd July 2009

McLachlan was lured to a secluded area by three boys, all under ten, where they had already set up the rope.

They turned on him and pushed his head into the loop, tightened the knot and left him for dead, hovering a few inches above the ground and choking. After a few moments Bradley managed to wriggle free and ran home in tears to his horrified grandmother.

He was taken to Queen Alexandra Hospital in Cosham, Portsmouth, with ropeburn marks on his head and neck. Police are appealing for information but admit that even if the boys are caught they are too young to be prosecuted.[512]

FIVE-YEAR-OLD GIRL BATTLING CANCER ATTACKED BY YOBS WHO TRIED TO SET HER ON FIRE

"A girl of five who is battling cancer is recovering today after two boys sprayed an aerosol in her face and tried to set her alight. Scarlett Hellewell had to be rescued by neighbours when the boys pinned her down and sprayed the deodorant in her face in Halifax, West Yorks. She escaped with just bruises after the deodorant failed to ignite.

A spokesman for West Yorkshire Police said: 'It is reported the girl was playing when she was approached by two young boys who kicked and punched her before spraying an aerosol in her face and attempting to set her alight. The match did not ignite.'

The two young boys, believed to be only ten and seven, ran off when someone came to Scarlett's help on Tuesday evening."[513]

TEENAGER, 16, WHO SMILED AS HE STABBED SCHOOLBOY TO DEATH ON FOOTBALL PITCH, IS JAILED FOR LIFE

"A teenager who stabbed an innocent 14-year-old boy to death simply because he went to a rival school was jailed for life yesterday.

The Old Bailey heard that Elijah Dayoni, 16, laughed as he knifed model pupil David Idowu in the chest. David, a devout Christian who wanted to become an aeronautical engineer, died in hospital three weeks later."[514]

---

[512] *Daily Mail*, 24th August 2009
[513] Ibid, 22nd August 2009
[514] Ibid, 16th January 2009

Gil Garcetti, District Attorney for Los Angeles County, remarks:

"It's incredible, the ability of the very young to commit the most horrendous crimes was unthinkable 20 years ago." [515]

Judge Susan Winfield, of Washington DC, stated:

"Youngsters used to shoot each other in the body. Then in the head. Now, they shoot each other in the face."[516]

Bruce Wiseman writes:

"Outside our windows, the peaceful streets of years past now harbour violence. In some neighbourhoods, gunfire pierces the night. Police helicopters fly overhead, scanning yards and alleys for runaway criminals.

We worry about our children. Once-quiet schools are now hothouses of drug-trafficking, promiscuity, and vice unimaginable in days gone by. We hear of an ever declining literacy rate, dwindling test scores, and of graduates who can't even find their home city on a map. We wonder how they will ever make it in the adult world.

In our homes, at our jobs, on our television screens, we see that the once-clear line between right and wrong has become grey and hazy. Virtue is held up to ridicule. The honest man is viewed as a fool. Criminal behaviour is now excused under the banner of 'irresistible impulse' and 'diminished capacity'.

Hardly anyone would argue with the statement that <u>something</u> has been eating at the moral fabric for decades now.... <u>No one questions that there is a palpable, destructive force</u>. In the United States, for example, people are at each other's throats over it. Liberals blame it on conservative policies, right wingers rebuke the left. Many in the religious community have held the entertainment industry accountable." [517]

---

[515] **Wilkerson, Isabel** "2 Boys, A Debt, a Gun, a Victim: The Face of Violence", *The New York Times*, 16th May 1994

[516] **Lacayo, Richard** "When Kids Go Bad", *Time*, 19th September 1994, p.61

[517] Wiseman, Bruce *Psychiatry – The Ultimate Betrayal*, op. cit., pp.5,6

Thunder in the distance

In the second book in this series, *Origins II – Holy War*, we will trace the origin of Wiseman's 'palpable, destructive force', which has wreaked so much havoc down the bloodstained pages of history. The search raises philosophical questions about the origin of evil, why bad things happen to good people, and why 'a loving God' would allow disasters, war and disease to befall us if he were omnipotent.

To Dawkins, the Christian God is a *"petty, unjust, unforgiving control freak; a vindictive, racist, infanticidal, genocidal, filicidal, malevolent bully."*[518] The Bible could even harm schoolchildren. God counters in Job 38, where he challenges Job with dozens of questions to show human ignorance. Some startling information is revealed in the process. Dawkins, like Job, is not required to answer the questions because he cannot.

"Then the LORD answered Job out of the whirlwind, and said: "Who is this who darkens counsel by words without knowledge? Now prepare yourself like a man; I will question you, and you shall answer Me.

Where were you when I laid the foundations of the Earth? Tell Me, if you have understanding. Who determined its measurements? Surely you know! Or who stretched the line upon it? To what were its foundations fastened? Or who laid its cornerstone when the morning stars sang together, and all the sons of God shouted for joy?

"Or who shut in the sea with doors when it burst forth and issued from the womb. When I made the clouds its garment, and thick darkness its swaddling band. When I fixed My limit for it and set bars and doors. When I said, 'This far you may come, but no farther, and here your proud waves must stop!' Have you commanded the morning since your days began, and caused the

---

[518] **Dawkins, Richard** *The God Delusion*, Bantam, London, 2006

dawn to know its place, that it might take hold of the ends of the earth, and the wicked be shaken out of it?

It takes on form like clay under a seal, and stands out like a garment. From the wicked their light is withheld, and the upraised arm is broken. Have you entered the springs of the sea? Or have you walked in search of the depths? Have the gates of death been revealed to you? Or have you seen the doors of the shadow of death? Have you comprehended the breadth of the Earth? Tell Me, if you know all this. Where is the way to the dwelling of light? And darkness, where is its place, that you may take it to its territory, that you may know the paths to its home? Do you know it because you were born then, or because the number of your days is great?"[519]

God carries on for four chapters and covers just about everything, including the dinosaurs behemoth and leviathan, "...which I made along with you." Job shrinks. God's right, we know nothing. We can't make a fly from scratch. We can't cure disease. We can't stop our youngsters from killing each other. Is it God arming schoolchildren with bullets and knives or the thoughts in their head? We have free will. We don't have to go to school today with the Kalashnikov. David Robertson pens a response to Dawkins:

"You seem to think that those of us who believe in God are in effect children who have not grown out of the need for an imaginary friend. Apart from the patronising aspect of this, the question arises to me that if the God of the Bible, or the God of the Catholics, or the God of anyone is as horrible as you state, how can belief in him be a consolation?"[520]

And:

---

[519] Job 38:1-21, *NKJV*, Thomas Nelson, USA

[520] **Robertson, David** *The Dawkins Letters,* Christian Focus Publications 2007, p.122

"It is one of the reasons that I believe in the God of the Bible – because without that Biblical worldview I have no real explanation of, nor defence against, the evil of which humans are capable."[521]

Two paths

In God's world, we can choose good over evil. In Dawkins' world, good and evil are invalid religious concepts. In Keith Richards' world, there's the left-hand path and right-hand path. In Robert Plant's world, there are two paths you can go by but in the long run, there's still time to change the path you're on. In God's world, we came from Spirit. In Dawkins' world, we came from a monkey. In God's world, we feel shame for the damage our actions cause. In the evolutionist's world, we feel no shame. We are the irreproachable consequence of our chemicals.

"It is completely right to say that since the evidence for evolution is so absolutely totally overwhelming, nobody who looks at it could possibly doubt that if they were sane and not stupid, so the only remaining possibility is that they're ignorant. And most people who don't believe in evolution are ignorant." [522]

God replies: **"Shall the one who contends with the Almighty correct Him? He who rebukes God, let him answer it."** (Job 40:2) It's not an argument you'll want to be in the middle of. To Dr Will Provine, Professor of the History of Biology at Cornell University, evolution is the ultimate God-fixer:

"No God. No life after death. No ultimate foundation for ethics. No ultimate meaning in life. And no human free will. All are deeply connected to an evolutionary perspective. You're here today and gone tomorrow. And that's all there is to it."

Like Richard Dawkins, Provine was originally a Christian whose study of evolution destroyed his faith:

---

[521] Ibid.

[522] Stein, Ben, *Expelled – No Intelligence Allowed*, op. cit.

"It starts by giving up an active deity. Then it gives up the hope that there's any life after death. When you give those two up, the rest follows fairly easily. You give up the hope that there's an imminent morality. And finally, there's no human free will. If you believe in evolution, you can't hope for there being free will. There's no hope whatsoever of there being any deep meaning in human life. We live. We die. And we're gone. We're absolutely gone when we die."[523]

Cross-dressing atheist Eddie Izzard is similarly unenamoured of the God Alien:

"I personally don't believe in any organised Gods because I don't see any organisation in the way the world has progressed. I always think if there is a God he would have flicked Hitler's head off." [524]

And Stalin's and Jeffrey Dahmer's and the Yorkshire Ripper's, no doubt. In fact, where is this God when a head needs a flicking?

We'll explore such philosophical questions in *Origins II,* but for now, let me rest the case for a created cosmos with a summary of the extraordinary implications of design. Faith is not required; only an extension of the logic used to explore the central theme of this book: That either someone made the Earth, or the Earth made itself.

Global implications for design – science

If evolution were true, we would have to accept it. The fact that Darwin's theory is shot so full of holes yet still revered speaks more for mankind's desire to escape accountability and rule the roost than for any rigour of scientific enquiry. Happily, evolution is not borne out in the complex order we observe in the world around us. The boggling detail found in hundreds of thousands of species of mammals, birds, reptiles, fish, insects, trees, flowers, grasses, weeds, fruits and vegetables shouts something far more profound. All are 'finished' and ideally suited to their environment. The

---

[523] Ibid.
[524] *Daily Mail,* 22nd January 2009, p.21

cumulative odds of this occurring by accident run to the power of millions. By contrast, the evolutionist claims that the universe has only been evolving for 17 billion years, or 5 x 10^{17} seconds. Man of our times Richard Dawkins may refuse to acknowledge the problems, but some of his colleagues are having second thoughts.

Oxford academic, Alister McGrath writes:

> Science has, in Dawkins' view, wrecked faith in God, relegating God to the margins of culture where he is embraced by deluded fanatics. There's an obvious problem, of course – namely, that rather a lot of scientists do believe in God. *The God Delusion* was published in 2006. In that same year, three other books were published by leading research scientists. Owen Gingrich, a noted Harvard astronomer, produced *God's Universe,* declaring that 'the universe has been created with intention and purpose, and that this belief does not interfere with the scientific enterprise'. Francis Collins published his *Language of God*, which argued that the wonder and ordering of nature pointed to a creator God, very much along the lines of the traditional Christian conception. In this book, Collins describes his own conversion from atheism to Christian faith. This hardly fits Dawkins' rigid insistence that real scientists are atheists.”[525]

Take highflying defector Professor Antony Flew, who migrated to 'deism' after a lifetime denying God in his writings:

THERE IS A GOD, LEADING ATHEIST CONCLUDES

"A British philosophy professor who has been a leading champion of atheism for more than a half-century has changed his mind. He now believes in God — more or less — <u>based on scientific evidence</u>, and he says so on a video released Thursday.

At age 81, after decades of insisting that belief is a mistake, the professor, Antony Flew, has concluded that some sort of intelligence or first cause must have created the universe. A super-intelligence is the only good explanation for the origin of life and the complexity of nature, Flew said in a telephone interview from England."[526]

---

[525] **McGrath, A** *The Dawkins Delusion?* SPCK, London, 2007, p.19-20
[526] www.msnbc.msn.com/id/6688917/

At the age of 84, Dr Flew published *There is a God: How the World's Most Notorious Atheist Changed His Mind* in 2007. Whether or not Antony's mortality was making itself felt, the evolutionist knives were out. Flew was a heretic who had renounced humanism and embraced…. God, it didn't bear thinking about. Spittle-flecked accusations that Flew had gone senile and his co-writer, Roy Varghese, had co-opted the work for Christian ends were denied by Flew in a statement put out by HarperCollins:

"My name is on the book and it represents exactly my opinions. I would not have a book issued in my name that I do not 100 percent agree with. I needed someone to do the actual writing because I'm 84 and that was Roy Varghese's role. The idea that someone manipulated me because I'm old is exactly wrong. I may be old but it is hard to manipulate me. This is my book and it represents my thinking."[527]

If the universe was designed, then it follows that it was made for a purpose and is daily maintained by some higher intelligence. The big surprise to astrophysics is that the universe is finite, and the big surprise to quantum physics is that the smallest particles cannot be subdivided under 10^{-33}cm or they lose locality and are 'everywhere at once'. With limits set at either end, the conclusion is that we are part of a highly elaborate 'virtual world' – a digital simulation, wherein reality is multi-layered and -faceted, and matter isn't matter at all but a sea of vibrating quantum energy.[528] The physical universe *isn't*, at least not in the sense that science has come to know it. Humans are nothing but oscillating particles, which are themselves comprised of Chopra's 'Thinking No-Stuff'. Theoretical physics examines 'string theory', which holds that there may be ten dimensions, only four of which are knowable (length, width, height and time, collectively known as 'space-time'). An Intelligence capable of putting this lot together must be both

---

[527] www.publishersweekly.com/article/CA6501078.html
[528] www.khouse.org

outside and inside of time, which he created, and omniscient (all-knowing), omnipotent (all-powerful) and omnipresent (everywhere at once) to get the job done.[529] Intricate laws and constants control everything. Most intriguingly, the universe has been made to be knowable to man, who comprehends his surroundings in a way impossible for any other creature.

If we are the special creation of a Designer who saw fit to make every hair on our heads and count them,[530] then nothing in our lives has happened by accident, *yet we have free will.* The implications are staggering. Whatever the God Alien is, he knows every thought and intention before we conceive them, *but he lets us conceive them.* He walks every step we take, pumps our heart, inflates our lungs and blinks our eyes, *yet we blink them.* He is within us, around us, above and below us, and when we die, nothing in this extraordinary Being dies.

The Word

Is the Designer a personal or impersonal life-force? If personal, God would want to make contact with the beings he placed in such a unique environment, not least to tell us why. Has such a contact happened? How can we tell? Suspicions turn to the religious books of the world and the Judeo-Christian Bible in particular. Thomas Schulz writes:

"Not one recognised religious leader, not Moses, Paul, Buddha, Mohammed, Confucius, etc., has ever claimed to be God; that is, with the exception of Jesus Christ. Christ is the only religious leader who has ever claimed to be Deity, and the only individual ever who has convinced a great portion of the world that He is God."[531]

---

[529] Isaiah 46:10; 57:15
[530] Matthew 10:30
[531] **Schultz, Thomas** *The Doctrine of the Purpose of Christ with an Emphasis upon the Hypostatic Union.* Dallas Theological Seminary, May 1962

C S Lewis writes:

"I am trying here to prevent anyone saying the really foolish thing that people often say…. "I'm ready to accept Jesus as a great moral teacher, but I don't accept his claim to be God." That is the sort of thing we must not say. A man who, as merely a man, said the sort of things Jesus said would not be a great moral teacher. He would either be a lunatic – on a level with the man who says he is a poached egg – or else he would be the Devil of Hell. You must make your choice. Either this man was, and is, the Son of God: or else a madman or something worse….. You can shut him up for a fool, you can spit at him and kill him as a demon; or you can fall at His feet and call Him Lord and God. But let us not come up with any patronising nonsense about his being a great human teacher. He has not left that open to us. He did not intend to." [532]

The Bible hangs itself firmly on the hook, providing an ideal chance to confirm or disprove its extraterrestrial pedigree. It claims the Designer made everything. It claims God sent his Son to Earth to die so that man could be reconciled with the Designer at death. The Bible claims to hold the secret to our ultimate fate. The Bible tells us a lot of things we should and should not be doing. Clearly a book claiming authority over such matters is one of the following:

1. Completely deluded
2. A hoax of pure wickedness
3. What it says it is.

The scriptures contain no mistakes in their original form (Hebrew, Aramaic and Greek). Unlike other writings, the Bible self-authenticates with a perfect record of acrostic signatures, micro, meta and macro codes, quantum language, prophetic evidence and scientific knowledge we would expect from an Entity outside of time.[533] Chuck Missler writes:

---

[532] Lewis, C S, op. cit.
[533] McDowell, Josh, *Evidence That Demands a Verdict,* op. cit.

"Throughout the Bible we find the 'fingerprints' of a supernatural message system. Numerous design features in the Biblical text defy coincidence and demonstrate that the Bible, which consists of sixty-six books penned by forty authors over thousands of years, <u>is an integrated message system</u>."[534]

The Bible has been read by more people and published in more languages than any other book in history, yet has been repeatedly defamed and many attempts made to stamp it out. If it truly is 'the Word of God', it follows that the Designer would have ensured its survival over thousands of years against insuperable odds through the most chaotic periods of history. Today, we still have the Bible. Bernard Ramm writes:

"A thousand times over, the death knell of the Bible has been sounded, the funeral procession formed, the inscription cut on the tombstone, and committal read. But somehow the corpse never stays put."[535]

Sidney Collett writes:

"François Voltaire, the noted French infidel who died in 1778, said that in one hundred years from his time, Christianity would be swept from existence and pass into history. But what has happened? Voltaire has passed into history and the circulation of the Bible has increased in almost all parts of the world." [536]

Geisler and Nix point out that only fifty years after Voltaire's death, the Geneva Bible Society was using his printing press and house to produce stacks of Bibles![537]

---

[534] www.khouse.org

[535] **Ramm, Bernard** *Protestant Christian Evidences*, Moody Press, 1957

[536] **Collett, Sidney** *All About the Bible*, Fleming H Revell Co, 1962

[537] Geisler, Norman L and William E Nix, *A General Introduction to the Bible,* op. cit.

If God came to Earth as a man…

…what would he be like? McDowell thinks the more pertinent question is, why come to Earth as a man at all?[538] To teach us? We could reasonably expect the Designer to be knowable – after all, we're told we were 'created in his image'. We could expect God to make an unusual entrance into the world. We would expect him to live a sin-free life impossible for any human. This would get our attention, especially as he lived among Jews who had a highly developed sense of what sin was. How about overcome death? Satisfy the inner spiritual yearning of man? Do deeds of unparalleled wonder before witnesses, change lives forever, manipulate nature, heal the sick, raise the dead, comfort the fearful, be humble and unworldly, have a lasting, global influence and give man the promise that his life was not in vain? Did Christ accomplish all this?

Josh McDowell concludes that:

"If Jesus was not God, then He deserves an Oscar." [539]

And Bernard Ramm:

"That a Galilean carpenter should so claim to be the Light of the world, and be so recognised after so many centuries, is best explained on the grounds of His divinity."[540]

We would expect 'God's Word' to contain the greatest words ever spoken:

"For God so loved the world that he gave his only begotten Son, that whosoever believeth in him should not perish, but have everlasting life. For God sent not his Son into the world to condemn the world, but that the world through him might be saved. He that believeth on him [Jesus] is not condemned, but he

---

[538] McDowell, Josh, *Evidence That Demands a Verdict,* op. cit. p.286

[539] Ibid.

[540] **Ramm, Bernard** *Protestant Christian Evidences*, Chicago: Moody Press, 1957

that believeth not is condemned already, because he hath not believed in the name of the only begotten Son of God. And this is the condemnation, that light is come into the world, and men loved darkness rather than light, because their deeds were evil." (John 3:16-19)

"Eye has not seen, nor ear heard, neither have entered into the heart of man, the things which God has prepared for those that love him." (1 Cor 2:9)

"Let not your heart be troubled; you believe in God, believe also in me. In My Father's house are many mansions; <u>if it were not so, I would have told you</u>. I go to prepare a place for you. And if I go to prepare a place for you, I will come again and receive you to myself; that where I am, there you may be also." (John 14:1-3)

"Whoever drinks of the water that I shall give him will never thirst. But the water I shall give him will become in him a fountain of water springing up into everlasting life." (John 4:14)

"Consider the lilies of the field, how they grow; they toil not, neither do they spin. And yet I say unto you that even Solomon in all his glory was not arrayed like one of these. Wherefore, if God so clothe the grass of the field, which today is, and tomorrow is cast into the oven, shall he not much more clothe you, O ye of little faith? Therefore take no thought, saying, 'What shall we eat?' or, 'What shall we drink?' or, 'Wherewithal shall we be clothed?' (For after all these things do the Gentiles seek). For your heavenly Father knoweth that ye have need of all these things. But seek ye first the kingdom of God and his righteousness, and all these things shall be added unto you." (Matt 6:28-33)

You shall know them by their fruits

What of the alternative – a world with no God? We've traced the socio-political implications of Darwin's theory to the worst crimes ever perpetrated. Evolution's atheist philosophies continue to wreak their havoc into our modern age. Crime, totalitarianism, murder, abortion, broken homes and marriage, euthanasia and assisted suicide, radical environmentalism, gay rights and the denigration of the mother/father family unit in favour of 'Do what thou wilt'. Evolution means heaven is empty, so no judgment, no hell, no sin, no ultimate point to why we are here. As Friedrich Nietzsche proclaimed:

"The world – including mankind – as it truly is, is without any purpose, and is nonsense!"

Nietzsche died in an insane asylum. Today in our mad, mad world, the bus adverts proclaim:

"There is probably no God. Now stop worrying and enjoy your life."[541]

Probably no God? Is that the best they can do?

But the public *is* worried. Even in values-lite Britain, a 2006 poll revealed that only 48% of us accept evolution as an explanation of our origins, in spite of the brainwashing.[542] Most hedge their bets, attempting to balance the freedom to do what they want with a 'good life' in case there's a reckoning. "Guilt!" moans Dawkins. Perhaps, but if there *is* a God, then he's God whether we like it or not. And he's free to do what he wants with us, whether we like it or not. What profit cursing God to his face if we are not in control of the game? A wise man might ask what God wants.

We know what he wants and we don't like it. We're held accountable by the law for what we do on Earth, why would we not be held accountable by the astonishing laws which govern the universe into which we were born? Why do we cling to moral law, which violates the most basic evolutionary principle of survival of

---

[541] *Daily Mail*, 22nd January 2009
[542] *Weekend* magazine, *Daily Mail*, 24th January 2009, p.12

the fittest? Is there something more to why we are here, because for this not to be so, we would have to accept that everything we've ever achieved, all the discoveries made, skills learned, children raised and 'I love you's' whispered have been the cruellest tricks of all. Is that what *you* think life's about? More to the point, is that what you'll think when you're old and infirm and take to your bed for the very last time?

Evolutionist David Attenborough wishes he did believe in God, at least to give him someone to blame for life's woes and some comfort in his final years:

"Oh sure, when you are in your 20s and 30s, life is swashbuckling stuff…. But I tell you, when you get to 82, your views are very different. You are less certain of everything."[543]

Death, the great leveller

David Attenborough hears the Reaper's call.[544] For his part, Richard Dawkins knows the death rate is still one per person with a 100% hit ratio and there's a day in the future with his name on it. And like us all, Richard will have to pass through Death's door alone, and then what? The fatal flaw in Dawkins' atheism is not so much that he's wrong, it's that Richard has *no clue* what awaits him after death, yet maintains his defiance anyway, hoping the lights pinch out for a blissful oblivion. As we've seen in this study, the odds don't look stellar.

In the physics realm, the indefinable part of Richard – his life/soul/spirit/ethereal – has zero mass. He'll weigh the same thirty seconds before death as he will thirty seconds after, but something with no mass will have passed. The indefinable life-force or 'software' that was Richard Dawkins.

---

[543] Ibid.

[544] **"I have said, Ye are gods; and all of you are children of the most High. But ye shall die like men and fall like one of the princes."** (Psa 82:6-7)

According to the Mass-Distance-Time (MDT) relativity cube in physics, if mass = zero, then time and distance are eternal.[545] Dawkins will find himself morphed into the Matrix for all time with barely a blink, or in theological terms, into the palm of God's right hand. And each of us will pass on in like fashion at the appointed time, and with our life-force will go none of our flats, houses or mansions; no Porsches, lip gloss, piles of gold, bulging muscles, Rolexes or Jimmy Choos. Born into this virtual world with nothing, we leave the same way. Spirit in, spirit out. And we never controlled the game for even a nano-second.

It's a sobering thought. Go to a graveyard and look at the old stones at the back. No-one puts flowers by them anymore. Those who once were alive and laughing have gone and no-one remembers them. They are lost to Earth but not to the Field. What did they achieve? Where are they now? Only the Designer knows, having drawn their energy back to himself for the destiny only he has determined.

Richard Dawkins calls his supporters 'brights' because they have achieved 'a higher level of consciousness' by deifying man and rejecting God. But how bright is the man who bites the hand that feeds him? Who rejects the Designer – indeed teaches other people's children to do the same – yet has neither knowledge nor control over what happens next? By scorning all non-material evidence in life's game of roulette, Dawkins has stacked his whole stash on the black. A 'bright' man might wish to take pause and consider the implications before pushing his chips across. Why did I live? What have I learned? What happens next?

Ecclesiastes 3:11 states:

"[God] has made everything beautiful in its time. He has also set eternity in the hearts of men, yet they cannot fathom what God has done from beginning to end."

---

[545] http://lofi.forum.physorg.com/The-MDT-Cube_3496.html

In memoriam

One last thought. Evolution kills but so does religion. No origins study can be just and complete without a look at the mess man's made of 'religion'. This is the subject of the second book in this series, *Origins II – Holy War*.

Millions have murdered and died in the name of God. Were the popes really that evil? Is religion dangerous? What further proofs are there for Eden, the Flood, Babel, Abraham, Moses and the Exodus? Did Jesus exist? Was he who he says he was or a fake? How do the Greeks and Romans fit in? What about the planet Mars, the Roman god of war? Why were early civilisations so terrified of a planet most of us can't even find in the night sky? What about Islam, Buddhism and other religions? What about the Saxons and Vikings? How did the races start? Are we justified in living our lives however we want, or are there rules to be obeyed on a cosmic scale with the universe taking notes?

Weighty questions indeed, and fit to be tackled in their entirety another time. For now, I will leave you in a cemetery somewhere in Indiana, USA, contemplating a tombstone, upon which is carved the epitaph:

Pause, stranger, when you pass me by
As you are now, so once was I
As I am now, so you will be
So prepare for death and follow me.

Some wag has scrawled underneath:

To follow you I'm not content
Until I know which way you went!

THE END

BIBLIOGRAPHY

Amundsen, Roald *The Northwest Passage*, London and New York, 1908

Arnold, Chester A *An Introduction to Paleobotany*, McGraw-Hill, New York, 1947

Astronomical Almanac, US Government Printing Office, Washington DC, 1989

Baugh, Carl *Dinosaur*, Promise Publishing, CA, USA, 1987

Behe, Michael *Darwin's Black Box*, Simon and Schuster, New York, 1996

Binzel, PE *Alive and Well*, American Media, 2000

Blavatsky, Helen P *The Secret Doctrine*, Theosophical University Press, 1989

Bruce, FF *The Books and the Parchments*, Revell Co, 1963

Bruce, FF *The New Testament Documents: Are They Reliable?* Inter-Varsity Press, 1964

Bryan, William J *In His Image*, Kessinger Publishing, 2004

Collett, Sidney *All About the Bible*, Fleming H Revell Co, 1962

Cooper, Bill *After the Flood*, New Wine Press, Colchester, 1995

Corner, EJH *Contemporary Botanical Thought*, Oliver and Boyd, for the Botanical Society of Edinburgh, 1961

Crane, S *The Montreal Conferences*, 1976

Cranfill, SA *They Came From Babel*, The Write House, 1994

Crick, F *Life Itself: Its Origin and Nature*, Simon and Schuster, New York, 1981

Crowley, Aleister *The Book of the Law*, Samuel Weiser Inc., 1989

Darwin, CR *Origin of Species*, 6th ed, New York University Press, orig. 1959

Darwin, CR *The Descent of Man and Selection in Relation to Sex*, John Murray, London, 1922

Davies Paul *The Cosmic Blueprint*, Simon and Schuster, New York, 1988

Dawkins, Richard *The Blind Watchmaker: Why the Evidence of Evolution Reveals a Universe Without Design*, Penguin Books, London, 1987

Dawkins, Richard *The God Delusion*, Bantam, London, 2006

Day, Phillip *Health Wars*, Credence, 2007

Day, Phillip *The ABC's of Disease*, Credence 2004

Day, Phillip *The Mind Game*, Credence Publications 2002

Dembski William A *The Third Mode of Explanation*, The Proceedings of the Wethersfield Institute, 1999. Published in *Science and Evidence for Design in the Universe*, Ignatius Press, San Francisco, 2000

Dembski, WA & Sean McDowell *Understanding Intelligent Design,* Harvest House, 2008

Denton, Michael *Evolution: A Theory in Crisis,* Adler & Adler, USA, 1986

Dunbar, CO and KM Waage *Historical Geology,* John Wiley and Sons, 1969

Durrant, Will *Die Napoleonische Ära,* Frankfurt, Berlin, 1982

Eiseley LC *The Immense Journey,* Vintage, New York, NY, 1957

Eldredge, Niles *Reinventing Darwin,* Wiley, New York, 1995

Foley, Henry & Steven S Sharfstein *Madness and Government,* American Psychiatric Press, Inc., Washington DC, 1983

French, Roger *The Man Who Lived in Three Centuries,* Natural Health Society of Australia, 2000

Garbutt, Paul *Assassin!* Ian Allan Ltd., England, 1942

Geisler, Norman L & William E Nix *A General Introduction to the Bible,* Moody Press, Chicago, 1968

Gilbert, Martin *History of the Twentieth Century,* HarperCollins, 2001

Gould, Stephen J *Ontogeny and Phylogeny,* Belknap Press, Cambridge MA, 1977

Grasse P-P *Evolution of Living Organisms Evidence for a New Theory of Transformation,* Academic Press, New York, NY, 1977

Grenz, S *A Primer on Postmodernism,* Eerdmans, Grand Rapids, USA, 1996

Guthrie, RD *Frozen Fauna of the Mammoth Steppe – The Story of Blue Babe,* University of Chicago Press, Chicago, IL, 1990

Haldane JBS "When I Am Dead", in *Possible Worlds: And Other Essays,* Chatto and Windus, London, 1932

Harcourt Brace Jovanovich *General Science,* 1989

Hermann, William & Paul Bacon *The Holocaust: From a Survivor of Verdun,* Harper & Row, New York, 1972

Heyford, Jack *Spirit Filled Bible* (NKJV), Thomas Nelson, 1991

Hitchens, Peter, *The Abolition of Britain,* Quartet Books, 1999

Hitler, Adolf *Mein Kampf,* translated by Ralph Manheim, Houghton Mifflin & Co., Boston, USA, 1971

Hoffman, Michael *Secret Societies and Psychological Warfare,* Wiswell Ruffin House, 1992

Holdaway, David *The Life of Jesus,* Sovereign World Ltd, Tonbridge, UK, 1997

Holmberg, Eric *The Allure of Rock,* Amercian Portrait Films, 1999

Holt R & W *Earth Science,* Holt McDougal, 1984

Horgan, John *The Undiscovered Mind,* The Free Press, New York, 1999

Hothersall, David *History of Psychology,* Temple University Press, Philadelphia, 1984

Hovind, K *Creation seminars series,* www.drdino.com

Howells, John G *World History of Psychiatry,* Brunner/Mazel, Inc. New York, 1975

Hoyle, F *Mathematics of Evolution,* Acorn Enterprises, Memphis, TN, 1999

Hoyle, F *The Intelligence Universe,* M Joseph, 1983

Hudson, Peter J *Where Do We Go From Here?* Mayfair Publishing, 1999

Hutton, SK *Among the Eskimos of Labrador,* London and Philadelphia 1912

Huxley, Thomas "Biogenesis and Abiogenesis", *Collected Essays of T H Huxley,* (1894) Macmillan and Co, London 1970

Jeffrey, G *Armageddon – Appointment With Destiny,* Waterbook Press, 1997

Kantor, JR *The Scientific Evolution of Psychology,* Principia Press, 1969

Karier, Clarence J *Scientists of the Mind,* University of Illinois Press, Chicago, 1986

Kerkut, GA *Implications of Evolution,* Pergamon Press, London, 1960

Lapon, Lenny *Mass Murderers in White Coats,* Springfield, Massachusetts, Psychiatric Genocide Research Institute, 1986

Leach, Charles *Our Bible. How We Got It,* Moody Press, 1898

Levi, Wendell *The Pigeon,* Sumter, SC, Levi Publishing Co Inc, 1977

Levin, HL *The Earth Through Time,* Saunders College Publishing, New York. 1992

Lewis, Richard *S A Continent for Science: The Antarctic Adventure,* Viking Press, New York, 1965

Lifton, Robert Jay *The Nazi Doctors,* Basic Books, 1986

Lipton, Bruce *The Biology of Belief,* Elite Books, USA, 2005

Ludwig, Mark *Artificial Life and Evolution,* American Eagle Press, 1993

Lyttleton, RA, *Mysteries of the Solar System,* Clarendon Press, Oxford, 1968

Martin Jobe and David Hames *Incredible Creatures that Defy Evolution,* www.explorationfilms.com

McCann, Alfred *God - or Gorilla?* Devin-Adair Co, New York, 1922

McDowell, Josh & Don Stewart *Answers to Tough Questions,* Here's Life Publishers, Inc., 1980

McDowell, Josh *Evidence That Demands a Verdict,* Here's Life Publishers, 1972

McGrath, A *The Dawkins Delusion,* SPCK, London, 2007

McTaggart, Lynne *The Field,* Element, 2003

Midgley M *Evolution as a Religion: Strange Hopes and Stranger Fears,* Methuen, London, 1986

Mielke, F *The Death Doctors,* Elek Books, London, 1962

Mindless, Harvey *Makers of Psychology: The Personal Factor,* Insight Books, New York, 1988

Missler, Chuck *Beyond Coincidence,* Coeur D'Alene, USA. www.khouse.org

Missler, Chuck *In the Beginning, there was Information,* audio presentation supplementary notes, Koinonia House, www.khouse.org

Morris, Henry *Many Infallible Proofs,* Master Books,1974

Morris, John *The Young Earth,* Master Books, 1994

Newton, Isaac *Mathematical Principles of Natural Philosophy,* University of California Press, 1978

Prentice Hall *Earth Science,* 1999

Prentice Hall *General Science,* 1992

Price, Weston A *Nutrition and Physical Degeneration,* London and New York, 1939

Ramm, Bernard *Protestant Christian Evidences,* Moody Press, 1957

Ransom, Steven & Phillip Day *The Truth About HIV,* Credence Publications, 2006

Reeves, H *The Origin of the Solar System,* John Wiley and Sons, New York, 1978

Rehwinkel, Alfred M *The Flood,* St. Louis, MO, Concordia, 1951

Richards, Jay W and Guillermo Gonzalez *The Privileged Planet,* Regnery Pub, 2004

Robertson, David *The Dawkins Letters,* Christian Focus Publications 2007

Röder, Thomas, Kubillus, Volker & Anthony Burwell *Psychiatry – The Men Behind Hitler,* Freedom Publishing, Los Angeles, 1995

Rose, MR *Darwin's Spectre: Evolutionary Biology in the Modern World,* Princeton University Press, Princeton NJ, 2000

Roseman, Mark *The Villa, the Lake, the Meeting: Wannsee and the Final Solution,* Allen Lane, 2002

Sagan, C & Ann Druyan *Comet,* Headline Book Publishing,1997

Sagan, Carl *Cosmos,* Macdonald, London, 1981

Sagan, Carl *Pale Blue Dot,* Ballantine Books Inc, 1997

Satinover, Jeffrey *The Truth Behind the Bible Code,* Sidgwick & Jackson, 1998

Schaff, Philip *Companion to the Greek Testament and the English Version,* Harper Brothers, New York, 1883

Schultz, Thomas *The Doctrine of the Purpose of Christ with an Emphasis upon the Hypostatic Union.* Dallas Theological Seminary, May 1962

Sharkey, Joe *Bedlam: Greed, Profiteering, and Fraud in a Mental Health System Gone Crazy,* St Martin's Press, New York, 1994

Sheldrake, Rupert *The Presence of the Past,* Inner Traditions Bear and Company, 2000

Shrag, Peter *Mind Control*, Pantheon Books, 1978

Simpson, George G *The Major Features of Evolution*, Columbia University Press, New York, 1953

Sodera, V *One Small Speck to Man*, Vij Sodera Productions, Bognor Regis, UK, 2003

Stahl, Barbara J *Problems in Evolution*, McGraw-Hill, New York, 1974

Stein, Ben *Expelled – No Intelligence Allowed*, Premise Media Corporation, 2008

Stone, Robert B *The Secret Life of Your Cells*, Whitford Press, 1989

Symonds, John & Kenneth Grant *The Confessions of Aleister Crowley*, Viking Penguin, 1989

Szasz, T *Insanity: The Idea and its Consequences*, John Wiley & Sons, New York, 1987

Szasz, T *The Manufacture of Madness*, Harper and Row, New York, 1970

Taylor, Renee *Hunza Health Secrets*, Keats Publishing, 1964

Taylor, Stuart Ross *Solar System Evolution: A New Perspective*, Cambridge University Press, 1992

The Privileged Planet documentary, www.illustramedia.com

Torrey, E Fuller *Nowhere to Go*, Harper & Row, New York, 1988

Unger, Merrill F *Unger's Bible Dictionary*, Moody Press, Chicago, 1971

Unlocking the Mystery of Life, Illustra Media, www.illustramedia.com

Jeremiah Films *The Evolution Conspiracy*, Hemet, CA, USA, www.jeremiahfilms.com

Valenstein, Elliot S *Blaming the Brain*, Free Press, New York, 1998

Velikovsky, Immanuel *Earth in Upheaval*, Garden City, New York, Doubleday & Co., 1955

Ward, Peter & Donald Brownlee *Rare Earth: Why Complex Life is Uncommon in the Universe*, Springer, 2009

Webster, Nesta H *World Revolution*, Constable & Co., London, 1921

Wertham, Frederic *A Sign For Cain: An Exploration of Human Violence*, Robert Hale Ltd, London, 1966

Williams, William *The Evolution of Man Scientifically Disproved*, Bibliobazaar, 2007

Wipple, Fred L *The Mystery of Comets*, Cambridge University Press, 1985

INDEX

398

Binger, Carl, 249
Biology, 322
Black Corps, The, 285
Black Sea theory, 189
Blair, Tony, 314, 324, 341
Blasphemy, 334
Blavatsky, Helena Petrovna, 261, 393
Blythman, Joanna, 364
Boleyn, Anne, 265
Bombardier beetle, 95
Book of the Law, 141, 261, 393
Bouhler, Philipp, 289
Boyle, Frank, 332
Brachiosaurus, 215
Brandenburg, 292
Brandt, Karl, 289
Brantley, Garry, 150, 151
Bresler, Johannes, 272, 275
British Army, 358
Brocket, Lady, 337
Brown, Walt, 195, 230
Brownlee, Donald, 57, 397
Bryan, William, 97, 98, 393
Bryce Canyon, 197
Buchenwald, 257
Buckland, William, 155
Buddha, 384
Buffon, Comte de, 153
Bulger, James, 375
Bürger-Prinz, Hans, 316, 317, 320
Byrne, Rhonda, 133

C

California, 263, 337, 373
Cambodia, 314
Cameron, Ewen, 136
Campbell, Charlie, 69, 363
Canada, 205, 255
Cancer, 357, 358, 359, 361, 410
Canton, M A, 373
Carbon dating, 201
Carbon monoxide, 292, 302

Catastrophism, 29
Catel, Werner, 289
Catholic Church, 265, 266
Cayce, Edgar, 161
Chalmers, Thomas, 155
Chamberlain, Houston Stewart, 274, 287
Chamberlain, Neville, 290
Chandler's Wobble, 226
Charterhouse, 13, 15, 17, 23, 56, 410
Chemical evolution, 118, 120
Child sacrifice, 262
China, 255
Chisholm, G Brock, 322, 323
Cho, Seung-Hui, 375
Chopra, Deepak, 127, 131, 383
Christianity, 245, 259, 261, 268, 270, 330
Church of England, 265
Churchill, Winston, 28, 285, 324
CIA (Central Intelligence Agency), 136, 137, 314
Cigarette smoking, 299
Citizen's Commission on Human Rights (CCHR), 263
Cleese, John, 327
Cobbett, William, 249
Cocaine, 259, 262
Cohen, Richard M, 11
Colby, William, 137
Colitis, 359
Collett, Sidney, 386
Colorado, 374
Colorado River, 203, 204
Colquhoun, James, 357
Columbia University, 258, 287, 321
Columbine High, 374
Comedy Channel, The, 334
Comets, 77
Communism, 33, 270, 311
Communist Manifesto, 270, 311
Concentration camps, 294, 302, 306, 317
Confucius, 384

400

F

G

H

401

Haldane, John, 44, 45, 394
Hall, G Stanley, 251
Hall, Richard, 251, 252
Hamburg, 276, 277, 279, 304, 315, 317, 320
Hanging, 337
Hanlon, Michael, 23
Harris, Eric, 374
Harsch, Joseph, 290
Harvard University, 30, 43, 90, 209, 211, 307, 382
Heart disease, 359, 361
Heaven, 162, 330, 349
Heidelberg, 317
Henry, Patrick, 35
Heroin, 262, 337
Heyde, Werner, 292, 295, 316, 319
Heydrich, Reinhard, 281, 297, 298, 299, 300, 302, 303, 305, 306, 310
High blood pressure, 359
Hill, Benny, 326
Himmler, Heinrich, 294, 300, 306, 310
Hitchens, Peter, 334, 346, 394
Hitler, Adolf, 18, 23, 31, 33, 34, 168, 239, 240, 247, 273, 277, 278, 281, 282, 283, 285, 287, 288, 289, 290, 294, 296, 299, 300, 301, 302, 304, 305, 306, 307, 308, 309, 310, 311, 314, 316, 318, 329, 381, 394, 396
Hittites, 310
Hoche, Alfred, 281, 315
Holdaway, David, 149, 394
Hollywood, 23, 74, 140, 207, 334, 337, 373
Holocaust, The, 275, 283, 394
Holy Spirit, 133, 135, 138, 330
Hothersall, David, 251
House of Israel, 169
House of Judah, 169
Houston, TX, 274, 287
Hovind, Kent, 35, 49, 66, 70, 75, 76, 77, 78, 83, 91, 178, 181, 189, 193,
194, 205, 219, 221, 227, 228, 230, 232, 233, 234, 395
Howard, Russell, 332
Hoyle, Fred, 69, 80, 121, 156, 157, 395
Hrdlicka, Ales, 89
Hubble, Edwin, 58, 68, 71
Hudson, Peter, 130, 132
Humanism, 267, 331
Humphries, Russell, 46
Hunzas, 358, 359
Hutchence, Michael, 337
Hutton, James, 154, 215, 357, 395
Hutton, Samuel, 357
Huxley, Thomas, 38
Hydroplate theory, 230
Hyperborea, 310
Hypocrisy, 265
Hysteria virilis, 276

I

I G Farben, 302
IBM Laboratories, 133
Ice Age, 226, 233
Illinois, 254, 395
Illuminati, 266, 267, 268, 270
Illuminism, 33
India, 359
Industrial Revolution, 73, 87
Ingolstadt University, 266
Insulin, 256
Insulin coma, 256
INXS, 337
Iowa State University, 47, 59
Israel, 139, 160, 168, 170, 171, 174, 302
Israelites, 169
Izzard, Eddie, 381

J

Jacob, 167
Jagger, Mick, 327, 328

402

James, William, 253, 254
Japan, 240, 282, 335
Jeffrey, Grant, 95, 142, 171, 172, 175, 381, 395, 396
Jerusalem, 133, 147, 168, 169, 170, 171, 172, 173
Jesuits, 266, 268, 312
Jesus Christ, 13, 27, 35, 133, 139, 146, 147, 149, 151, 152, 156, 157, 164, 168, 177, 178, 185, 245, 265, 326, 328, 330, 331, 338, 343, 346, 348, 384, 385, 387, 392, 394
Jews, 168, 169, 170, 246, 265, 292, 297, 298, 299, 300, 301, 302, 306, 310
Johanson, Donald, 90
John Hopkins University, 91
Josephus, Flavius, 147, 173
Judaism, 270
Jung, Carl, 329
Jupiter, 56, 67

K

Kantor, J R, 264
Karier, Clarence J, 253
Katyn massacre, 312, 313, 314
Katzen-Ellenbogen, Edwin, 257
Kaufbeuren, 304
Kaufmann therapy, 277
Keith, Sir A, 27, 28, 308, 327, 328, 380
Kent, England, 410
Khmer Rouge, 314
Kihn, Berthold, 319
King Edward VII, 272
King Henry VIII, 265
King Nebuchadnezzar (Babylon), 169, 170
King's Cross, London, 336
Kinkel, Kip, 373
Kipling, Rudyard, 272
Kitts, David, 92
Klebold, Dylan, 374

Klee, Ernst, 295, 296, 299, 316, 319
Knigge, Baron Adolph von, 267, 268
Koresh, David, 137, 138
Kraepelin, Emil, 250, 255, 256, 257, 282, 286
Krafft-Ebing, Richard von, 273
Kranz, Heinrich, 320
Krebs Jr, Ernst T, 360
Kremlin, 314
Kretschmer, Ernst, 319
Kun, Béla, 280

L

Labour Party, 324
Lake Champlain, 221, 222
Lamarck, Jean, 153
Lang, Jacob, 268
Laplace, Pierre, 153
Large Hadron Collider, 23
Larson, Alan, 263
Latin, 279
LaVey, Anton, 344, 345
Lawrence, T ('of Arabia'), 174
Lead, 335
League of Nations, 174
Leary, Timothy, 262
Lecter, Hannibal, 346
Lehner, Ludwig, 293
Leipzig, 251, 281, 289
Lemelsen, General, 300
Lenin, V, 28, 31, 280, 311, 347
Lennon, John, 327, 329, 330, 331, 334
Levi, 141, 169
Leviathan, 216
Lewis, C S, 385
Lewis, Jerry Lee, 287
Lewontin, Richard, 43, 44
Lidice, 306
Liebknecht, Karl, 280
Linden, Herbert, 289
Lipson, H, 23, 24
Lipton, Bruce, 44, 115, 116, 135, 395

404

Morris, John, 16, 75, 109, 188, 196, 197, 203
Morrison, Jim, 15, 135
Mortensen, Terry, 153, 156
Morton, Andrew, 337
Moscow, 280
Moseley, Willie, 372
Moses, 94, 384
Most, Mickey, 330
Mount Everest, 193
Mount Rushmore, 54
Mount Wilson Observatory, 58
MTV, 334
Munich, 283, 284, 285, 288, 296, 297, 304, 318, 319
Murder, 248, 265, 289, 292, 297, 299, 301, 334, 335, 373
Murdoch, Rupert, 349

N

Narut, Thomas, 137
Nathanson, Bernard, 365
National Academy of Sciences, 41
National Geographic, 78
National Institute of Mental Health (NIMH), 321
National Socialists. *See* Nazis
Natural History Museum, 18, 243
Nazis, 283, 287, 288, 292, 296, 297, 298, 300, 301, 311, 316, 317, 318
Nazism, 27, 34, 256, 285, 288, 309
Nebraska Man, 91
Nebular Hypothesis, 67, 68
Nechilli Eskimos, 358
Negroes, 246
Nelson, Paul, 86, 123
Neo-Darwinism, 242
Neurotransmitters, 374
New Age, 33, 261, 270
New Jersey, 257
New World Order, 267, 270, 331

New York, 249, 250, 256, 258, 259, 260, 275, 287, 321, 323, 338, 377, 394, 395, 396, 397
New York Times, 377
Newcastle University, 24
Newspapers, 304, 336, 350
Newton, Sir Isaac, 237
Niagara Falls, 195, 205, 232
Nietzsche, Friedrich, 244, 245, 246, 253, 274, 275
Nihilism, 70, 72
NKVD, 313
Noah, 180
Noah's Flood, 75, 109, 143, 156, 179, 180, 182, 183, 184, 185, 186, 187, 189, 190, 191, 193, 194, 195, 196, 197, 200, 201, 203, 204, 205, 206, 207, 208, 209, 215, 216, 217, 219, 220, 221, 223, 226, 227, 228, 229, 231, 233, 369, 392, 393, 396
Nocebo, 129
Non-lethal weapons, 137, 138
Nonne, Max, 276
Normandy, 304
Nostradame, Michel de, 161
Nuremburg, 292, 293, 300

O

Oard, Michael, 213
On the Origin of Species, 14, 23, 26, 28, 81, 94, 201
Ono, Yoko, 329
Oort Cloud, 77
Operation Barbarossa, 297, 300, 301
Operation Gnadentod, 292
Order of the Golden Cross, 266
Oregon, 374
Orwell, George, 325
Ouillette, Shawn, 373
Oxford University, 25, 108, 155, 310, 359
Oxygen, 79, 180

Religion, 240, 245, 252, 253, 259, 260, 264, 267, 268, 270, 271, 279, 331, 334, 348
Richards, Jay, 59, 73
Richards, Keith, 327
Ritalin, 373
Robertson, David, 78, 226, 308, 309, 379, 396
Roche's Limit, 227
Röder et al, 277, 278, 279, 287, 304, 315, 316, 317, 318
Romanes, 88
Romig, Joseph H, 357
Roseman, Mark, 299, 300, 301, 396
Rosicrucians, 266, 268
Ross, Hugh, 145
Rousseau, 269
Royal Greenwich Observatory, 75
Rüdin, Ernst, 282, 283, 284, 285, 288, 303, 318, 319, 320
Rush, Benjamin, 248
Russia, 137, 138, 240, 275, 280, 301, 307, 312

S

Sado-masochism, 334
Sagan, Carl, 42, 43, 44, 54, 56, 57, 77, 140, 396
Saint-Emmeran, 268
Salant, Richard, 12
San Andreas Fault, 193
Sanskrit, 141
Sarajevo, 274
Satan, 19, 168, 261, 322, 328, 329, 330, 342, 344, 345
Satanism, 34, 330, 344, 345, 346, 374
Satinover, Jeffrey, 142, 396
Saturn, 56, 67, 78, 226
Satyavrata, 189
Saul, Andrew, 356
Sawade, Dr (Werner Heyde), 316
Saxe-Gotha, 268

Scallion, Gordon M, 161
Schaff, Philip, 149, 150, 396
Schlechta, Karl, 244
Schneider, Carl, 319
Schulz, Johannes H, 317
Schulz, Thomas, 317, 384
Schweitzer, Albert, 352
Search for Extraterrestrial Life (SETI), 23
Second Law of Thermodynamics, 13, 29, 37, 71, 73, 242
Sedatives, 337
Sedgwick, Adam, 155
Selective serotonin re-uptake inhibitors (SSRI's), 374
Serbia, 274
Serotonin, 374
Sheldrake, Rupert, 134, 135, 396
Silesia, 290
Simony, 265
Simpson, Don, 337
Simpson, George, 211
Singer, Peter, 32
Smallpox, 258
Smithsonian Institution, 243
Sobibor, 302
Sodera, Vij, 18, 155, 397
Somme, Battle of the, 276
South Carolina, 372
Southampton University, 24
Soviet Union, 255, 297, 300
Spartacists, 280
Spartacus, 267, 307
Spielberg, Steven, 281
Springfield, OR, 374
SS, The, 281, 292, 297, 301, 303, 304, 305, 306
St Anthony Falls, 203
St George, 218
Stahl, Barbara, 107, 108, 397
Stalin, Josef, 280, 311, 312, 314
Stalingrad, 301
Stammheim, 317
Stark, Carl, 273

407

ABOUT THE AUTHOR

Phillip Day was born in England in 1960. He was educated at the leading British education establishments Selwyn and Charterhouse, and throughout his '20's had a successful entrepreneurial career founding businesses in sales and marketing. With a firm grounding in business and the ways of the media, Phillip's research career began after he became interested in wars going on in the realms of health and politics over issues that  were being deliberately withheld or misreported to the public.

His research into AIDS and cancer, as two examples of the establishment's entrenched scientific error and brazen profiteering to society's cost, culminated in two books that have captured the public's imagination: *Cancer: Why We're Still Dying To Know The Truth* and *The Truth About HIV*. Phillip Day has written twelve books on health and today his speaking schedule takes him all over the world, lecturing on the subject of entrenched scientific error.

Phillip Day heads the publishing and research organisation Credence and lives in Kent, England.